COMPUTING
SYSTEM
FUNDAMENTALS

An Approach
Based on Microcomputers

COMPUTING
SYSTEM
FUNDAMENTALS

An Approach
Based on Microcomputers

KENNETH J. DANHOF
CAROL L. SMITH
Southern Illinois University at Carbondale

▲▼ ADDISON-WESLEY PUBLISHING COMPANY

Reading, Massachusetts • Menlo Park, California
London • Amsterdam • Don Mills, Ontario • Sydney

This book is in the
ADDISON-WESLEY SERIES IN COMPUTER SCIENCE

Consulting Editor: Michael A. Harrison

Library of Congress Cataloging in Publication Data

Danhof, Kenneth J
  Computing system fundamentals.

  Includes bibliographical references and index.
  1. Electronic digital computers. 2. Microcomputers.
I. Smith, Carol L., joint author. II. Title.
QA76.5.D252   001.6'4   79-14933
ISBN 0-201-01298-7

ISBN 0-201-01298-7
ABCDEFGH-MA-89876543210

PREFACE

This book is intended as a textbook for an introductory course on computer organization and systems at the sophomore or junior level. As such it corresponds to the CS3 course described in the ACM 1978 curriculum guidelines. The primary prerequisite is a first course in programming with a high-level language such as FORTRAN or PL/1.

There are two salient features in the approach taken in this textbook. First, there is the matter of teaching the fundamentals of computer hardware and software (and the interplay between the two) and doing this in an unrestricted hands-on environment. The second feature is the incorporation of the most recent development of computer technology, the microprocessor, into the computer science curriculum.

Relative to the first issue, it is generally recognized that the future computer science or computer engineering student must understand both the hardware and software aspects of computers. Although in the past computer science curricula have tended to be either heavily software- or heavily hardware-oriented, the most recent curriculum specifications suggest a greater unification of hardware and software within one discipline. In fact, both the recent ACM and IEEE curriculum guidelines suggest the use of minicomputers or microcomputers in a hands-on laboratory situation as a means of achieving this goal. This text constitutes a realization of this approach.

Returning to the second basic feature of the book, we believe that, while the microcomputer revolution is currently spreading through various application areas, it has not really affected the computer science curriculum itself to a significant extent. This book is designed to correct the situation. It is apparent that not only should the microcomputer be clearly understood by computer science students, but that it is at precisely this level that one can best view and study the entire system. The course is constructed to utilize the microcomputer both as an object of study and as a laboratory tool. The low cost of microcomputers makes it possible to give each student essentially unlimited hands-on access to a microcomputer.

The course is structured in terms of programming "levels" and four "modules" support the development. Module I (Chapters 1-5) introduces the specific microcomputers to be studied—the Motorola 6800 and the Intel 8085. In this module, the student is taken from the machine language level to the assembly language level. Chapters 2 and 3 are devoted to the instruction sets of the two microprocessors. Chapter 4 introduces the basic programming constructs and compares the two instruction sets. Chapter 5 covers basic hardware components and discusses system architecture for the two microcomputers.

Module II (Chapters 6 and 7) introduces the students to system I/O programming. Chapter 6 covers typical cassette punch and load routines and Chapter 7 describes more general loaders and a simple text editor.

In Module III (Chapters 8, 9, 10), the students are introduced to a high-level programming language—PL/M. Chapter 8 describes PL/M and the corresponding structured-programming concepts. Chapter 9 covers the concepts involved in writing a two-pass assembler and thereby prepares the student for the task of producing a small resident assembler on the microcomputer. The last chapter in this module, Chapter 10, describes other software support packages that are typically found in a resident system and explores the microcode support for the machine-language level of the machine.

Module IV (Chapters 11 and 12) contains a discussion of interrupt I/O and some of the many application areas of microprocessors. Following a consideration of interrupt and parallel I/O support on each of the two systems, case studies are made of particular applications.

While moving through these four modules, the student transforms her or his own microcomputer from an initial naked piece of hardware into a functioning small computer system containing a loader, a text editor, and a resident assembler. Moreover, the student has written the programs that support this system.

The course presupposes a rather modest laboratory, which includes the microcomputers themselves (at least one of which has an extended memory) and a terminal. In addition, a support system centered around a computer sufficiently large to handle the necessary software development packages and a link between the support system and the microcomputers is needed. It should be noted that the ACM curriculum 1978 specifications recommend a laboratory of just this sort for computer science departments.

Although it is possible to cover most of the material in a three-hour, one-semester course, it may be desirable to omit some of the material in a given situation. It is possible, for example, to consider only one of the two microcomputers, or to provide the students with some of the programs (such as the text editor) which they might otherwise write. Moreover, various sections of the text (such as parts of Chapter 10 and much of Module IV) might be regarded as optional material. An Instructor's Manual, which includes solutions to selected exercises and a description of a possible supporting microcomputer laboratory, is available. In addition, supporting software packages are available from the Computer Science Department, Southern Illinois University at Carbondale. These include the PL/M STAR Compiler and associated cross assemblers for the M6800 and I8085, as well as linkers and simulators for the two machines.

The authors wish to acknowledge Clovis Tondo, Debra May, Linda Foran, and Jeff Marks for their assistance in the development of the software support packages and David Alvin for his considerable help in developing the microcomputer laboratory and its support system. We are further indebted to the CS 306 students who took the course on an "experimental" basis and provided many helpful comments. Finally, we wish to thank our typists, June Blonde and Glenda Russell, who suffered through the several versions of the manuscript.

The course was developed with support from the National Science Foundation grant number SER77–02523.

Carbondale, Illinois   K.J.D.
July, 1980   C.L.S.

CONTENTS

MODULE I   WORKING WITH THE BASIC MACHINE

Chapter 1   An Overview of Computer Organization   **1**
    1.1   Computing systems in general   1
    1.2   The basic hardware components   6
    1.3   Instruction formats   14
    1.4   Addressing modes   20
    1.5   Maxis, minis, and micros   24

Chapter 2   The Motorola M6800 Instruction Set   **27**
    2.1   Chapter overview   27
    2.2   The microprocessor unit   27
    2.3   Accumulator and memory reference instructions   31
    2.4   Index register and stack pointer instructions   41
    2.5   Jump and branch instructions   44
    2.6   Condition code register instructions   49

Chapter 3   The Intel 8085 Instruction Set   **51**
    3.1   Chapter overview   51
    3.2   The microprocessor unit   51
    3.3   Data transfer instructions   54
    3.4   Arithmetic instructions   58
    3.5   Logical instructions   60
    3.6   Branch control instructions   63
    3.7   Stack, input/output, and machine control instructions   65

Chapter 4   Programming with the M6800 and the I8085   **69**

  4.1   Programming techniques   69
  4.2   Comparison of the two instruction sets   91
  4.3   Program development techniques   93

Chapter 5   Introduction to Microcomputer Architecture   **97**

  5.1   Basic circuits   97
  5.2   Microprocessors and associated components   102
  5.3   Hardware support for input/output functions   108

MODULE II   INTERFACING WITH OTHER SYSTEMS

Chapter 6   Automating the Loading Process   **121**

  6.1   Microcomputer development systems and systems programs   121
  6.2   A typical cassette interface   122

Chapter 7   System Interface Programs   **137**

  7.1   Bootstrap and absolute loaders   137
  7.2   Relocating loaders   140
  7.3   Linking loaders   143
  7.4   Text editors   149

MODULE III   BUILDING A RESIDENT SOFTWARE SYSTEM

Chapter 8   High-Level Language Programming   **153**

  8.1   The PL/M programming language   153
  8.2   Structured programming and software engineering   180
  8.3   High-level versus assembly-language versus conventional
             machine-language programming   190

Chapter 9   Assembly Language Support   **195**

  9.1   The assembler function   195
  9.2   Macro assemblers   212
  9.3   Conditional assembly   222
  9.4   Cross, resident, and self-assemblers   225

Chapter 10   Advanced System Software Support   **227**

  10.1   Compilers   227
  10.2   Simulators and debuggers   241
  10.3   Traversing the levels   247

**MODULE IV   MICROPROCESSOR APPLICATIONS
AND INTERRUPT I/O**

Chapter 11   Microprocessor Interrupt Systems   253
    11.1   Interrupt-driven I/O   253
    11.2   An example using interrupt I/O   263

Chapter 12   Applications and Future Directions   267
    12.1   Utilizing microprocessors in dedicated systems   267
    12.2   Interprocessor communication   270
    12.3   Future directions   274

    Appendixes

    A   ASCII Code   277
    B   M6800 Instructions Listed Numerically by Opcode   281
    C   I8085 Instructions Listed Numerically by Opcode   285
    D   Motorola M6800 and Assembler Conventions   289
    E   Intel 8085 Assembler Conventions   299
    F   PL/M STAR Syntax Specification   309
    G   PL/M STAR Built-in Functions   317

    Bibliography   321

    Index   325

CHAPTER ONE

AN OVERVIEW OF COMPUTER ORGANIZATION

1.1 COMPUTING SYSTEMS IN GENERAL

In framing a definition of what constitutes a computing system, we tend to be heavily biased by the types of interaction we have had with such a system. For the most part, modern computing systems are viewed as mysterious machines that are capable of performing wondrous tasks, such as computing space-flight paths or predicting election results, and/or making disastrous mistakes, such as refusing to acknowledge that you paid last month's bill.

The mystique about the nature of computing systems has been reinforced by the lack of physical contact that is permitted with the machine. This situation is common even within a computer-science curriculum. Although beginning students in computer science are exposed to the process of programming (giving instructions to) computing systems, this exposure tends to reinforce the mystical illusion rather than dispel it. These students normally deal with a machine that seems to require meaningless commands and all too often returns meaningless messages. It is rare that beginning students even get to see the machine, which is usually locked away in a secure room and attended by the high priests of the field, i.e., computer operators, programmers, and technicians.

The objective of this text is to unravel the mysteries surrounding computers and thereby derive an accurate definition for a computing system. Our premise is that the best way to accomplish this is to encourage close interaction with these systems. For this reason our text uses microcomputer systems as case studies. For the time being we define microcomputers as small, inexpensive computers. These two attributes—i.e., small physical size and low cost—make these systems ideal for our use.

One point that should be stressed is that, while we are using microcomputers as case studies, we are really investigating computing system concepts that are common to all computing systems, even the large expensive ones that are locked away in secure rooms. Although microcomputers are currently being sold in neighborhood electronics shops and used in computer games, they are not toy systems. This fact is emphasized by the comparison figures shown in Table 1.1. In this table we compare the IBM 7090 computer, a very popular machine manufactured by International Business Machines in 1960, with a typical microcomputer system based on the M6800 microprocessor develorea by Motorola in 1970. The figures in this table highlight the fact that, despite the small cost of microcomputers, the computing power of these machines is significant. The cycle time listed in the table is a measure of the amount of time needed to transfer information in the computer. The cycle time for the M6800 is less than the cycle time for the IBM 7090, but the former has a smaller information unit.

The fact that microprocessors are used in an ever increasing number of applications, including automotive parts, point-of-sale terminals, and games, is a result of the low cost and small size of these components. We should not overlook the fact that they are also powerful computing machines. Since we are stressing the power of microprocessors and emphasizing the fact that we'll be studying computing concepts that are relevant for all computers, an obvious question is "Why do some computing systems sell for over a million dollars while others are marketed for under 300 dollars?" The distinction between large machines (maxis), medium-sized machines (minis) and small machines (micros) will be discussed in Sec. 1.5, after we have introduced enough computer terminology to make the discussion meaningful.

Table 1.1
IBM 7090/M6800 Comparisons

	IBM 7090	M6800
Cost	$3,000,000.00	$3,000.00
Cycle time	2.18×10^{-6} sec	1.0×10^{-6} sec
Memory	32768 units unit width: 36	65536 units unit width: 8

1.1.1 The Components of a Computing System

Computing systems consist of several components, not just the electronic circuits that are called the *hardware* components of the system. In a typical computing system we'll find a blend of hardware, software, and firmware components. The term *software* is used to refer to a set of programs or instructions that are executed by the hardware. Hardware can be viewed as a very inflexible part of a computing system; i.e., the electronic components are fixed and can be changed only with great difficulty. Software, on the other hand, is quite flexible since it is relatively easy to change one or more instructions. In terms of flexibility, firmware lies somewhere between hardware and software. *Firm-*

ware is a program or set of instructions, but it is normally encoded in a medium that makes it relatively difficult to change. The use of firmware is advantageous for programs that are never (or seldom) altered since firmware media are generally faster and less expensive than typical software media.

In studying computing systems, we must discuss hardware, software, firmware, and the interaction between these components. When viewed as a whole, computing systems are quite complex and seem to defy total comprehension. To overcome the complexity factor, we will investigate these systems in terms of a set of levels, moving to a new level only when we completely understand the preceding levels. The analysis of computing systems in terms of levels has been described in Tanenbaum (1976). We briefly review this approach in the following paragraphs.

1.1.2 Levels of Computing Systems

While computing systems taken in totality are very complex, the basic computer is actually a very simplistic device when viewed at its lowest level. At this level computers are viewed as machines that can only execute (directly in the hardware) instructions encoded in a language consisting entirely of 0's and 1's, i.e., the computer's machine language. Let us say that this language is at level L1.

Even though we can write programs in L1, it soon becomes very tedious and difficult. To overcome this problem, the computing system designer usually develops a new set of instructions that are more convenient for humans to use. These instructions form a new language, e.g., L2. Now the designer must specify a way of running L2 programs on the original machine. There are two ways of attacking this problem—*translation* and *interpretation.*

In the case of *translation,* an L1 program called a *translator* is used to replace each instruction of an L2 program by L1 instructions that perform the same function. Thus the translator accepts an L2 program as input and outputs an equivalent L1 program, which may then be executed on the machine.

Interpretation involves writing an L1 program (an *interpreter*) that will again accept L2 programs as input data. The interpreter decodes each L2 instruction and immediately executes an equivalent set of L1 instructions. Note that an equivalent L1 program is not created, i.e., each L2 instruction is decoded and directly executed. Thus two processes (interpretation and execution of the L2 program) are occurring simultaneously.

Translation and interpretation are methods of moving from one level (L2) to another (L1). Ordinary users are unaware of level transversal; e.g., FORTRAN programmers might feel that they are using a FORTRAN machine, just as the L2 and L1 programmers feel that they are using L2 and L1 machines, respectively. However, the L1 programmer is using a *real machine* while the L2 and FORTRAN programmers are using *virtual machines.* The L1 machine is real because L1 programs are directly executed in the hardware. L2 is a virtual machine since L2 programs must be either translated or interpreted to the L1 level before they are executed.

Early computers had only one level—the conventional machine language (CML) level. Modern computing systems are organized in terms of several levels. The notion of a two-level system was suggested by M. Wilkes in England (Wilkes, 1951). This machine was designed to have a built-in (unchangeable) interpreter, which would execute machine-language programs. In this approach, machine-language instructions were simulated, by the interpreter, with "microinstructions." At present, the micro level is common on most machines. The reader should be warned at this point not to confuse the use of the term micro in this context with the use of micro in microcomputer or microprocessor. The built-in unchangeable interpreter mentioned here is a firmware component of the system, which is used to define the control component of a computer. The instructions found in the interpreter were termed microinstructions because basic CML-level instructions were defined in terms of these lower-level instructions. In practice, the term *microprogramming* refers to the programming of the control function of a system; it does not refer to writing programs for microcomputers. A microcomputer may have a micro level also; i.e., its control function may be defined by a set of microprograms.

In the 1950's software components called *assemblers* and *compilers* were developed, and they added additional levels to the system. An assembler is a translator that supports an *assembly language,* i.e., a language that is very close to the CML-level instructions, but it is encoded in terms of mnemonic instructions and symbolic names. Compilers, which are also translators, support the so-called *high-level languages* (FORTRAN, PL/1, or PASCAL), which contain constructs that are quite dissimilar from the CML level and are designed to make programming much easier.

A final level was added in the 1960's when major advances were made in operating systems. *Operating systems* (OS) are software components that control the use of system resources and provide access to other software or hardware functions.

Figure 1.1 shows the levels available on most modern computing systems, together with the normal methods of level transversal. Note that two arrows emanate from the OS level, one to the CML level and one to the MP level. This is because the OS level actually consists of a mixture of OS-level and CML-level instructions. The OS instructions require interpretation down to the CML level, while the CML instructions can be passed directly to the MP level.

The five-level structure of Fig. 1.1 will be present in the computing systems we will examine in this text. In particular, we will develop a microcomputer system in the context of these levels.

Within the context of the hardware, software, and firmware components of a system, we should note that there are no rules that state at what level a function should be implemented. In some machines, for example, a multiply instruction is directly supported by the hardware while, in others, it must be

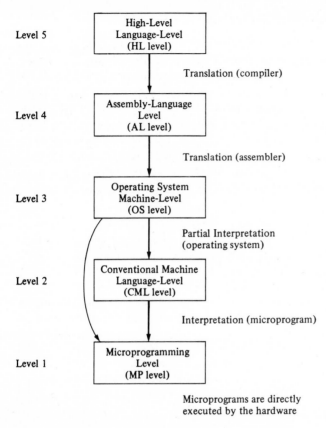

Fig. 1.1 Computing system levels.

simulated in the software. This is true of the more complex functions also. For instance, while we defined translators as software components, this definition is only generally, but not always, true. For example, on the SYMBOL-2R system, the translator is a hardware component (Anderberg, Smith, 1973). Hardware and software are functionally equivalent; i.e., any operation performed by software can be built directly into the hardware, and any instruction executed by the hardware can be simulated in the software. This observation applies to firmware also. In this text we will refer to functions as existing in the form in which they are typically implemented. The decision as to whether a function should be implemented in hardware, software, or firmware is usually dictated by economics rather than feasibility.

We begin our investigation of computer systems at the CML level. Although not the lowest level in modern machines, this is the level described in manufacturers' "Principles of Operation" manuals, and it was historically the lowest level.

1.2 THE BASIC HARDWARE COMPONENTS

A minimal computing-system configuration requires at least the following hardware components: Central processor unit (CPU), Memory, and input/output (I/O) interfaces. These might be arranged as shown in Fig. 1.2. The buses serve as links between the various hardware components and are generally bidirectional. The number of lines in (or width of) these buses varies depending on the particular bus and the system.

The CPU—often called the *microprocessor* (μP) in the case of micro-computers—is the core of any computing system. It includes a *control unit* (CU), an *arithmetic logic unit* (ALU), and various *registers* (Fig. 1.3).

Among the registers, we would typically expect to find the following:

1. *Accumulators* (one or more), which generally hold the results of the various operations being performed on the data. These registers would normally be of the same width (be composed of the same number of bits) as the data bus.

2. A *program counter* (PC), which at any time contains the address of the next instruction to be executed. This would normally be of the same width as the address bus.

3. A *condition code* or flag register, which consists of various flags indicating conditions such as arithmetic overflow or carry, a result "zero," etc.

Finally, we would expect to find other special-purpose registers that could be used to facilitate the accessing of memory. Registers such as index registers and stack pointers would fit into this category.

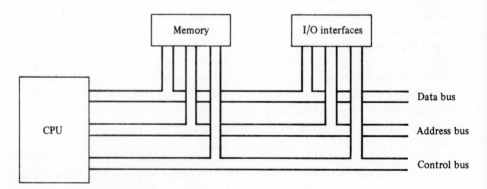

Fig. 1.2 Minimal computing system.

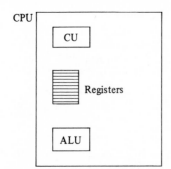

Fig. 1.3 Central processing unit.

In the basic operation of the computer, the following sequence of steps is taken:

1. The CPU fetches a machine-language instruction from the memory location indicated by the PC.

2. The PC is then updated to point to the next instruction.

3. The fetched instruction is decoded and executed by the CU.

4. Go to step (1).

The ALU facilitates those instructions calling for arithmetic or logical operations.

1.2.1 Number Systems

As we shall see later, a digital computer is constructed from two-state binary devices that can be either on or off. We shall refer to these states as 1 and 0, respectively. Such an individual binary device, or more precisely, the information it contains, is referred to as a *bit* (BInary digiT). The registers and memory units mentioned above might be regarded as groupings of these binary devices. Generally however, access to registers would be somewhat easier and faster than access to memory.

Since computers are constructed from binary devices, it is natural to utilize the binary (base 2) number system for the internal representation of numbers. Binary numbers involve only the two digits 0 and 1; and in the binary representation of an integer, each digit is weighted according to its position. Thus the value of the six-bit binary number $b_5 b_4 b_3 b_2 b_1 b_0$ is

$$b_5 \cdot 2^5 + b_4 \cdot 2^4 + b_3 \cdot 2^3 + b_2 \cdot 2^2 + b_1 \cdot 2^1 + b_0 \cdot 2^0.$$

Note that this is consistent with the usual interpretation of the digits comprising an integer. For example, the decimal (base 10) integer 324 is evaluated as $3 \cdot 10^2 + 2 \cdot 10^1 + 4 \cdot 10^0$.

The term *word* is often used to refer to the most commonly manipulated group of bits in a computer. Note that when words of size n bits are used, positive integers from $000\cdots0 = 0$ up through $11\cdots1 = 2^n - 1$ can be represented; or we may say that 2^n different numbers (or characters) can be represented or encoded by using words of size n.

Two other number systems, which are closely associated with the binary system and which are often used in conjunction with digital computing systems, are the octal (base 8) and hexadecimal (base 16) systems. The octal system utilizes the eight digits 0, 1, . . . ,7; the hexadecimal system utilizes the 16 digits 0,1, . . . ,9,A,B,C,D,E,F, corresponding to the integers 0,1,2, . . . ,15, respectively. In either system, the digits comprising the representation of a number are once again weighted on a positional basis. Thus the value of the four-digit octal number $n_3 n_2 n_1 n_0$ is

$$n_3 \cdot 8^3 + n_2 \cdot 8^2 + n_1 \cdot 8^1 + n_0 \cdot 8^0.$$

Similarly, the hexadecimal number 4B7 is evaluated as

$$4 \cdot 16^2 + B \cdot 16^1 + 7 \cdot 16^0 \qquad \text{or} \qquad 1207.$$

When working with numbers in different bases, it is customary to specify the base by suffixing an appropriate letter on the string of digits. We shall use the letters B, Q, H, and D to denote binary, octal, hexadecimal, and decimal numbers, respectively. If the letter is omitted, the default value is assumed to be D (decimal). Thus we may restate the example of the preceding paragraph by writing 4B7H = 1207D.

Since 8 and 16 are powers of 2, there is a close relationship between the binary number system and the octal and hexadecimal number systems. In particular, each group of three binary digits (which represents a number between 0 and 7, inclusively) corresponds to a single octal digit. Similarly, each group of four binary digits (which represents a number between 0 and 15, inclusively) corresponds to a single hexadecimal digit. Thus octal and hexadecimal numbers are useful for abbreviating longer binary numbers. For example, the number 11000101B may be compressed to C5H since 1100 in binary (or 12D) becomes C in hexadecimal, and 0101 in binary (or 5D) becomes 5 in hexadecimal. Alternatively, we may arrange 11000101B in groups of three starting from the right and abbreviate it in octal as 305Q.

The process used to convert a number to the decimal or base 10 representation from another base is implicit in the above discussion. Specifically, a number $d_k \cdots d_0$ in base B representation is converted to decimal representation by writing it as

$$d_k \cdot B^k + \cdots + d_0 \cdot B^0.$$

In order to convert a number N from a base 10 representation to another, say base B, representation, we can use the method of repeated division. Specifically, N divided by B yields a quotient Q_1 and a remainder R_1. R_1 is the least significant digit of the base B representation of N. Then Q_1 divided by B yields a second quotient Q_2 and remainder R_2. R_2 is the next smallest significant digit in the base B representation of N, etc. This process is illustrated by finding the hexadecimal representation of the decimal number 372:

$$372/16 = 23, \quad \text{remainder 4;}$$
$$23/16 = 1, \quad \text{remainder 7;}$$
$$1/16 = 0, \quad \text{remainder 1.}$$

Hence, 174H is the hexadecimal representation of 372D.

1.2.2 Representing Negative Integers

The preceding discussion has been concerned only with the representation of positive integers. A common way of handling negative numbers is to use the most significant bit (leftmost) as a sign bit, with 0 indicating a positive number and 1 a negative number. Thus, for example, with a word size of six bits, using the leftmost bit for the sign and the remaining five bits for the magnitude, all integers between -31 and 31 can be represented. This is called the *sign/magnitude* system. Table 1.2 below gives several examples of integers represented in the sign/magnitude system.

Table 1.2
Representing integers

Decimal number	Six-bit Sign/magnitude representation	Six-bit One's complement representation	Six-bit Two's complement representation
+31	011111	011111	011111
+23	010111	010111	010111
+17	010001	010001	010001
+ 6	000110	000110	000110
+ 0	000000	000000	000000
− 0	100000	111111	000000
− 6	100110	111001	111010
−17	110001	101110	101111
−23	110111	101000	101001
−31	111111	100000	100001

A second method of representing negative integers is the *one's complement* system. Here the representation of a negative number is obtained from the sign/magnitude representation of corresponding positive number by *complementing* each bit. Thus if we assume a word size of six bits, the one's complement representation of $+17$ is obtained by complementing each bit of -17 or 010001 to give 101110. Table 1.2 again illustrates the representation of various positive and negative integers in the one's complement system. Note that in both the sign/magnitude and the one's complement systems, $+0$ and -0 have distinct representations.

The *two's complement* system provides yet another technique for representing negative integers. The two's complement of an integer is obtained by adding 1 (using binary addition) to the one's complement of the integer. Thus, again assuming a word size of six bits, the two's complement representation of -6 is obtained by adding 1 to 111001, producing 111010. Table 1.2 includes the representations of various integers in the two's complement system. Note that in all the systems we have considered, the high-order bit is 0 for positive integers and 1 for negative integers.

1.2.3 Integer Arithmetic

The two's complement system will be used for the representation of integers in the machines that will be considered in this book. With this system, addition can be done directly without having to first examine the signs of the numbers involved. In particular, addition is the only operation needed since subtraction can be performed by adding the negative of the number, that is, $A - B = A + (-B)$. Moreover, the addition process yields information about the magnitude of the resulting sum. Relative to the addition operation, we single out two of the various possible carries, namely a *carry in* to the sign bit and a *carry out* of the sign bit. When using the two's complement system, a binary addition that results in exactly one of these two possible carries has produced a sum that is too large to fit into one word. In other words, the occurrence of exactly one of these two carries signals *overflow*. This feature is illustrated in greater detail in the examples of Table 1.3 below. Here again, a word size of six bits is assumed.

Most computers provide some means of signaling to the programmer when an overflow occurs. It is clear that such an overflow signal can be made available through the hardware as a function of the two carries noted above.

A "carry flag" is available on most computers to indicate whether or not a carry out of the high-order (sign) bit occurred as the result of an addition operation. Typically the carry flag would also be used to indicate whether or not a borrow occurred as the result of a subtraction operation.

Table 1.3
Two's complement arithmetic

Addition example	Two's complement arithmetic	
7	000111	
4	000100	No carries
	001011	
8	001000	Two carries
− 4	111100	No overflow
	000100	
5	000101	
− 7	111001	No carries
	111110	
− 5	111011	Two carries
−15	110001	No overflow
	101100	
− 26	100110	One carry
− 9	110111	Overflow
	011101	
17	010001	One carry
21	010101	Overflow
	100110	

When using the two's complement system and a word size of n bits, all integers from -2^{n-1} to $+2^{n-1}-1$ can be represented; the binary string $100\cdots0$ is taken as -2^{n-1} and is unique in that it is its own two's complement.

1.2.4 Logical Operations

The arithmetic operations discussed in the preceding section are utilized primarily on numeric data. Computers also generally provide a set of logical operations, which can be useful when dealing with nonnumeric data. Although the specific operations that are available vary from one computer to another, the operations of AND, OR, EXCLUSIVE OR, and COMP (NEGATION) are typical. AND, OR, and EXCLUSIVE OR are binary (two-operand) operations; COMP is a unary (one-operand) operation. In all cases the operands are individual bits; the operations are extended to groups of bits by applying the operations to the respective bits (or pairs of bits).

In what follows, we shall often denote AND by the symbol $\cdot$, OR by $+$, EXCLUSIVE OR by $\oplus$, and COMP by $^-$. Table 1.4 defines the four logical operations.

Table 1.4
Definitions of logical operations

X	Y	$X \cdot Y$	$X + Y$	$X \oplus Y$	$\bar{X}$
0	0	0	0	0	1
0	1	0	1	1	1
1	0	0	1	1	0
1	1	1	1	0	0

As an example to illustrate how these operations are extended to groups of bits, we let A and B be the six-bit strings 010101 and 001110, respectively. We now apply the operations one bit at a time. For example,

$$
\begin{array}{rr}
A & 010101 \\
B & 001110 \\
\hline
A \cdot B & 000100
\end{array}
$$

Similarly, $A + B = 011111$, $A \oplus B = 011011$, and $\bar{A} = 101010$.

1.2.5 Nonnumeric Data

In addition to representing numbers, binary words are often used to represent nonnumeric data such as alphabetic characters. To achieve this, each character (letter, digit, punctuation mark) is encoded by a different pattern of bits. As noted earlier, assuming a word size of n bits, up to 2^n different characters can be encoded.

For most applications, more than $64 = 2^6$ characters are needed and thus seven- or eight-bit character codes must be used. One widely used seven-bit code is the American Standard Code for Information Interchange (or ASCII) code. The most common eight-bit code is the IBM EBCDIC code. We shall be primarily concerned with the ASCII code, extended to eight bits by setting the leftmost bit to zero. A listing of this code appears in Appendix A.

Some equipment will modify a particular code by adding a *parity check bit*. Setting this bit so that the total number of 1's in each extended code word is even (odd) is called establishing even (odd) parity. For example, by adding a parity check bit on the left to establish even parity,

1011000	becomes	11011000,

and

0011011	becomes	00011011.

In many data-transmission environments, interference or "noise" in the transmission channel will occasionally cause a bit value to be changed. A parity check bit is often used to aid in detecting such errors, for, if all trans-

mitted words have even parity, an error occurring in any one bit during transmission will cause a word to have odd parity and hence the error can be
detected by checking parity upon reception. (Note that errors in two bits or
any even number of bits will go undetected with this technique.) When there is
a relatively low probability of an error occurring in any particular bit, the
addition of a parity check bit provides a fairly efficient error-detection
technique.

The term *byte* is often used to refer to a group of bits used by a particular
computer to encode a single character. A normally equivalent definition of
byte is that it is the *smallest addressable unit* of memory in a computer. For us,
a byte, and the width of the data bus, will generally consist of eight bits.
Address buses in our computing systems will generally be 16 bits wide. Note
that this implies the potential for addressing 2^{16} units or bytes of memory.
($2^{10} = 1024$ is often abbreviated as 1K; 2^{16} then becomes 64K).

EXERCISES

1. Find the decimal representations of each of the following numbers:

   a) 2AH   b) 10111001B   c) 734Q

   d) C5BH   e) 162Q

2. Find both the octal and hexadecimal representations of each of the following
   numbers:

   a) 274   b) 101101101B

   c) 1237   d) 399D

3. Write each of the following decimal integers in the two's complement system
   using an eight-bit word:

   a) 17   b) −1   c) 62

   d) −126   e) 111

4. Assuming an eight-bit word, what decimal integer is represented, in the two's
   complement system, by each of the following?

   a) 01101110   b) 10010011   c) 10000000

   d) 01111111   e) 10101010

5. Let $X = 01101110$ and $Y = 10010011$. Find $X \cdot \bar{Y}$, $\bar{X} \cdot Y$, and $X + Y$.
   Compare $X \oplus Y$ with $(X \cdot \bar{Y}) + (\bar{X} \cdot Y)$.

Laboratory Assignment
This exercise is designed to introduce you to the monitor functions on your microcomputer and should be carried out with the help of your microcomputer's user's
manual.

1. Find the keyboard key that places you in the "Register Examine" mode. What
   number representation system is used by your microcomputer?

2. Enter the memory examine mode. Note the contents of some specific location. Now modify the contents of this location and subsequently confirm the effects of your modification. Does the monitor provide any efficient means of examining successive memory locations?

3. Determine your microcomputer's "halt" instruction. Write a short program (possibly a sample program from the user's manual) and load your program in memory. Now have your microcomputer execute the program. Examine the effects of your program's execution.

4. Does your microcomputer's monitor provide any capability for halting an executing program at some point internal to the program? Examine any such facilities.

1.3 INSTRUCTION FORMATS

In the previous sections, we have informally referred to a program as a set of instructions for a computer. In this section we examine some typical formats that are used in representing and encoding instructions.

1.3.1 Addresses in Instructions

Instructions specify some operation that is denoted by an opcode where an *opcode,* short for *op*eration *code*, is simply an encoding used to denote an operation. In addition, if the operation requires data, one or more addresses (specifying where the data can be found) are included in the instruction. For this discussion we'll assume that data is referenced by specifying (in the instruction) the address of the memory location holding the data. The number of addresses present in a given instruction will vary from one processor to another and will even vary among the instructions of a given processor. In the following paragraphs we will confine our attention to binary arithmetic operations—i.e., arithmetic operations involving two operands—and indicate how these operations might be represented on various machines.

In addition to requiring two operands, binary arithmetic operations of course determine a result. Within this context, we might use an instruction with four fields, i.e.,

```
opcode      address1 ,address2 ,address3
```

As a specific example of this, consider

```
ADD       A , B , C   ; C = A + B
```

In this and subsequent examples, we are using a semicolon (;) to indicate a comment. Comments are used to specify the meaning of the instruction. For this example, address1 (A) and address2 (B) specify the operands of the ADD instruction, while address3 (C) specifies the result address, i.e., the address where the sum is stored. Instructions such as the above are typical on a three-address machine. On such a machine, the FORTRAN statement A = (B*C) − D might be replaced by the following AL statements:

```
MULT        B , C , T 1        ; T 1 = B * C
SUB         T 1 , D , A        ; A = T 1 − D
```

In this example, a temporary location (T1) has been introduced to hold the intermediate value (B*C). Some care must be taken in rewriting the FORTRAN statements in AL code. In particular, we must make sure that we preserve the original FORTRAN meaning—that is, A takes on the value of (B*C) − D and *the values of* B, *C, and* D *do not change.* In light of the above,

```
MULT        B, C, A        ; A = B * C
SUB         A , D , A       ; A = A − D
```

would be an appropriate three-address AL representation, whereas

```
MULT        B, C, B        ; B = B * C
SUB         B, D, A        ; A = B − D
```

would not, since the value of B is changed.

Three-address instructions tend to be "costly" in terms of the amount of space they require in order to store all three addresses and in terms of their execution time (e.g., more time is required to fetch all three addresses). For this reason two-address instructions, in which one of the operand addresses doubles as the result address, are more common; e.g.,

```
ADD         A , B        ; B = A + B
MOV         X , Y        ; Y = X
```

In a two-address machine, the FORTRAN statement A = (B*C) − D might be represented as

```
MOV         C , T 1        ; T 1 = C
MULT        B , T 1        ; T 1 = B * T 1
MOV         D , A          ; A = D
SUB         T 1 , A        ; A = T 1 − A
```

By using the accumulator (ACC) as an implied operand, two-address instructions can be compressed into one-address instructions; e.g.,

```
LOAD        A        ; ACC = A
ADD         X        ; ACC = ACC + X
STORE       Y        ; Y = ACC
```

In a one-address format we can represent the FORTRAN statement A = (B*C) − D as

```
LOAD        B        ; ACC = B
MULT        C        ; ACC = ACC * C
SUB         D        ; ACC = ACC − D
STORE       A        ; A = ACC
```

One can go even further in removing addresses from instructions and consider a zero-address instruction format. In this format, both the operand addresses and the result address must be implied. To accomplish this, a data structure known as a stack is maintained in the computer's memory. A *stack* is organized such that elements may be placed on it (via a PUSH operation) or removed from it (via a POP operation). Entries (deletions) are always made to (from) the top of the stack. For binary operations—e.g., ADD, SUB, MULT, etc.—it is assumed that the top two entries on the stack are the operands. The result is placed back on the stack; e.g.,

```
PUSH      A      |    A    |   ← Top of stack.

PUSH      B      |    B    |   ← Top of stack
                 |    A    |

ADD              |  A+B    |   ← Top of stack
```

The diagrams are used to illustrate the effect of the instructions on the stack. The entries in the stack denote the values of the operands, e.g., for "PUSH A", A's value is placed on the stack. An internal pointer, often called the *stack pointer,* is used on machines that support zero-address formats. This pointer is adjusted automatically by the instructions that add elements to or delete elements from the stack so that the stack pointer always indicates the current top of the stack. In the zero address format, the FORTRAN statement $A = (B*C) - D$ becomes

```
PUSH      B      |    B    |   ← Top of stack

PUSH      C      |    C    |   ← Top of stack
                 |    B    |

MULT             |  B*C    |   ← Top of stack

PUSH      D      |    D    |   ← Top of stack
                 |  B*C    |

SUB              | (B*C)-D |   ← Top of stack

POP       A      |         |   Empty stack
```

As a result of the "POP A", A is assigned the value of $(B*C) - D$—that is, the value at the top of the stack when the POP is executed. Note that, after this instruction is executed, the stack is empty. Also note that this format uses both one-address instructions (PUSH and POP) and zero-address instructions (ADD, SUB, and MULT).

1.3.2 Encoding Instructions

Instructions consisting of opcodes and addresses must be encoded as 0's and 1's, just as numbers and character data are. Instruction size refers to the number of bits needed to encode an instruction. There are several factors that influence instruction size. We consider some of these below.

One influence on instruction size is the number of different operations that can be performed on a machine. Obviously we must have enough bits to uniquely encode all of the opcodes for these operations. If we use n bits to encode the opcode, then 2^n distinct opcodes can be represented; e.g., for $n = 5$, we can have 32 different opcodes.

In determining the number of bits necessary to represent an address, we need to consider the total number of addresses in the address space and the memory unit that is specified by an address. Consider, for example, a machine that supports a memory space consisting of 4096 (4K) words, where each word consists of two eight-bit bytes. If we let a memory address denote a word, then we need 12 bits ($2^{12} = 4096$) to encode an address. If, on the other hand, we use an address to denote a byte, we'll need 13 bits ($2^{13} = 8192$) to encode an address. We could even consider giving an address to each bit; and for this case, 16 bits are needed to represent an address, since there are 65536 bits on the machine ($2^{16} = 65536$). The smallest addressable quantity on a machine determines the memory resolution of the machine. A bit-addressable machine would have the finest memory resolution, but it would require the largest number of bits to specify an address.

The determination of memory resolution has an impact on the programming of certain tasks. To illustrate this point, consider machine A, which is byte-addressable, versus machine B, which is word-addressable. We will assume that machine A uses 13 bits to specify an address, while machine B uses 12 bits. Instruction size will therefore be slightly larger for machine A. Let us further assume that on both machines, eight bits, or a byte, is used to encode a character. Within this framework, consider the comparative ease (or difficulty) in implementing two common programming techniques: large memory-movement operations and character compares.

Large memory-movement operations—i.e., moving the contents of n locations beginning at address X to n locations beginning at address Y—is more efficiently performed by using a larger memory-resolution factor. For example, if we assume that machines A and B both use an instruction that moves the contents of one memory unit to another in accomplishing the memory-movement operation, then machine A will have to execute such an instruction twice as often as machine B will. This is a result of the fact that, on machine A, each such operation will move a byte value, whereas a word value is moved for the same operation on machine B.

In general, comparison operations are more easily performed when the memory resolution of the machine matches the comparison item. For example, in comparing word values, a single comparison would suffice on machine B while two comparisons would be needed on machine A. If we consider byte comparisons, the advantage lies with machine A, where a single comparison would compare two byte values. If the memory resolution is larger than the comparison item, we can consider two solutions: one that conserves space and one that conserves time. Consider, for example, searching for an occurrence of character$_r$ in memory starting at location X on machine B. From the programmer's point of view, it would be easier to implement this if only one character were stored per word, with the remainder of the word used to hold some constant value (v), thus,

word 1		word 2		word 3		
v	character$_1$	v	character$_2$	v	character$_3$	. . .

Using this scheme a loop could be set up that would compare each word fetched from memory with the word

v	character$_r$

While this method is easy to program it does waste space since it uses twice as much space as is necessary to hold the character values in memory. To conserve memory the characters should be stored as shown below, i.e., two characters per word.

word 1		word 2		word 3		
character$_1$	character$_2$	character$_3$	character$_4$	character$_5$	character$_6$	. . .

The space conservation implies a penalty on machine B, however. In searching for character$_r$, a loop could be used, but each pass through the loop would require splitting the fetched memory word into two word values; for example,

v	character$_i$

v	character$_j$

and then comparing these values with

v	character$_r$

This solution would require extra instructions and more processing time.

Instruction size is equal to the sum of the bits required to encode the opcode and the bits required to encode the addresses needed for the instruction. If we consider the three-, two-, one-, and zero-address instruction formats discussed earlier in this section, it is obvious that instruction size is larger for formats requiring more addresses (assuming the number of bits needed for an address is held constant). The space saved by using a shorter format, one requiring fewer addresses, is offset somewhat by the fact that a given problem generally requires more instructions to encode using a shorter format than it would require if a longer format were used. However, shorter formats tend to be more conservative on storage even when this factor is considered.

The relationships between instruction size, word size, and byte size are designed to minimize or totally eliminate any wasted space. To achieve this, word size should be a multiple of byte size, and instruction size should be a multiple of word size. Flexibility can be gained without wasting space by permitting variable-sized instructions within the same machine. For example, both two-address and one-address formats could be used on the same machine by using a bit in the instruction itself to indicate which format is being used.

The bit-transfer rate—i.e., the number of bits per second that can be read from memory—is another factor that influences instruction size. If S denotes the number of bits in an instruction and B the bit transfer rate, then I, the number of instructions the CPU can execute in one second, should be close to SB, for, if I is less than SB, the CPU is being overloaded, since more instructions can be read from memory in one second than the CPU can execute in that time. On the other hand, if I is greater than SB, the CPU will be idle part of the time while waiting for new instructions to arrive.

EXERCISES

1. Write the AL code for the FORTRAN statement

$$X = (Y + Z) - (M* N)$$

   using three, two, one, and zero addressing formats. Use the instructions shown in this section for each format.

2. The FLEX computer has a total of 35 instructions. Of these, fifteen require two six-bit addresses, ten require one eight-bit address, and twenty require no addresses. Devise an efficient scheme for encoding these instructions, one instruction per word. (*Hint.* Use an *expanding opcode* scheme; that is, using four bits, let 0000, . . . , 1110 encode the fifteen two-address instructions. Then let 1111 serve as the initial segment of the opcode for the remaining thirty instructions. Now repeat the process for the ten instructions with one address, etc.)

3. Assume you have decided to manufacture a processor with a word size of 12 bits. An instruction in the processor will be one word in length. Discuss the advantages and disadvantages of each of the following architecture proposals.

    a) i) 32 one-address instructions, where an address is represented in seven bits;
        ii) six bits are used to represent a character.

    b) i) 48 one-address instructions, where an address is represented in six bits;
        ii) eight bits are used to represent a character.

1.4 ADDRESSING MODES

In addition to specifying addresses, an instruction must indicate how the addresses should be interpreted. As we shall see, some flexibility in the interpretation of addresses is essential.

The most natural form of addressing is *direct addressing*. In this mode, the actual location of the operand is given by the indicated address as specified in the instruction. For example,

ADD   5

would imply that the contents of memory location 5 is to be added to the accumulator. In discussing addressing modes, we shall want to determine the *effective address* (EA) specified by the indicated address and the addressing mode. The EA is the actual location of the operand. As indicated above, for direct addressing the location of the operand is given by the indicated address, so for this example EA = location 5.

Example (direct addressing)

Before	Instruction	After
ACC [4]		ACC [7]
	ADD 5	
Location		Location
5 [3]		5 [3]

If a processor has a set of high-speed registers available, it will support a form of *register addressing*. In this mode the location of the operand is the specified register. For example,

ADD   R5

would imply that the contents of register 5 (EA = register 5) are added to the accumulator. Since there are relatively few registers in processors, as compared to the number of memory locations, register addressing is very economical with respect to the number of bits needed to specify an address. Register addressing is actually a specialized form of direct addressing.

Example (register addressing)

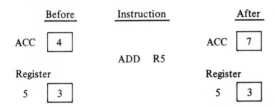

Although direct addressing is straightforward and readily applicable to many types of problems, it becomes awkward in certain situations. For example, when we must successively access a sequence of consecutive memory locations, it is convenient to have some built-in facility for address modification. One technique for achieving this is *indirect addressing*. In the indirect-addressing mode the effective address is contained in the indicated address. For example, if we use parentheses* to indicate the indirect mode, then

$$ADD \qquad (5)$$

would imply that the contents of the location found in location 5 are added to the accumulator. For this example, EA = (location 5).

Example (indirect addressing)

	Before	Instruction		After
ACC	4		ACC	6
		ADD (5)		
Location			Location	
5	3		5	3
Location			Location	
3	2		3	2

A second common method for effecting efficient address modification is to utilize a special hardware register known as an *index register*. The *indexed addressing* mode is available on processors that have an index register. The general rule for finding the effective address in this mode is to add the contents

---

*The use of parentheses around a location to denote the contents of that location is very common in the literature.

of the index register to the indicated address (offset). If we use "X" to denote the indexed addressing mode, then

$$\text{ADD} \qquad 5 \text{, X}$$

would imply that the contents of the location determined by adding 5 to the index register are added to the accumulator. In this example $EA = 5 + $ (index register).

Example (indexed addressing)

Before	Instruction	After

ACC [4]   ACC [12]

                        ADD   5,X

Index
register [2]   Index
                                                    register [2]

Location   Location
7 [8]   7 [8]

An additional addressing mode found on many processors is the *relative addressing* mode. In this mode the address of the operand is specified "relative to" the address of the current instruction. For example, if we use "%" to denote the relative addressing mode, then

$$\text{ADD} \qquad \% \, 4$$

would imply that the contents of the location that is determined by adding 4 to the current value of the instruction counter are to be added to the accumulator. In this regard, it should be noted that when a given instruction is being executed, the instruction counter normally will point to the following instruction. Thus, if the instruction

$$\text{ADD} \qquad \% \, 4$$

were at location 100, we would have $EA = 101 + 4$, so that the contents of location 105 would be added to the accumulator.

Example (relative addressing)

Before	Instruction	After

ACC [4]   100 ADD %4   ACC [7]
                  101   —
                  102   —
                  103   —
                  104   —
                  105   3

Another addressing mode found on many processors is the *immediate addressing* mode. In this mode, the value appearing in the operand field (i.e., the specified address) is itself the operand. Since we have defined the effective address to be the location of the operand, for immediate addressing the effective address is the address of the operand within the instruction. If we use "#" to denote immediate addressing, then

        ADD   # 5

would imply that the number 5 is to be added to the accumulator.

Example (immediate addressing)

Before	Instruction	After
ACC $\boxed{4}$	ADD #5	ACC $\boxed{9}$

Most processors utilize instructions that do not naturally fit into any of the modes listed above. These include instructions whose mode is effectively determined by the function they perform. Instructions of this form are said to be in the *implied addressing* mode. An example of this group would be a "clear accumulator" instruction.

In Chapters 2 and 3 we will analyze the instruction sets and addressing modes found on two specific microcomputers: the Motorola M6800 and the Intel 8085.

EXERCISES

1. Given the following initial conditions:

  ACC $\boxed{4}$ Index register $\boxed{1}$

  Register

  3 $\boxed{2}$

  Location

  4 $\boxed{2}$

  Location

  7 $\boxed{4}$

Indicate how you can add "2" to ACC using (a) direct addressing, (b) register addressing, (c) indirect addressing, (d) indexed addressing, and (e) immediate addressing.

2. The PDP-8 minicomputer uses a paging scheme in accessing main memory. Memory is divided into pages, where each page consists of one hundred and twenty-eight 12-bit words. The instruction format is given below.

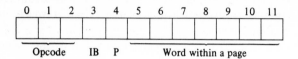

Bits 0–2: opcode
Bit   3: Indirect bit
           (Bit 3 = 0 implies direct addressing, Bit 3 = 1 implies indirect addressing.)
Bit   4: Page bit
           (Bit 4 = 0 implies a reference to page 0, Bit 4 = 1 implies a reference to the current page, which is determined from the program counter.)

```
0                   4  5                        11
 _____  _____
| Current page       || Word within current page |
 ‾‾‾‾‾‾‾‾‾‾‾‾‾‾‾‾‾‾‾‾  ‾‾‾‾‾‾‾‾‾‾‾‾‾‾‾‾‾‾‾‾‾‾‾‾‾
```
                    Program counter

How much of main memory is directly addressable under this scheme? How much is indirectly addressable?

3. Assume that X and N are memory locations with (N) a positive integer. Suppose one wishes to add the contents of X, X + 1, . . . , X + (N) using the accumulator to keep the running sum. Discuss the problems of doing this if only direct addressing is available. How would the presence of an indirect addressing capability ease the problem? How could an indexed addressing capability be utilized to solve the problem?

1.5 MAXIS, MINIS, AND MICROS

It is fairly common today to speak of a computer hardware system belonging to one of three groups: the maxi or large computer group, the mini or medium-sized computer group, or the micro or small computer group. The most visible distinction between these groups is the cost of these systems. Microcomputers, often viewed as a computer on a "chip," can cost as little as a few hundred dollars. A minicomputer, sometimes called a computer on a "board," is generally priced in the $20,000 to $100,000 range, depending on peripherals. Large maxicomputers can cost several million dollars.

There are certain physical characteristics that currently differ in these systems. For example, as of 1978, word size on microcomputers is usually eight bits, on minicomputers it is generally in the 12–16-bit range, and for maxicomputers 32 bits is typical. Relative to memory capacity, large computers have memory sizes ranging up to several million bytes; for minis maximum memory sizes of 64K to 128K are typical; and for micros the corresponding figures might be 32K to 64K. Instruction set size is another easy-to-measure difference, with the larger machines supporting larger numbers of instructions.

While the characteristics listed above are valid distinctions for 1978, it would be very misleading to classify a system on only these properties. Microcomputer manufacturers are already developing 16-bit and 32-bit microcomputers, and memory capacity is expanding for both micros and minis.

A more fundamental distinction can be based on the *computing power* of these systems; computing power denotes a measure of the amount of computing that can be done by a system in a given amount of time. Computing power is related to instruction speed, which varies considerably in these systems; from 200,000 instructions/second in micros to several million instructions/second in fast maxicomputers. In addition, the utilization of the CPU affects computing power; e.g., a slow processor that is used 100 percent of the time may exhibit more computing power than a faster processor that is used only 10 percent of the time.

It is in fact very common that the CPU remains idle during a large percentage of the time that a program is being processed. This is due to the fact that programs quite often engage in input and output activities, and these activities are several orders of magnitude slower than the CPU itself. For example, a program that is looping in an input/process/output loop may spend only one percent of the time processing (CPU active) and 99 percent of the time performing input/output (CPU idle). A major distinction between maxis, minis, and micros can be made on the basis of computing power. Maxis are primarily intended for use in a multi-user environment. To support this environment, a fast processor that is capable of operating with close to 100 percent CPU utilization is necessary. Micros are generally intended for use in a single-user environment where CPU utilization is not an important factor.

REFERENCES AND SUPPORTIVE MATERIAL

Section 1.1. The overview of computing systems is made in terms of the "levels" approach followed by Tanenbaum, 1976. Additional reference material on each of the respective levels appears at the end of the chapters discussing these particular levels.

Sections 1.2, 1.3, 1.4, 1.5. Much of the material in these sections is assumed to be background material. As such, it is available in various forms in most introductory texts on computing systems including: Gear, 1974; Stone, 1972; and Tanenbaum, 1976. Osborne (1976) and Leventhal (1976) are introductory texts which deal specifically with microcomputers and are recommended for their supportive coverage of much of the material in this text. Finally, Garner (1965) is recommended as a specific reference on concepts of binary-number systems.

1. Anderberg, J. W., and C. L. Smith [1973], "High-level language translation in SYMBOL-2R." SIGPLAN Notices, 8:11.

2. Garner, H. L. [1965], "Number systems and arithmetic." in *Advances in Computers.* **6**, Academic Press.

3. Gear, C. W. [1974], *Computer Organization and Programming.* New York: McGraw-Hill.

4. Leventhal, L. A. [1978], *Introduction to Microprocessors: Software, Hardware, Programming.* Englewood Cliffs, N.J.: Prentice-Hall.

5. Osborne, A. [1976], *An Introduction to Microcomputers, Volume I: Basic Concepts.* Berkeley, California: Adam Osborne and Associates, Inc.

6. Stone, H. S. [1972], *Introduction to Computer Organization and Data Structures.* New York: McGraw-Hill.

7. Tanenbaum, A. S. [1976], *Structured Computer Organization.* Englewood Cliffs, N.J.: Prentice-Hall.

8. Wilkes, M. V. [1951], "The best way to design an automatic calculating machine." Manchester University Computer Inaugural Conference, July 1951.

CHAPTER TWO

THE MOTOROLA M6800
INSTRUCTION SET

2.1 CHAPTER OVERVIEW

In this chapter we shall take a close look at the Motorola M6800 microprocessor (hereafter referred to as the M6800) and its instruction set. We begin by considering the organization of the CPU and then look at the individual instructions. The instructions are presented in rather natural groups and typical instructions from each group are examined with respect to the action they effect, the flags they set, etc. Later, in Chapter 4, we shall consider various program segments composed of M6800 instructions.

2.2 THE MICROPROCESSOR UNIT

Programming a computer at the CML level requires that the programmer have a detailed knowledge of the program-accessible registers that are available in the CPU. The registers that are accessible on the M6800 are noted in Fig. 2.1.

The M6800 has two eight-bit accumlators, denoted by ACCA and ACCB, and a single 16-bit index register (XR) that is used to support the indexed addressing mode. The program counter (PC) and the stack pointer (SP) are 16-bit special-purposes registers. The PC controls the execution of a program in that, at any given point in a computation, the PC holds the address of the next instruction that will be executed. The SP, via the value it holds, defines a stack structure in memory. The SP value, which is an address, specifies *the next free byte available in the stack.* In other words, if SP holds the value m, then the next push-type operation (see Sec. 1.3.1) would place a byte value in memory location m. The M6800 stack expands toward lower memory as elements are added to the stack, and contracts toward higher memory as elements are deleted. For example, if SP holds the value m, then an attempt to push value v in the stack would result in value v being placed in location m and SP

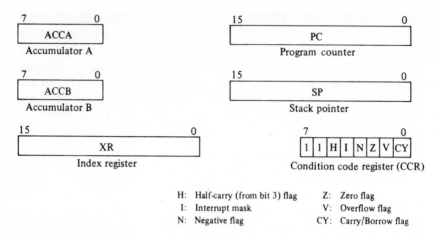

H: Half-carry (from bit 3) flag   Z: Zero flag
I: Interrupt mask   V: Overflow flag
N: Negative flag   CY: Carry/Borrow flag

Fig. 2.1 M6800 program accessible registers.

taking on the value $m - 1$. For a pull operation, again assuming that we start with SP $= m$, the byte value held in location $m + 1$ is popped and SP is set to $m + 1$.

The Condition Code Register (CCR) contains six bit values that can be used by a programmer. These values are held in bits 0–5 of the CCR. As indicated in Fig. 2.1, bits 6 and 7 always read as a logical 1 and therefore contain no useful information.

Bit 4 of the CCR indicates the status of the interrupt system of the M6800. A 0 value in bit 4 indicates that the interrupt system is enabled, a 1 indicates that it is disabled. (The significance of this is explored in Chapter 5.)

The remaining five values provide information concerning the result of a previous operation. Bit 2, for example, is set (to 1) if the previous operation produced a zero result and reset (to 0) if the result was nonzero. The negative flag, bit 3, is set if the result was negative and reset if it was positive. The M6800 uses two's complement arithmetic, so a negative result is indicated whenever bit 7, the most signficant bit, is set.

The carry/borrow flag (CY), bit 0, is set after an addition operation if there was a carry from bit 7 of the result, and reset otherwise. For a subtraction or a comparison operation, the CY flag is set if the absolute value of the second operand is larger than the absolute value of the first operand, and reset otherwise.

Bit 5 of the CCR, the half-carry flag, is set only when an addition operation results in a carry-out of bit 3 of the result. The half-carry flag is not used for subtraction or comparison operations, but rather in doing decimal (as opposed to binary) additions.

The V flag, bit 1 of the CCR, is used to signal that an overflow has occurred as a result of the previous operation. An overflow condition is said to exist whenever the result is too large to be stored as an eight-bit value—i.e., if the result is greater than 127 or less than -128. This condition can be detected by examining the sign bits of the two operands and the sign bit of the result. An abnormal sign change (e.g., adding two positive numbers and getting a negative result) signals an overflow. The overflow conditions for addition and subtraction are shown in Table 2.1, where

$$a_7 = \text{sign bit of first operand,}$$
$$b_7 = \text{sign bit of second operand,}$$
$$r_7 = \text{sign bit of result.}$$

The M6800 supports variable-length instruction formats. Instructions may be one, two or three bytes in length, with the opcode always being the first byte. Both one-address and zero-address instructions are used. In multiple-byte instructions, the second and third bytes of the instruction contain address information.

The M6800 supports the direct, indexed, relative, register, immediate, and implied addressing modes. There are actually two forms of direct addressing supported on this processor depending on the number of bytes used to specify the address. The direct addressing mode, in which the effective address is specified in two bytes, is referred to as *extended addressing* in Motorola's literature. The term "direct addressing" is then reserved for the restricted case where the effective address is specified by one byte. Hence, direct addressing is limited to those locations in the range 0 to 255 (decimal).

Table 2.1
Overflow conditions

(a) Addition				(b) Subtraction			
a_7	b_7	r_7	v	a_7	b_7	r_7	v
0	0	0	0	0	0	0	0
0	0	1	1	0	0	1	0
0	1	0	0	0	1	0	0
0	1	1	0	0	1	1	1
1	0	0	0	1	0	0	1
1	0	1	0	1	0	1	0
1	1	0	1	1	1	0	0
1	1	1	0	1	1	1	0

In a similar manner, when relative addressing is used, only one byte is used to specify the relative offset. The offset is interpreted as a two's complement binary number in the range -128 to $+127$ (decimal). In the M6800 system, relative addressing is used only in conjunction with certain transfer-of-control statements. The one-byte limit on the offset thereby implies that transfer of control by these instructions is limited to range PC + 127 and PC -128, where PC is the updated PC value.

Indexed addressing also has a one-byte limit on the offset value that can be used in conjunction with the index register. This offset is always interpreted as a positive number in the range 0 to 255 (decimal).

The M6800 processor supports 72 basic instructions that can be subdivided into four groups on the basis of the hardware components they reference; the groups are:

1. Accumulator and memory reference instructions,

2. Index register and stack-manipulation instructions,

3. Jump and branch instructions (which modify the PC),

4. Condition code register instructions.

The remaining sections of this chapter discuss these groups in detail. A listing of the M6800 instructions in numeric order by opcode can be found in Appendix B.

A number of symbols and abbreviations are used in the instruction tables that define these instructions. For example, c refers to the number of clock cycles and b to the number of program bytes needed for a given instruction. The ACTION field of these tables describes the semantics of an operation. In this field, "M" is used to denote the operand of the instruction. When the immediate mode is used, M represents the immediate data. For the direct- and extended-addressing modes, M denotes the contents of the address found in the instruction; that is, M $\equiv$ (address). If the indexed mode is used, M represents the contents of the memory location found by adding the contents of the index register (XR) to the offset specified as a part of the instruction; that is, M $\equiv$ (offset + (XR)).

For each operation, the opcode, the number of instruction bytes, and the number of clock cycles needed are specified for each addressing mode that can be used with the operation. A blank entry under a given addressing mode signifies that the addressing mode is not used with the operation.

Whenever it is necessary to distinguish between the most significant byte and the least significant byte of a 16-byte value, the subscript h is used to denote the *high* or most significant byte while the subscript l will denote the *low* or least significant byte.

EXERCISES

1. For each of the following operations, indicate the values of the N, Z, V, and CY flags after the operation is performed.
   a) 1FH + 3CH   b) 9CH − 9DH   c) −8FH − 1BH
   d) 9AH + 9CH   e) 7FH + 34H

2. What benefit is derived from the fact that the M6800 supports two forms of direct addressing?

2.3 ACCUMULATOR AND MEMORY REFERENCE INSTRUCTIONS

This instruction group is by far the largest of the four groups previously mentioned. For clarification we can subdivide this group into four subgroups based on the actions they perform: arithmetic instructions, logical instructions, data testing, and data movement/handling.

2.3.1 Arithmetic Instructions

The instructions in this group are listed in Table 2.2. The flag bits that are affected are noted. These bits are set to 1 when the specified condition is true, and reset to 0 otherwise.

Examples

a) The ADDA instruction adds the contents of A to a specified operand and places the result in A. If the extended mode is used with this operation, three bytes are needed to encode the instruction. The second and third bytes specify the address. For example, if (A) = 04H and (0123H) = 05H, then the instruction BB0123H would change (A) to 09H. Note that the 16-bit address value is stored in most significant byte/least significant byte order in the instruction encoding.

b) The ABA instruction adds the contents of A to the contents of B and stores the result in A. If (A) = AAH and (B) = CCH, then after execution of ABA, which is encoded as 1BH, we would have (A) = 76H. Furthermore, the CCR would be changed with CY = V = 1.

c) The ADCB instruction adds the contents of B, a specified operand, and the current CY value, and stores the result in B. If used with the indexed mode, this is a two-byte instruction with the second byte containing the offset. If (B) = 15H, (XR) = 0100H, (CY) = 1, and (0103H) = 05H, then after execution of the instruction A903H we would have (B) = 1BH and CY would be reset to 0. Recall that for the indexed mode M ≡ (offset + (XR)) which, for this example, is (03H + 0100H) = (0103H) = 05H.

Table 2.2
Arithmetic instructions

Operation	Mnemonic	Addressing modes														Action	Flag bits affected
		IMMED			DIRECT			INDEX			EXTND			IMPLD				
		OP	c	b	OP	c	b	OP	c	b	OP	c	b	OP	c	b		
Add	ADDA	8B	2	2	9B	3	2	AB	5	2	BB	4	3				(A)←(A) + M	H,N,Z,V,CY
	ADDB	CB	2	2	DB	3	2	EB	5	2	FB	4	3				(B)←(B) + M	H,N,Z,V,CY
Add acmltrs.	ABA													1B	2	1	(A)←(A) + (B)	H,N,Z,V,CY
Add with carry	ADCA	89	2	2	99	3	2	A9	5	2	B9	4	3				(A)←(A) + M + (CY)	H,N,Z,V,CY
	ADCB	C9	2	2	D9	3	2	E9	5	2	F9	4	3				(B)←(B) + M + (CY)	H,N,Z,V,CY
Complement, 2's	NEG							60	7	2	70	6	3				M←00 − M	N,Z,V,CY ② ③
(negate)	NEGA													40	2	1	(A)←00 − (A)	N,Z,V,CY ② ③
	NEGB													50	2	1	(B)←00 − (B)	N,Z,V,CY ② ③
Decimal adjust, A	DAA													19	2	1	Converts binary to BCD format	N,Z,V,CY ①
Subtract	SUBA	80	2	2	90	3	2	A0	5	2	B0	4	3				(A)←(A) − M	N,Z,V,CY
	SUBB	C0	2	2	D0	3	2	E0	5	2	F0	4	3				(B)←(B) − M	N,Z,V,CY
Subtract acmltrs.	SBA													10	2	1	(A)←(A) − (B)	N,Z,V,CY
Subtr. with carry	SBCA	82	2	2	92	3	2	A2	5	2	B2	4	3				(A)←(A) − M − (CY)	N,Z,V,CY
	SBCB	C2	2	2	D2	3	2	E2	5	2	F2	4	3				(B)←(B) − M − (CY)	N,Z,V,CY

① BCD, which stands for Binary Coded Decimal, is a way of representing numbers in which each decimal digit is encoded by its corresponding hexadecimal digit.
② CY is set unless result is 00H.
③ V is set if result is 80H.

d) The NEGA instruction places in A the two's complement of (A). If (A) = 0FH, then after execution of the instruction NEGA (40H), (A) = F1H, and in the CCR, N = 1.

e) The SUBA instruction subtracts a specified operand from the contents of accumulator A. When used with the immediate mode, this is a two-byte instruction where the second byte contains an immediate eight-bit value. If (A) = 1FH, then after execution of the instruction 8015H, (A) = 0AH; that is, 1FH − 15H = 0AH.

f) The SBCB instruction subtracts a specified operand and the current CY value from accumulator B. When used with the direct-addressing mode, this is a two-byte instruction, where the second byte represents an address in the range 00H to FFH. Assuming (B) = BCH, (CY) = 1, and (78H) = 7BH, then after execution of the instruction D278H, (B) = 40H and in the CCR, CY = 0 and V = 1.

2.3.2 Logical Instructions

The M6800 supports the four logical operations mentioned in Sec. 1.2.4; AND, OR, COMP, and EXCLUSIVE OR. Table 2.3 contains a listing of the logical instructions.

Examples

a) The EORB can be used with the immediate-, direct-, indexed-, or extended-addressing modes. The effect is the exclusive ORing of the contents of B with the specified operand. In the extended mode this is a three-byte instruction. For example, if (B) = ACH and (0100H) = C5H, then the effect of the instruction F80100H would be to set (B) = 69H with N, Z, and V = 0.

b) With (A) = ACH, the instruction encoded as 840FH—that is, ANDA in the immediate mode—would set (A) = 0CH with N, Z, and V = 0.

2.3.3 Data Test Instructions

Table 2.4 contains a listing of the instructions in this group. The effect of these instructions is to set or reset certain flag bits in the condition code register; all other registers and locations used by these instructions remain unchanged.

Table 2.3
Logical instructions

Operation	Mnemonic	Addressing modes													Action	Flag bits affected
		IMMED			DIRECT			INDEX			EXTND			IMPLD			
		OP	c	b	OP	c	b	OP	c	b	OP	c	b	OP	c	b		
And	ANDA	84	2	2	94	3	2	A4	5	2	B4	4	3				$(A)\leftarrow(A)\cdot M$	N,Z; V = 0
	ANDB	C4	2	2	D4	3	2	E4	5	2	F4	4	3				$(B)\leftarrow(B)\cdot M$	N,Z; V = 0
Complement, 1's	COM							63	7	2	73	6	3				$M\leftarrow\bar{M}$	N,Z; V = 0,CY = 1
	COMA													43	2	1	$(A)\leftarrow(\bar{A})$	N,Z; V = 0,CY = 1
	COMB													53	2	1	$(B)\leftarrow(\bar{B})$	N,Z; V = 0,CY = 1
Exclusive OR	EORA	88	2	2	98	3	2	A8	5	2	B8	4	3				$(A)\leftarrow(A)\oplus M$	N,Z; V = 0
	EORB	C8	2	2	D8	3	2	E8	5	2	F8	4	3				$(B)\leftarrow(B)\oplus M$	N,Z; V = 0
Or, Inclusive	ORAA	8A	2	2	9A	3	2	AA	5	2	BA	4	3				$(A)\leftarrow(A)+M$	N,Z; V = 0
	ORAB	CA	2	2	DA	3	2	EA	5	2	FA	4	3				$(B)\leftarrow(B)+M$	N,Z; V = 0

Table 2.4
Data test instructions

Operation	Mnemonic	IMMED			DIRECT			INDEX			EXTND			IMPLD			Test made on:	Flag bits affected
		OP	c	b	OP	c	b	OP	c	b	OP	c	b	OP	c	b		
Bit test	BITA	85	2	2	95	3	2	A5	5	2	B5	4	3				A • M	N,Z;V = 0
	BITB	C5	2	2	D5	3	2	E5	5	2	F5	4	3				B • M	N,Z;V = 0
Compare	CMPA	81	2	2	91	3	2	A1	5	2	B1	4	3				A − M	N,Z,V,CY
	CMPB	C1	2	2	D1	3	2	E1	5	2	F1	4	3				B − M	N,Z,V,CY
Compare acmltrs.	CBA													11	2	1	A − B	N,Z,V,CY
Test, zero, or	TST							6D	7	2	7D	6	3				M − 00	N,Z;V = CY = 0
minus	TSTA													4D	2	1	A − 00	N,Z;V = CY = 0
	TSTB													5D	2	1	B − 00	N,Z;V = CY = 0

Examples

a) The BITA instruction performs a logical AND on the contents of A
and the specified operand and sets the N and Z flags depending on the
result. This instruction can be used to test whether certain bits in A are
set. For example, if (A) = 06H, then the instruction 8502H (BITA
with immediate operand 02H) sets $N = 0$ and $Z = 0$. Since the Z flag
is 0 and bit 1 of the immediate operand was set, this implies that bit 1
of A was set. For the instruction 8501H (BITA with immediate oper-
and 01H), N = 0 and Z = 1, which implies that bit 0 of A was reset.

b) The CBA instruction subtracts the contents of B from A and sets the
condition codes appropriately. If (A) = CAH and (B) = ACH, then
CBA sets CY = 1 and N, Z, and V = 0.

2.3.4 Data-Handling Instructions

The M6800 instructions that support data-handling operations are listed in
Table 2.5. Included in this group are clear, increment, decrement, load, store,
rotate, shift, push, pull, and register transfer operations. The push and pull
operations (that is, PSHA, PSHB, PULA, and PULB) are used in conjunction
with the M6800 stack. In the ACTION fields of these instructions, $M_{SP} =$
((SP)).

Examples

a) The CLRA and CLRB instructions can be used to clear (set to 00H)
the contents of A and B, respectively. The CLR instruction can be used
in conjunction with the indexed- or extended-addressing modes to clear
the contents of an arbitrary memory location. The instruction
750110H—CLR with extended address 0110H—sets (0110H) to 00H.

b) The LDAA and LDAB instructions can be used to load a specified
operand into A and B, respectively. These instructions can be used with
the immediate-, direct-, indexed-, and extended-addressing modes. For
example, assume that (XR) = 0200H, (0200H) = 04H, and (0201H)
= 08H. The instruction A600H (LDAA in the indexed mode) would
set (A) = 04H. Similarly, E601H (LDAB in the indexed mode) would
set (B) = 08H.

c) The push operations available on the M6800 consist of the PSHA and
PSHB, which push the contents of A and B, respectively, onto the
stack. The pop operations, PULA and PULB, pop eight-bit values off
the stack to A and B, respectively. Note that, in the semantic descrip-

tions of these instructions, the modification of the SP is indicated; that is, SP is incremented for PULA and PULB, and it is decremented for PSHA and PSHB. The effect of the modification is noted in the example illustrated below. For this example, assume we start with (A) = 02H, (B) = 04H, and (SP) = 0200H. With the configuration, we trace the following operations:

Operation	Action
PSHA	(0200H = 02H, (SP) = 01FFH
PSHB	(01FFH) = 04H, (SP) = 01FEH
PULA	(SP) = 01FFH, (A) = 04H
PULB	(SP) = 0200H, (B) = 02H

d) The shift and rotate instructions operate on a single eight-bit operand. The rotate right and left operations rotate through the carry, thus performing a nine-bit circular rotate. The arithmetic shifts effectively perform a multiplication by two (arithmetic left) and a division by two (arithmetic right). The logical shift right shifts a zero into bit 7. To compare these operations, we will consider the effect of various rotates and shifts on a common value. For each of the following, assume we start with (A) = 86H and (CY) = 1.

Operation	Action
RORA	(A) = C3H, (CY), (Z) = 0, (V), (N) = 1
LSRA	(A) = 43H, (CY), (Z), (V),(N) = 0
ASLA	(A) = 0CH, (Z), (N) = 0, (V),(CY) = 1
ROLA	(A) = 0DH, (Z), (N) = 0, (V), (CY) = 1

EXERCISES

1. Hand-load and execute the program segments that are shown below. Indicate all changes in the computer's internal state (registers, memory locations, condition codes) that result from executing these segments. Clear accumulators A and B before running each of these segments.

   Since the address range of valid memory locations varies in different microcomputers, the notation xy has been used in these segments to denote the most significant byte of an address. In running these segments you should replace xy by hex digits that will denote valid memory on your computer. For example, if 0100H–01FFH are valid addresses on your microcomputer, then xy00 becomes 0100, xy01 becomes 0101, etc.

Table 2.5
Data-handling instructions

Operation	Mnemonic	IMMED			DIRECT			INDEX			EXTND			IMPLD			Action	Flag bits affected
		OP	c	b	OP	c	b	OP	c	b	OP	c	b	OP	c	b		
Clear	CLR							6F	7	2	7F	6	3				M←00	N = V = CY = 0,Z = 1
	CLRA													4F	2	1	(A)←00	N = V = CY = 0,Z = 1
	CLRB													5F	2	1	(B)←00	N = V = CY = 0,Z = 1
Decrement	DEC							6A	7	2	7A	6	3				M←M − 1	N,Z ①
	DECA													4A	2	1	(A)←(A) − 1	N,Z ①
	DECB													5A	2	1	(B)←(B) − 1	N,Z ①
Increment	INC							6C	7	2	7C	6	3				M←M + 1	N,Z ②
	INCA													4C	2	1	(A)←(A) + 1	N,Z ②
	INCB													5C	2	1	(B)←(B) + 1	N,Z ②
Load acmltr.	LDAA	86	2	2	96	3	2	A6	5	2	B6	4	3				(A)←M	N,Z; V = 0
	LDAB	C6	2	2	D6	3	2	E6	5	2	F6	4	3				(B)←M	N,Z; V = 0
Push data	PSHA													36	4	1	M_{SP}←(A),(SP)←(SP) − 1	none
	PSHB													37	4	1	M_{SP}←(B),(SP)←(SP) − 1	none
Pull data	PULA													32	4	1	(SP)←(SP) + 1,(A)←M_{SP}	none
	PULB													33	4	1	(SP)←(SP) + 1,(B)←M_{SP}	none
Rotate left	ROL							69	7	2	79	6	3				M	
	ROLA													49	2	1	(A)	
	ROLB													59	2	1	(B)	N,Z,CY ③

Addressing modes

Operation	Mnemonic									Boolean/Arithmetic Operation	Cond. Code
Rotate right	ROR	66	7	2	76	6	3	46	2	1	M	N,Z,CY ①
	RORA										(A) $\; CY \leftarrow \boxed{} \rightarrow b_7 \quad b_0$	
	RORB							56	2	1	(B)	
Shift left, arithmetic	ASL	68	7	2	78	6	3	48	2	1	M	N,Z,CY ①
	ASLA										(A) $\; CY \leftarrow \boxed{} \leftarrow 0 \quad b_7 \quad b_0$	
	ASLB							58	2	1	(B)	
Shift right, arithmetic	ASR	67	7	2	77	6	3	47	2	1	M	N,Z,CY ①
	ASRA										(A) $\; b_7 \; \boxed{} \rightarrow CY \quad b_0$	
	ASRB							57	2	1	(B)	
Shift right, logical	LSR	64	7	2	74	6	3	44	2	1	M	Z,CY,N = 0 ③
	LSRA										(A) $\; 0 \rightarrow \boxed{} \rightarrow CY \quad b_7 \quad b_0$	
	LSRB							54	2	1	(B)	
Store acmltr.	STAA	A7	6	2	B7	5	3	97	4	2	M←(A)	N,Z; V = 0
	STAB	E7	6	2	F7	5	3	D7	4	2	M←(B)	N,Z; V = 0
Transfer acmltrs.	TAB							16	2	1	(B)←(A)	N,Z; V = 0
	TBA							17	2	1	(A)←(B)	N,Z; V = 0

① The flag bit V is set if the operand = 10000000 prior to execution.
② The flag bit V is set if the operand = 01111111 prior to execution.
③ Flag bit V is set equal to result of N ⊕ CY after shift has occurred.

The SWI instruction (3FH) has been used in these segments as the return-to-monitor or halt-execution instruction. If some other instruction is used in your system to terminate execution, the SWI should be changed appropriately.

	Location	Hex code			
a)	0000	9B	03		ADDA direct
	0002	3F			SWI
	0003	01			data
b)	xy00	BB	xy	04	ADDA extended
	xy03	3F			SWI
	xy04	02			data
c)	xy00	8B	03		ADDA immediate
	xy02	3F			SWI
d)	xy00	70	xy	04	NEG extended
	xy03	3F			SWI
	xy04	01			data
e)	xy00	40			NEGA
	xy01	3F			SWI
f)	xy00	84	0F		ANDA immediate
	xy02	3F			SWI
g)	xy00	BA	xy	04	ORA extended
	xy03	3F			SWI
	xy04	1F			data
h)	0000	91	03		CMPA direct
	0002	3F			SWI
	0003	01			data
i)	xy00	F1	xy	04	CMPB extended
	xy03	3F			SWI
	xy04	00			data
j)	xy00	4D			TSTA
	xy01	3F			SWI
k)	xy00	4A			DECA
	xy01	3F			SWI
l)	xy00	7C	xy	04	INC extended
	xy03	3F			SWI
	xy04	05			data
m)	xy00	B6	xy	08	LDAA extended
	xy03	48			ASLA
	xy04	B7	xy	08	STAA extended
	xy07	3F			SWI
	xy08	01			data

2. Write an M6800 hex program that will add the contents of locations 0030H, 0031H, and 0032H and store the sum in location 0040H. Your program should use direct addressing and use accumulator A to form the sum. Single-step (execute one instruction at a time) through the program to verify its operation.

3. Given the following register and memory configuration:

(A) = 00	(0000) = 10	(0100) = 20
(B) = 01	(0001) = 11	(0101) = 21
	(0002) = 12	(0102) = 22
	(0003) = 13	(0103) = 23
	(0004) = 14	(0104) = 24
	(0005) = 15	(0105) = 25
	(0006) = 16	(0106) = 26

Specify the effect of the following:

a) 97 04   b) D7 05   c) 96 00   d) C6 04

e) F6 01 01   f) 5F   g) 7F 01 06

Assume that each case starts anew from the initial configuration.

4. Assume that memory is configured as follows:

Location	Contents
0100	86
0101	3F
0102	16
0103	BB
0104	01
0105	08
0106	1B
0107	3F
0108	02

Further, assume that (PC) = 0100H, so that execution will begin with the instruction found at location 0100H, and that 3FH is a halt-execution instruction. With respect to the memory configuration given above:

a) How many instructions will be executed?

b) List, in order of execution, the instructions (and addressing modes) that will be executed.

c) What are the contents of A and B at the end of execution of the program?

2.4 INDEX REGISTER AND STACK POINTER INSTRUCTIONS

In the previous section we have seen instructions that have used the values found in the XR and SP registers, that is, PULA, PSHB, LDAA with the indexed addressing mode, etc. The XR and SP instructions listed in Table 2.6 provide for setting, storing, modifying, and testing the values in these registers.

Table 2.6
Index register and stack-pointer instructions

Operation	Mnemonic	Addressing modes														Action	Flag bits affected
		IMMED			DIRECT			INDEX			EXTND			IMPLD			
		OP	c	b	OP	c	b	OP	c	b	OP	c	b	OP	c	b		
Compare Index Reg	CPX	8C	3	3	9C	4	2	AC	6	2	BC	5	3				(XR) − [M : M + 1]	Z,V,N
Decrement Index Reg	DEX													09	4	1	(XR)→(XR) − 1	Z
Decrement Stack Pntr	DES													34	4	1	(SP)→(SP) − 1	none
Increment Index Reg	INX													08	4	1	(XR)→(XR) + 1	Z
Increment Stack Pntr	INS													31	4	1	(SP)→(SP) + 1	none
Load Index Reg	LDX	CE	3	3	DE	4	2	EE	6	2	FE	5	3				(XR)→[M : M + 1]	Z,N,V = 0
Load Stack Pntr	LDS	8E	3	3	9E	4	2	AE	6	2	BE	5	3				(SP)→[M : M + 1]	Z,N,V = 0
Store Index Reg	STX				DF	5	2	EF	7	2	FF	6	3				[M : M + 1]→(XR)	Z,N,V = 0
Store Stack Pntr	STS				9F	5	2	AF	7	2	BF	6	3				[M : M + 1]→(SP)	Z,N,V = 0
Index Reg Stack Pntr	TXS													35	4	1	(SP)→(XR) − 1	none
Stack Pntr Index Reg	TSX													30	4	1	(XR)→(SP) + 1	none

Since the SP and XR are 16-bit registers, these instructions operate on 16-bit rather than eight-bit values. As a result the N and V flags are set in a slightly different manner than before; N is set if bit 15 of the result is 1 and V is set if the result cannot be represented in 16 bits.

The notation [M : M + 1] has been used to represent the 16-bit operand value used by some of these instructions. In the immediate mode [M : M + 1] denotes the 16-bit immediate operand found in bytes 2 and 3 of the instruction. For the direct and extended addressing modes [M : M + 1] denotes a 16-bit value whose most significant byte is (address) and whose least significant byte is (address + 1), where address is the extended or direct address value specified in the instruction. In the indexed mode [M : M + 1] specifies a 16-bit value whose most significant byte is (offset + (XR)) and whose least significant byte is (offset + (XR) + 1), where offset is specified in the instruction.

EXERCISES

1. Hand-load and execute the following program segments. Indicate all changes in the computer's internal state (registers, memory locations, condition codes) that result from executing these segments. Clear accumulators A and B before running each of these segments.

    The notation used in this exercise is described in Exercise 1 following Sec. 2.3.4.

	Location	Hex code			
a)	*xy*00	CE	*xy*	08	LDX immediate
	*xy*03	A6	00		LDAA indexed
	*xy*05	E6	01		LDAB indexed
	*xy*07	3F			SWI
	*xy*08	02			data
	*xy*09	03			data
b)	*xy*00	BF	*xy*	04	STS extended
	*xy*03	3F			SWI
c)	*xy*00	30			TSX
	*xy*01	3F			SWI
d)	*xy*00	FE	*xy*	0B	LDX extended
	*xy*03	4F			CLRA
	*xy*04	AB	00		ADDA indexed
	*xy*06	AB	01		ADDA indexed
	*xy*08	AB	02		ADDA indexed
	*xy*0A	3F			SWI
	*xy*0B	*xy*			data
	*xy*0C	00			data
	*xy*0D	02			data
	*xy*0E	03			data
	*xy*0F	04			data

2. Assume that (SP) is as usual, the address of the next free location on the stack. Find a sequence of two M6800 instructions that will load ACCA with the contents of the memory location whose address is (SP) + 4.

3. Specify the effect of the following M6800 program.

Location	Hex code
0000	CE 00 06
0003	EE 01
0005	3F
0006	01
0007	02
0008	03

4. Put 00, 01, 02, 03, 04, 05 in locations 0100, 0101, . . . , 0105, respectively. You are to bring these numbers to A and push them on the stack. Note if (XR) = 0100, the number I can be put on top of the stack with:

    LDAA in the indexed mode with offset I
    PSHA

    Conversely, the number on the top of the stack can be brought to location 0100 + J with:

    PULA
    STAA   in the indexed mode with offset J.
    Using these ideas, write a program that halts with 02, 04, 03, 05, 00, and 01 in locations 0100, 0101, . . . , 0105, respectively.

5. For each of the following cases, write an M6800 segment to load accumulator A with the indicated number.

    a) (0025)   b) 25   c) (25 + (XR))   d) ((XR))

2.5 JUMP AND BRANCH INSTRUCTIONS

Table 2–7 lists the Jump and Branch instructions for the M6800. Apart from the fact that an interrupt (and in particular, the SWI instruction) sets flag bit I = 1, these instructions do not affect the flag bits.

Note that the relative-addressing mode applies in the case of the branch instructions and, since the address must be specified in one byte, the branch is limited to the range − 128 to + 127 bytes of the branch instruction itself. The relationship between the specified relative address R (viewed as a two's complement binary number), the updated PC (the address of the first byte of the branch instruction plus two) and the destination D is given by D = PC + R. A branch beyond the range − 128 to + 127 requires the JMP instruction.

The conditional branch instructions consist of seven pairs of complementary instructions. BMI and BPL test the sign bit N and branch according as the previous result was negative or positive, respectively. BEQ and BNE test the zero-status bit Z to see whether the result of the previous operation was zero. These are useful following the CMP and BIT instructions. BVC and BVS test the state of the V bit to determine whether an arithmetic overflow occurred on the previous operation. BCC and BCS test the state of the C bit. These are useful for testing relative magnitudes when the values are regarded as unsigned binary integers in the range 00H to FFH. BHI and BLS are essentially complements of BCC and BCS. BHI tests if $C = Z = 0$ and will cause a branch if accumulator value is greater than the operand.

The remaining two pairs are used to test results on values regarded as signed numbers in the range -128 to $+127$. BLT and BGE test the status bits for $N \oplus V = 1,0$, respectively. BLE and BGT test the status bits for $Z + (N \oplus V) = 1,0$, respectively. We might summarize the relationships between those conditional branches and the various inequality relations as follows:

Relation	Signed integer data	Unsigned integer data
$<$	BLT	BCS
$\geq$	BGE	BCC
$\leq$	BLE	BLS
$>$	BGT	BHI

The operations of Branch to Subroutine (BSR) and Jump to Subroutine (JSR) are similar except for range. BSR requires fewer instruction bytes than JSR (two bytes compared with three bytes) and is one cycle faster. Execution of either instruction causes a return address—the updated PC, which contains the address of the instruction immediately following the BSR or JSR to be saved on the stack. The Return from Subroutine (RTS) instruction causes the return address to be retrieved from the stack and loaded into the program counter.

The Software Interrupt (SWI) and Wait for Interrupt (WAI) instructions cause all of the microprocessor's internal registers (except SP) to be stacked. SWI then fetches the starting address of an "interrupt routine" from a fixed memory location. The Return from Interrupt instruction (RTI) is used at the end of the interrupt routine to restore the register contents and return control to the main program. Interrupts are used in connection with I/O problems and we shall consider them in detail in later chapters.

Table 2.7
Jump and Branch instructions

Operation	Mnemonic	Addressing modes									Branch test (Branch taken if test is true)
		RELATIVE OP c b			INDEX OP c b	EXTND OP c b	IMPLD OP c b				
Branch Always	BRA	20	4	2							None
Branch if Carry Clear	BCC	24	4	2							$C = 0$
Branch if Carry Set	BCS	25	4	2							$C = 1$
Branch if = Zero	BEQ	27	4	2							$Z = 1$
Branch if ≥ Zero	BGE	2C	4	2							$N \oplus V = 0$
Branch if > Zero	BGT	2E	4	2							$Z + (N \oplus V) = 0$
Branch if Higher	BHI	22	4	2							$C + Z = 0$
Branch if ≤ Zero	BLE	2F	4	2							$Z + (N \oplus V) = 1$
Branch if Lower or Same	BLS	23	4	2							$C + Z = 1$
Branch if < Zero	BLT	2D	4	2							$N \oplus V = 1$
Branch if Minus	BMI	2B	4	2							$N = 1$

Description	Mnemonic						Notes
Branch if not Equal Zero	BNE	26	4	2			$Z = 0$
Branch if Overflow Clear	BVC	28	4	2			$V = 0$
Branch if Overflow Set	BVS	29	4	2			$V = 1$
Branch if Plus	BPL	2A	4	2			$N = 0$
Branch to Subroutine	BSR	8D	8	2			①
Jump	JMP	6E	4	2	7E 3 3		②
Jump to Subroutine	JSR	AD	8	2	BD 9 3		③
No Operation	NOP	01	2	1			Advances PC only
Return From Interrupt	RTI	3B	10	1			④
Return From Subroutine	RTS	39	5	1			⑤
Software Interrupt	SWI	3F	12	1			⑥
Wait for Interrupt	WAI	3E	9	1			⑥

① PC_l pushed onto stack, $(SP) \rightarrow (SP) - 1$. PC_h pushed onto stack, $(SP) \rightarrow (SP) - 1$, $(PC) \rightarrow (PC)$ + relative offset.

② For extended addressing, $(PC) \rightarrow$ address. For indexed addressing, $(PC) \rightarrow$ offset + (XR).

③ PC_l pushed onto stack, $(SP) \rightarrow (SP) - 1$. PC_h pushed onto stack, $(SP) \rightarrow (SP) - 1$. For extended addressing, $(PC) \rightarrow$ address. For indexed addressing, $(PC) \rightarrow$ offset + (XR).

④ The stack is popped seven times which reestablishes, in the order indicated, the following values: (CCR), (B), (A), (XR_h), (XR_l), (PC_h), (PC_l). $(SP) \rightarrow (SP) + 7$.

⑤ (PC_h) and (PC_l) are popped from the stack. $(SP) \rightarrow (SP) + 2$.

⑥ The following values are pushed onto the stack in the order given: (PC_l), (PC_h), (XR_l), (XR_h), (A), (B) and (CCR). $(SP) \rightarrow (SP) - 7$. For the SWI, the I flag is set to 1, $(PC_h) \rightarrow (OFF8H)$ and $(PC_l) \rightarrow (OFF9H)$. For the WAI, the microprocessor enters a wait state until an interrupt is signalled.

EXERCISES

1. Assume that location 0100 contains 20H, i.e., the BRA opcode. Indicate the destination of the branch if 0101 contains:

   a) 00H   b) FEH   c) 06H   d) E4H

2. a) Write a sequence of M6800 hex instructions that could be executed starting at 0100H and would transfer to location 0120H if bit 5 of accumulator A is set; halt with a 3FH otherwise.

   b) Write a sequence of M6800 hex instructions that could be executed starting at 0100H and would transfer to location 0240 if bit 5 of accumulator A is set; halt with a 3FH otherwise.

3. Write a sequence of M6800 hex instructions that could be executed starting at 0100H and will transfer to location 0120H if:

   a) (A) < (B), where (A) and (B) are regarded as eight-bit two's complement signed numbers.

   b) (A) < (B), where (A) and (B) are treated as eight-bit unsigned binary numbers.

4. Find values for (A), (0100H) so that following execution of the instruction CMPA in the extended mode with address 0100H:

   i) BLS but not BLE is satisfied.
   ii) BLT but not BCS is satisfied.

   Explain why (A) < (0100H) if and only if $N \oplus V = 1$ following execution of CMPA 0100H (extended addressing).

5. Assume that on the M6800, memory is configured as shown below and that execution begins with (PC) = 0100H.

Location	Contents (in hex)
0100	CE
0101	01
0102	00
0103	4F
0104	F6
0105	08
0106	1B
0107	3F
0108	F0
0109	21

   a) Trace the execution of the program.

   b) If the program is illegal, state why.

   c) Indicate the contents of the registers upon termination of the program (or at the point where it becomes illegal). Use ?? to denote an unknown value.

   ACCA =   ACCB =   XR =   PC =   SP =

2.6 CONDITION CODE REGISTER INSTRUCTIONS

Table 2.8 lists the instructions of this group. Note that the effect of an operation on the flag bits is clearly indicated by the action of that operation. All of the instructions of this group are in the implied addressing mode.

The instructions of this final group give the programmer direct control over the I, V, and C flag bits and indirect control (through accumulator A, using TAP) of all of the flag bits of the condition code register.

Table 2.8
Condition code register instructions

Operation	Mnemonic	OP c b	Action
Clear carry	CLC	0C 2 1	$(CY) \leftarrow 0$
Clear interrupt mask	CLI	0E 2 1	$(I) \leftarrow 0$
Clear overflow	CLV	0A 2 1	$(V) \leftarrow 0$
Set carry	SEC	0D 2 1	$(CY) \leftarrow 1$
Set interrupt mask	SEI	0F 2 1	$(I) \leftarrow 1$
Set overflow	SEV	0B 2 1	$(V) \leftarrow 1$
Transfer A to CCR	TAP	06 2 1	$(CCR) \leftarrow (A)$
Transfer CCR to A	TPA	07 2 1	$(A) \leftarrow (CCR)$

REFERENCES AND SUPPORTIVE MATERIAL

The presentation of the M6800 instructions, and in particular the groupings of these instructions, followed in this chapter, have been derived in part from Motorola's supporting literature. Specifically, Motorola (1976a) includes block diagrams, technical information, and instruction tables for the M6800, as well as detailed specifications for other components of the M6800 system. Motorola (1976b) is essentially a "Principles of Operation" manual for the M6800 and contains a thorough discussion of the various instructions. Motorola (1975) contains detailed discussions of all components of the M6800 system, as well as a complete coverage of many application possibilities.

1. Motorola [1976a]. "M6800 Microcomputer: System Design Data," Motorola Semiconductor Products Inc., Box 20912, Phoenix, Arizona.

2. Motorola [1976b]. "M6800 Programming Reference Manual," Motorola Semiconductor Products, Inc., Box 20912, Phoenix, Arizona.

3. Motorola [1975]. "M6800 Microprocessor Applications Manual," Motorola Semiconductor Products, Inc., Box 20912, Phoenix, Arizona.

CHAPTER THREE

THE INTEL 8085 INSTRUCTION SET

3.1 CHAPTER OVERVIEW

This chapter consists of a discussion of the Intel 8085 microprocessor (here-after referred to as the I8085) and its instruction set. After looking at the organization of the CPU and its registers, we consider the individual instructions, which are presented in natural groupings and are discussed with respect to the action they effect. Later, in Chapter 4, we consider various program segments composed of I8085 instructions.

3.2 THE MICROPROCESSOR UNIT

The CPU of the I8085 has several registers that can be accessed by a programmer. These registers are depicted in Fig. 3.1.

The I8085 has a single eight-bit accumulator, which is denoted by A. In addition, there are six eight-bit registers, B, C, D, E, H, and L, which can, with certain instructions, be grouped into three 16-bit pairs—that is, B–C, D–E, and H–L. The accumulator itself can be grouped with the I8085 condition code register. This grouping is referred to as the Program Status Word (PSW).

The program counter (PC) and the stack pointer (SP) are 16-bit special-purpose registers. The PC controls the execution of a program in that, at any given point in a computation, the PC holds the address of the next instruction that will be executed. The SP, via the value it holds, defines a stack structure in memory. The SP value specifies *the address of the top byte value in the stack*. Although the I8085 is an eight-bit machine, all push and pop operations involve 16-bit quantities. A 16-bit quantity is stored on the stack in least significant byte/most significant byte order; i.e., the least significant byte is on the top of the stack, so SP will point to it. The I8085 stack expands toward lower memory as elements are added to the stack, and contracts toward higher

51

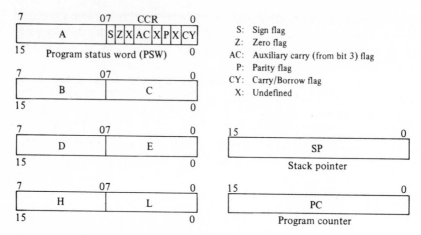

Fig. 3.1 I8085 program accessible registers.

memory as elements are deleted. For example, if SP holds the value *m,* then an attempt to push a 16-bit value *v* on the stack would result in the most significant byte of *v* being placed in location *m* − 1 and the least significant byte in location *m* − 2. Furthermore, SP would be set to *m* − 2. For a pull operation, again assuming we start with SP = *m,* a 16-bit quantity consisting of the contents of locations *m* + 1 and *m* would be popped. The contents of location *m* + 1 would be the most significant byte, the contents of *m* the least significant byte. In this case, SP would be set to SP + 2.

The condition code register (CCR) contains five bit values that can be used by the programmer and three undefined bits; bit 1, bit 3, and bit 5. The five defined bits provide information concerning the result of a previous operation. Bit 6, for example, is set (to 1) if the previous operation produced a zero result, and reset (to 0) if the result was nonzero. The sign flag, bit 7, is set if the result was negative, and reset if it was positive. The I8085 uses two's complement arithmetic, so a negative result is indicated whenever bit 7 of the result, the most significant bit, is set.

The carry/borrow flag (CY), bit 0, is set after an addition operation if there was a carry from bit 7 of the result, and reset otherwise. For a subtraction or a comparison operation, the CY flag is set if there was a borrow into bit 7 of the result.

The auxiliary carry flag, bit 4, is set when an addition operation results in a carry-out of bit 3 of the result, or when a subtraction or comparison operation results in a borrow into bit 3 of the result.

The P flag of the condition code register, bit 2, indicates the parity of the result (see Sec. 1.2.5). This bit is set for even parity and reset for odd parity.

The I8085 supports variable-length instruction formats, with instructions being one, two, or three bytes in length. The opcode always occupies the first byte. In multiple-byte instructions, the second and third bytes of the instruction contain address information. The I8085 supports one-address and zero-address instructions. It also supports a restricted form of a two-address instruction, in which both addresses are register specifications.

The direct-, indirect-, register-, immediate-, and implied-addressing modes are supported on the I8085. The H–L register pair is used extensively in connection with indirect addressing. The B–C and D–E pairs are used to a lesser extent with indirect addressing.

The I8085 supports 80 basic instructions, which can be subdivided into five groups on the basis of the functions they perform. These groups are:

1. Data transfer instructions,

2. Arithmetic instructions,

3. Logical instructions,

4. Branch control instructions,

5. Stack, input/output, and machine control instructions.

The remaining sections of this chapter discuss these groups in detail. A listing of the I8085 instructions in numeric order by opcode can be found in Appendix C.

A number of symbols and abbreviations are used in the instruction tables that define these instructions. The letter b denotes the number of program bytes and the letter c the number of machine cycles relative to a given instruction. In addition, "adr" denotes a 16-bit address, "data 8" an eight-bit data quantity, "data 16" a 16-bit data quantity, "r" an eight-bit register, "rp" a 16-bit register pair, "port" an eight-bit I/O device address, and "M" the memory location that is indirectly addressed through the H–L register pair. Parentheses are used in the table to denote the contents of a register or a memory location.

In the I8085 opcodes, the registers are denoted by patterns of three bits as follows:

Register	Pattern
A	111
B	000
C	001
D	010
E	011
H	100
L	101

The bit pattern 110 is used to denote M. In the instruction tables, some of the opcodes contain the patterns *ddd* and/or *sss*. These patterns stand for the source (*sss*) and destination (*ddd*) register bit patterns. For example, if *sss* appears in an opcode and register D is the source register, then 010 will occupy the positions where *sss* appears.

A similar technique is used to represent the register pairs. In this case *rp* will appear in an opcode and should be replaced by the two-bit pattern that denotes the appropriate pair, i.e.,

Register pair	Pattern
B–C	00
D–E	01
H–L	10
SP	11

Whenever it is necessary to distinguish between the most significant byte and the least significant byte of a 16-bit value, the subscript *h* is used to denote the (high) most significant byte, while the subscript *l* (low) will denote the least significant byte.

EXERCISES

1. For each of the following operations, indicate the values of the S, Z, P, and CY flags after the operation is performed.

    a) 1FH + 3CH   b) 9CH – 9DH   c) – 8FH – 1BH
    d) 9AH + 9CH   e) 7FH + 34H

3.3 DATA TRANSFER INSTRUCTIONS

The I8085 provides instructions for data movement between registers and between memory and registers. These instructions are listed in Table 3.1. None of the condition code flags are affected by the instructions in this group.

Examples

a) Assuming the following:

    (H) = 01H   (L) = 23H   (A) = 04H   (0123H) = 72H,

    consider the instruction MOV A,M. The opcode for this instruction would be 01111110B or 7EH; that is, for r_1 the designation is A and for r_2 the source is M. After execution of this instruction, we would have (A) = 72H, with everything else unchanged. Note that this is a one-byte instruction that requires seven machine cycles to complete execution.

Table 3.1
Data transfer instructions

Operation	Mnemonic	OP	c	b	Addressing mode	Action
Move	MOV r_1,r_2	01dddsss	4	1	register	$(r_1) \leftarrow (r_2)$ ①
	MOV M,r	01110sss	7	1	indirect	$(M) \leftarrow (r)$
	MOV r,M	01ddd110	7	1	indirect	$(r) \leftarrow (M)$
Exchange	XCHG	EB	1	1	register	$(H) \leftrightarrow (D)$
						$(L) \leftrightarrow (E)$
Move immediate	MVI r, data8	00ddd110	2	2	immediate	$(r) \leftarrow$ data8
	MVI M,data8	36	3	2	immediate indirect	$(M) \leftarrow$ data8
Load immediate	LXI rp, data16	00rp0001	3	3	immediate	$(rp) \leftarrow$ data16
Load	LDA adr	3A	4	3	direct	$(A) \leftarrow (adr)$
	LHLD adr	2A	5	3	direct	$(L) \leftarrow (adr),$
						$(H) \leftarrow (adr+1)$
	LDAX D	1A	2	1	indirect	$(A) \leftarrow ((D-E))$
	LDAX B	0A	2	1	indirect	$(A) \leftarrow ((B-C))$
Store	STA adr	32	4	3	direct	$(adr) \leftarrow (A)$
	SHLD adr	22	5	3	direct	$(adr) \leftarrow (L)$
						$(adr+1) \leftarrow (H)$
	STAX D	12	2	1	indirect	$((D-E)) \leftarrow (A)$
	STAX B	02	2	1	indirect	$((B-C)) \leftarrow (A)$

① r_1 and r_2 cannot both be M.

b) The MOV r_1, r_2 instruction provides an eight-bit register transfer operation; for example, MOV B,D moves the contents of D into B, with D unaffected by the transfer. The XCHG instruction functions as a 16-bit register exchange operation between the D–E and H–L pairs. For example, if

(H) = 01H,   (L) = 02H,   (D) = 03H,   and   (E) = 04H,

then after an XCHG instruction we would have

(H) = 03H,   (L) = 04H,   (D) = 01H   and   (E) = 02H.

c) Both eight-bit and 16-bit immediate data transfers are possible on the I8085. MVI B, 78H, for example, puts the immediate data value 78H into register B. This is a two-byte instruction, with the second byte holding the immediate data; for example, the MVI B, 78H instruction would be encoded as 0678H. Immediate 16-bit moves into the register pairs can be accomplished with the LXI instruction. For example LXI B,1F02H will place 1FH into register B, and 02H into register C. Note that the register pair is specified by the first element of the pair. The LXI instruction is a three-byte instruction, with the second and third bytes used to hold the immediate data. On the I8085, 16-bit values are held in least significant byte/most significant byte order. As a result, the LXI B,1F02H instruction would be encoded as 01021F.

d)   LDA and the LHLD instructions are examples of the direct addressing mode capability of the I8085 processor. A 16-bit address is specified as part of these instructions, occupying the second and third bytes of the instruction. The LDA instructions move the contents of the specified location into accumulator A. For example, if (0123H) = 72H, then LDA 0123H would transfer 72H into A. The address is stored in least significant byte/most significant byte order, so LDA 0123H would be encoded as 3A2301H. The LHLD provides for a 16-bit transfer from memory to the H–L register pair. LHLD 1345H, for example, would move the contents of memory location 1345H into register L and the contents of location 1346H into register H.

e) Indirect addressing through a register pair other than the H–L pair can be achieved using the LDAX and STAX instructions. For example, if

(D) = 24H,   (E) = 01H,   and   (A) = 20H,

after execution of the instruction STAX D, we would have

(A) = 20H   and   (2401H) = 20H.

EXERCISES

1. Hand-load and execute the program segments that are listed below. Indicate all changes in the computer's internal state (registers, memory locations, condition codes) that result from these segments. Clear the accumulator before running each segment.

Since the address range of valid memory locations varies in different microcomputers, the notation *xy* has been used in these segments to denote the most significant byte of an address. In running these segments you should replace *xy* by hex digits that will denote valid memory on your computer. For example, if 0100H–01FFH are valid addresses on your microcomputer, then *xy*00 becomes 0100, *xy*01 becomes 0101, etc.

The HLT instruction (76H) has been used in these segments as the return-to-monitor or halt instruction. If some other instruction is used in your system to terminate execution, the HLT should be changed appropriately.

a) | Location | Hex code |
|---|---|

*xy*00	32	10	*xy*	STA	adr
*xy*03	76			HLT	

b)
*xy*00	01	44	55	LXI	B,data16
*xy*03	76			HLT	

c)
*xy*00	0E	66	MVI	C,data8
*xy*02	76		HLT	

d)
*xy*00	11	05	*xy*	LXI	D,data16
*xy*03	1A			LDAX	D
*xy*04	76			HLT	
*xy*05	02			data	

e)
*xy*00	11	10	*xy*	LXI	D,data16
*xy*03	EB			XCHG	
*xy*04	77			MOV	M,A
*xy*05	76			HLT	

2. Specify the hex encoding for each of the following instructions.

   a) MOV   D,L   b) MOV   H,M   c) MVI   M,1FH
   d) LXI   D,024FH   e) SHLD   0245H

3. Specify the effect of each of the following program segments.

   a) LXI   H,2010H   where (A) = 14H
      MOV   A,M   (2010H) = 20H

   b) LHLD 2010H   where (A) = 14H
      MOV   A,M   (2010H) = 11H
                                  (2011H) = 20H

   c) LXI   B,2010H   where (A) = 14H
      STAX B   (2010H) = 40H

   d) LXI   D,2010H   where (2010H) = 15H
      LXI   H,2020H   (2011H) = 16H
      XCHG   (2020H) = 17H
      SHLD 2020H   (2021H) = 18H

4. Assume that memory is configured as follows:

Location	Contents	Location	Contents
2000	2A	2006	76
2001	08	2007	76
2002	20	2008	10
2003	7E	2009	20
2004	47	2010	78
2005	3E		

Further assume that (PC) = 2000H, so that execution will begin with the instruction found at location 2000H, and that 76H is a halt instruction. With respect to the memory configuration given above:

a) How many instructions will be executed?

b) List, in order of execution, the instructions (and addressing modes) that will be executed.

c) What are the contents of A and B at the end of execution of the program?

5. Give an example of an instruction from the Data Transfer Instruction group whose execution always results in absolutely no change in the computer's internal configuration; i.e., it is a meaningless instruction.

3.4 ARITHMETIC INSTRUCTIONS

The I8085 processor supports various forms of addition and subtraction operations. These instructions are listed in Table 3.2. Note that the instructions in this group affect the flag bits in the condition code register. These bits are set to 1 when the specified condition is true, and reset to 0 otherwise.

Examples

a) Given the following initial conditions,

(A) = 05H,   (E) = 03H,   and   (CY) = 1,

after execution of the instruction ADC E (which is 8BH), we would have (A) = 09H, with CY, Z, P, and S = 0.

b) The DCR and INR instructions, respectively, decrement and increment a specified eight-bit value; for example, INR C increments C by 1. The DCX and INX instructions operate on register pairs and can therefore be used to decrement or increment a 16-bit value. This distinction is noted in the following example: If (B) = 01H and (C) = 00H, then, after execution of the instruction DCR C, we would have (B) = 01H, (C) = FFH, with P, Z = 0 and S = 1. On the other hand, a DCX B instruction, using the same initial configuration, would yield (B) = 00H and (C) = FFH. No flag bits would be changed for this instruction.

c) The DAD instruction provides for a 16-bit addition between the contents of the H–L register pair and any of the other register pairs, with the result left in the H–L pair. For example, if (H) = 02H, (L) = F7H, (D) = 31H, and (E) = A2H, then, after execution of the instruction DAD D, we would have (H) = 34H and (L) = 99H, with CY = 0.

Table 3.2
Arithmetic instructions

Operation	Mnemonic	OP	c	b	Addressing mode	Action	Flag bits affected
Add	ADD r	10000sss	1	1	register	$(A) \leftarrow (A) + (r)$	all
	ADD M	86	2	1	indirect	$(A) \leftarrow (A) + (M)$	all
Add immediate	ADI data8	C6	2	2	immediate	$(A) \leftarrow (A) + data8$	all
Add with carry	ADC r	10001sss	1	1	register	$(A) \leftarrow (A) + (r) + (CY)$	all
	ADC M	8E	2	1	indirect	$(A) \leftarrow (A) + (M) + (CY)$	all
Add immediate with carry	ACI data8	CE	2	2	immediate	$(A) \leftarrow (A) + data8 + (CY)$	all
Subtract	SUB r	10010sss	1	1	register	$(A) \leftarrow (A) - (r)$	all
	SUB M	96	2	1	indirect	$(A) \leftarrow (A) - (M)$	all
Subtract immediate	SUI data8	D6	2	2	immediate	$(A) \leftarrow (A) - data8$	all
Subtract with borrow	SBB r	10011sss	1	1	register	$(A) \leftarrow (A) - (r) - (CY)$	all
	SBB M	9E	2	1	indirect	$(A) \leftarrow (A) - (M) - (CY)$	all
Subtract immediate with borrow	SBI data8	DE	2	2	immediate	$(A) \leftarrow (A) - data8 - (CY)$	all
Increment	INR r	00ddd100	1	1	register	$(r) \leftarrow (r) + 1$	Z,S,P,AC
	INR M	34	3	1	indirect	$(M) \leftarrow (M) + 1$	Z,S,P,AC
	INX rp	00rp0011	1	1	register	$(rp) \leftarrow (rp) + 1$	none
Decrement	DCR r	00ddd101	1	1	register	$(r) \leftarrow (r) - 1$	Z,S,P,AC
	DCR M	35	3	1	indirect	$(M) \leftarrow (M) - 1$	Z,S,P,AC
	DCX rp	00rp1011	1	1	register	$(rp) \leftarrow (rp) - 1$	none
Add register pair	DAD rp	00rp1001	3	1	register	$(H\text{-}L) \leftarrow (H\text{-}L) + (rp)$	CY
Decimal adjust	DAA	27	1	1	implied	(A) adjusted to BCD[1]	all

1. BCD, which stands for Binary Coded Decimal, is a way of representing numbers in which each decimal digit is encoded by its corresponding hexadecimal digit.

EXERCISES

1. Hand-load and execute the program segments that are shown below. Indicate
    all changes in the computer's internal state (registers, memory locations, condi-
    tion codes) that result from these segments. Clear the accumulator before run-
    ning each segment.

    The notation used in these segments is explained in Exercise 1 following
    Sec. 3.3.

a)	Location	Hex code		
	xy00	03	INX	B
	xy01	76	HLT	
b)	xy00	D6 FF	SUI	data8
	xy02	76	HLT	
c)	xy00	09	DAD	B
	xy01	76	HLT	
d)	xy00	2A 05 xy	LHLD	adr
	xy03	86	ADD M	
	xy04	76	HLT	
	xy05	06	data	
	xy06	20	data	

3.5 LOGICAL INSTRUCTIONS

The four logical operations mentioned in Sec. 1.2.4—that is, AND, OR,
COMP, and EXCLUSIVE OR—are supported by the I8085 instruction set. In
addition, Intel groups some compare, rotate, and condition code operations in
its set of logical instructions. The instructions in this group are listed in Table
3.3.

Examples

a) The CMP instruction compares the specified byte with the contents of
   the accumulator and sets the flag bits of the CCR accordingly. The
   values being compared remain unchanged. If, for example,
   $(A) = -1BH$ and $(D) = 05H$, after execution of the instruction
   CMP D, we would have $Z = 0$ and $CY = 0$.

b) The instruction *Rotate Accumulator Left* transfers the high-order bit of
   the accumulator to CY and then rotates the contents of the accumulator one bit position to the left. The value of CY prior to execution of
   the RAL becomes the value of bit 0 of the accumulator after execution
   of the instruction. For example, if $(A) = AAH$ and $CY = 0$, then,
   after the execution of RAL, we would have $(A) = 54H$ with $CY = 1$.

Table 3.3
Logical instructions

Operation	Mnemonic	OP	c	b	Addressing mode	Action	Flag bits affected
And	ANA r	10100sss	1	1	register	$(A) \leftarrow (A) \cdot (r)$	all ①
	ANA M	A6	2	1	indirect	$(A) \leftarrow (A) \cdot (M)$	all ①
	ANI data8	E6	2	2	immediate	$(A) \leftarrow (A) \cdot \text{data8}$	all ①
Exclusive or	XRA r	10101sss	1	1	register	$(A) \leftarrow (A) \oplus (r)$	all ②
	XRA M	AE	2	1	indirect	$(A) \leftarrow (A) \oplus (M)$	all ②
	XRI data8	EE	2	2	immediate	$(A) \leftarrow (A) \oplus \text{data8}$	all ②
Or	ORA r	10110sss	1	1	register	$(A) \leftarrow (A) + (r)$	all ②
	ORA M	B6	2	1	indirect	$(A) \leftarrow (A) + (M)$	all ②
	ORI data8	F6	2	2	immediate	$(A) \leftarrow (A) + \text{data8}$	all ②
Compare	CMP r	10111sss	1	1	register	$(A) - (r)$	all
	CMP M	BE	2	1	indirect	$(A) - (M)$	all
	CPI data8	FE	2	2	immediate	$(A) - \text{data8}$	all
Rotate	RLC	07	1	1	implied	$CY \; b_7 \; A \; b_0$	CY
	RRC	0F	1	1	implied	$CY \; b_7 \; A \; b_0$	CY
Rotate through carry	RAL	17	1	1	implied	$CY \; b_7 \; A \; b_0$	CY
	RAR	1F	1	1	implied	$CY \; b_7 \; A \; b_0$	CY
Complement (1's) accumulator	CMA	2F	1	1	implied	$(A) \leftarrow (\overline{A})$	none
Complement carry	CMC	3F	1	1	implied	$(CY) \leftarrow (\overline{CY})$	CY
Set carry	STC	37	1	1	implied	$(CY) \leftarrow 1$	CY

① $(CY) \leftarrow 0$, $(AC) \leftarrow 1$
② $(CY), (AC) \leftarrow 0$

EXERCISES

1. Hand-load and execute the program segments that are shown below. Indicate all changes in the computer's internal state (registers, memory locations, condition codes) that result from these segments. Clear the accumulator before running each segment.

   The notation used in these segments is explained in Exercise 1 following Sec. 3.3.

Location	Hex code	
a) $xy00$	2F	CMA
$xy01$	76	HLT
b) $xy00$	EE 0F	XRI data8
$xy02$	76	HLT
c) $xy00$	B8	CMP B
$xy01$	76	HLT
d) $xy00$	37	STC
$xy01$	1F	RAR
$xy02$	76	HLT

2. Write an I8085 program to add the contents of locations $xy20$, $xy21$, and $xy22$ and store the result in location $xy30$. The xy notation should be replaced by hex digits that represent valid memory for your computer. Your program should use indirect addressing.

   After your program executes properly, you should single-step through it (execute one instruction one at a time) and note the partial sums forming in the accumulator.

3. Given the following initial register and memory configuration,

(A) = 02	(2010) = 2B
(B) = A6	(2011) = C4
(C) = BB	(2012) = 56
(D) = 20	(2013) = 1F
(E) = 14	(2014) = E9
(H) = 20	
(L) = 12	

   determine the effect of each of the following (assuming that each case starts independently from the initial configuration):

   a) 54   b) 1E FE   c) 86   d) 09
   e) 1A   f) F6 F0   g) 34   h) 22 20 10

4. What is the effect of the following I8085 program?

Location	Hex code	Location	Hex Codes
2000	3A 0A 20	2009	76
2003	2F	200A	00
2004	07	200B	0D
2005	2A 0B 20	200C	20
2008	77		

5. The indexed addressing mode is not utilized in the I8085. Indicate how indexed addressing can be simulated; for example, how can one load the accumulator with the contents of location X + (H-L) where X is a two-digit hexadecimal number?

6. For each of the following cases, write a segment to load the accumulator with the indicated number.

    a) (2025)   b) 25   c) (25 + (H-L))   d) ((H − L))

3.6 BRANCH CONTROL INSTRUCTIONS

This group of instructions includes a number of conditional transfers. The conditional transfers examine the status of one of the flags Z, C, P, S. The conditions and their three-bit encodings ccc are as follows:

Condition		ccc
NZ	Z = 0	000
Z	Z = 1	001
NC	CY = 0	010
C	CY = 1	011
PO	P = 0	100
PE	P = 1	101
P	S = 0	110
M	S = 1	111

Condition flags are not affected by any instruction in this group. The instructions of this Branch Control Group are listed in Table 3.4.

As indicated above, the conditional Jump (and Call) instructions consist of four pairs of complementary instructions, one pair for each of the flag bits Z, C, S, and P. JP and JM test the status of the sign bit to determine whether or not the result of the previous operation was positive or negative, respectively. JZ and JNZ, which test the status of the zero bit, are useful, following Compare instructions, to test for the possibility of equality between the operands. JC and JNC test the carry bit and are useful for testing relative magnitudes when values are regarded as unsigned binary numbers in the range 00H to FFH. Following a comparison (CMP), for example, JC will cause a branch if the value in the accumulator is less than the value of the operand; JNC will cause a branch if the value in the accumulator is greater than or equal to the value of the operand. JPE and JPO test the status of the parity bit.

The Call instructions are used for branching to subroutines. As with the branch instructions, there is one unconditional Call and four pairs of complementary conditional Call instructions. Execution of a Call instruction causes a return address—the address of the first byte of the next instruction—to be

Table 3.4
Branch control instructions

Operation	Mnemonic	OP	c	b	Addressing mode	Action
Jump	JMP adr	C3	3	3	direct	$(PC) \leftarrow adr$
Jump on condition	Jcond adr	11ccc010	2/3	3	direct	$(PC) \leftarrow adr$ if cond
Call	CALL adr	CD	5	3	direct	$((SP)-1) \leftarrow (PC_h)$, $((SP)-2) \leftarrow (PC_l)$, $(SP) \leftarrow (SP)-2, (PC) \leftarrow adr$
Call on condition	Ccond adr	11ccc100	2/5	3	direct	If cond is true, then $((SP)-1) \leftarrow (PC_h)$, $((SP)-2) \leftarrow (PC_l)$, $(SP) \leftarrow (SP)-2$, $(PC) \leftarrow adr$
Return	RET	C9	3	1	implied	$(PC_l) \leftarrow ((SP))$, $(PC_h) \leftarrow ((SP)+1)$, $(SP) \leftarrow (SP)+2$
Return on condition	Rcond	11ccc000	1/3	1	implied	If cond is true, then $(PC_l) \leftarrow ((SP))$, $(PC_h) \leftarrow ((SP)+1)$, $(SP) \leftarrow (SP)+2$
Restart	RST n $0 \leq n \leq 7$	11NNN111	3	1	implied	$((SP)-1) \leftarrow (PC_h)$, $((SP)-2) \leftarrow (PC_l)$, $(SP) \leftarrow (SP)-2$ $(PC) \leftarrow 8*NNN$
Transfer H-L to PC	PCHL	E9	1	1	implied	$(PC) \leftarrow (H-L)$

saved on the stack. A jump is then made to the address specified in the Call instruction.

The Return instruction and the conditional returns (which again test the same four pairs of conditions as the Jump and the Call) cause the return address to be retrieved from the stack and loaded into the program counter.

Example

a) The Call, Conditional Call, and Restart instructions all save the updated PC on the stack before transferring control. The Call and Restart are unconditional transfers while Ccond is a conditional transfer. The call instructions specify the transfer address as part of the instruction. The Restart is a special transfer in that it allows a transfer to one of eight specific locations in lower core,

00H,   08H,   10H,   18H,   20H,   28H,   30H,   or   38H.

The value n that is specified in the instruction in bits 5, 4, and 3 determines the particular location. RST 3, for example, is encoded as DFH with bits 5, 4, and 3 being 011. Execution of this instruction results in the updated PC being saved on the stack and then $(PC) \leftarrow 8 \cdot 011$ or 18H.

3.7 STACK, INPUT/OUTPUT, AND MACHINE CONTROL INSTRUCTIONS

This final group of instructions is given in Table 3.5.

The PUSH, POP, XTHL, and SPHL instructions provide for programmed control of the stack. The stack pointer, SP, can be initialized or reset using the SPHL instruction, which moves the contents of the H–L register pair to SP. The XTHL instruction interchanges the two bytes at the top of the stack with the contents of the H–L pair. PUSH (POP) is used to add (delete) two eight-bit values to (from) the stack.

The IN and OUT instructions function, respectively, as input and output operations on the I8085. Both of these instructions are two bytes in length, where the second byte specifies an input or output port. An eight-bit value is output from the accumulator or input to the accumulator. The RIM and SIM instructions can also be used for input and output as well as for reading or setting (resetting) the interrupt masks. IN, OUT, RIM, and SIM are discussed in greater detail in Chapter 5.

Examples

a) If (B) = 04H, (C) = F3H, and (SP) = 2030H, then, after execution of PUSH B, we would have (202FH) = 04H, (202EH) = F3H, and (SP) = 202EH.

b) Given (H) = 32H, (L) = 4AH, (SP) = 2030H, (2030H) = 54H, and (2031H) = 76H, then, after execution of XTHL, we would have (H) = 76H, (L) = 54H, (2030H) = 4AH and (2031H) = 32H. SP is unaffected.

EXERCISES

1. Assume that (SP) is, as usual, the address of the top element on the stack for the I8085. Find an efficient way of loading the accumulator with the byte of data whose address is (SP) + 5.

Table 3.5
Stack, input/output, and machine control instructions

Operation	Mnemonic	OP	c	b	Address-ing mode	Action	Flag bits affected
Push	PUSH rp ①	11rp0101	3	1	implied	$((SP)-1) \leftarrow (rp_h)$, $((SP)-2) \leftarrow (rp_h)$, $(SP) \leftarrow (SP)-2$	none
	PUSH PSW	F5	3	1	implied	$((SP)-1) \leftarrow (A)$, $((SP)-2) \leftarrow (CCR)$, $(SP) \leftarrow (SP)-2$	none
Pop	POP rp ①	11rp0001	3	1	implied	$(rp_l) \leftarrow ((SP))$, $(rp_h) \leftarrow ((SP)+1)$, $(SP) \leftarrow (SP+2)$	none
	POP PSW	F1	3	1	implied	$(CCR) \leftarrow ((SP))$, $(A) \leftarrow ((SP)+1)$, $(SP) \leftarrow (SP)+2$	all
Exchange	XTHL	E3	5	1	implied	$(L) \leftrightarrow ((SP))$, $(H) \leftrightarrow ((SP)+1)$	none
Transfer	SPHL	F9	1	1	implied	$(SP) \leftarrow (H\text{-}L)$	none
Input	IN port	DB	3	2	direct	$(A) \leftarrow (port)$	none
Output	OUT port	D3	3	2	direct	$(port) \leftarrow (A)$	none
Enable interrupts	EI	FB	1	1	implied	Interrupts enabled	none
Disable interrupts	DI	F3	1	1	implied	Interrupts disabled	none
Halt	HLT	76	1	1	implied	Processor stopped	none
No op	NOP	00	1	1	implied	none	none
Read interrupt mask	RIM	20	1	1	implied	$(A) \leftarrow$ int. masks	none
Set interrupt mask	SIM	30	1	1	implied	int. masks $\leftarrow (A)$	none

① rp = SP may not be specified.

2. Suppose we wish to view a byte of data as a signed integer in the range
   + 127 to − 128. Devise a short segment that will test if $(A) < (M)$,
   where M is the address specified in the H–L register pair and branch to
   location 2050 if this condition is true.

3. Assume that, on the I8085, memory is configured as shown below and that execution begins with (PC) = 2000H.

Location	Contents (in hex)
2000	2A
2001	08
2002	20
2003	46
2004	23
2005	4E
2006	0A
2007	76
2008	09
2009	20
200A	0A

a) Trace the execution of the program.

b) If the program is illegal, state why.

c) Indicate the contents of the registers upon termination of the program (or at the point where it becomes illegal). Use ?? to denote an unknown value.

A =   B =   C =

D =   E =   SP =

H =   L =   PC =

REFERENCES AND SUPPORTIVE MATERIAL

The material in this chapter has been organized and presented in a manner similar to that followed in Intel's supporting literature for the I8085. Intel (1977a) contains a complete technical discussion of the I8085, as well as tables of its instructions. This manual also covers the other components in the I8085 system. A thorough discussion of the individual I8085 instructions appears in Intel (1977b).

1. Intel [1977a]. "MCS-85 User's Manual," Intel Corporation, 3065 Bowers Ave., Santa Clara, California.

2. Intel [1977b]. "8080/8085 Assembly-Language Programming Manual," Intel Corporation, 3065 Bowers Ave., Santa Clara, California.

CHAPTER FOUR

PROGRAMMING WITH THE M6800 AND THE I8085

4.1 PROGRAMMING TECHNIQUES

In this chapter we shall expand our discussion of the M6800 and I8085 instruction sets by analyzing the realizations of some standard programming concepts within these instruction sets. This will also provide us with a means of making an initial comparison of the two instruction sets.

Our analysis will follow the "levels" approach outlined in Chapter 1; that is, for a given high-level (level 5) construct, we shall examine the AL (level 4) and OS* (level 3) representations of the construct for each of the two microprocessors being considered.

The various assembler-language concepts used are discussed briefly as they are introduced; and a more complete presentation of the two assemblers appears in Appendixes D and E, respectively. This chapter concludes with a discussion of the transition from AL program representations to CML/OS representations.

The high-level versions of the various examples in this chapter will be presented using an *ad hoc* high-level language. This not only allows us to utilize statements that are typical and self-explanatory, but also frees us from the restrictions imposed by any particular language.

Specifically, each program will be bound by a *begin* statement and an *end* statement. All variables must be declared; a variable declared as integer will be represented internally in one byte. Such a variable can be assigned an initial value using *init*. Our high-level language will also utilize the assignment statement.

---

* The OS-level representations are almost identical with the CML (level 2) representations.

Example 1 (*Simple assignment*)

High-level representation

```
begin
    integer Q init (4);
    integer P;
    P = Q
end
```

M6800 representations

OS Code			AL Code		
Location	Hex code				
		*	SIMPLE ASSIGNMENT		
			NAM	EXAMP1	
0100			ORG	0100H	
0100	B6 01 07		LDA A	Q	ACCA←(Q)
0103	B7 01 08		STA A	P	(P)←ACCA
0106	3F		SWI		
0107	04	Q	FCB	4	
0108		P	RMB	1	
			END		

Recall that the numbers followed by an "H" in this AL program are hexadecimal numbers, while those not followed by an "H" denote decimal numbers.

The assembler directives used in the M6800 AL representation (NAM, ORG, RMB, FCB, and END) are described in detail in Appendix D. We shall briefly describe their use in this example.

The NAM directive is required at the beginning of an M6800 assembly-language program. Its purpose is to name the program module; in this case, "EXAMP1" is the specified name. The END directive marks the end of the assembler program.

The program has been arbitrarily set to be located beginning at location 0100H with the ORG directive; i.e., storage for the program instructions and data will be assigned starting at 0100H. Note that this implies that the extended addressing mode will be used in accessing the variables P and Q, since P is associated with location 0108H and Q with 0107H.

In the high-level representation, two variables have been declared and one of them, "Q", has been given an initial value of 4. These are accommodated in the AL representation with the FCB (Form Constant Byte) and RMB (Reserve Memory Byte) directives. The RMB simply reserves the specified number of bytes of storage, while the FCB reserves a byte of storage and initializes this byte to the designated constant.

I8085 representations

OS Code				AL Code		
Location	Hex code					
			;	SIMPLE ASSIGNMENT		
				NAME	EXAMP1	
2000				ORG	2000H	
2000	3A	07	20	LDA	Q	; A←(Q)
2003	32	08	20	STA	P	; (P)←A
2006	76			HLT		
2007	04		Q:	DB	4	
2008			P:	DS	1	
				END		

Details on the I8085 assembler can be found in Appendix E. The ORG and END directives serve the same function here that they did for the M6800 assembler. The DS (Define storage) directive reserves the specified number of bytes of storage, while the DB (Define byte) directive reserves a byte of storage and initializes this byte to the designated constant (4, in this case).

The M6800 and I8085 assembly languages use different conventions for including comments in an AL program. For the I8085, a semicolon is used to signal the beginning of a comment. Comments in the M6800 assembly language are separated from the last operand by at least one blank. In addition, for the M6800, an asterisk in column 1 is used to signal that the entire line is a comment.

The use of labels in each of the AL code representations should also be noted. In particular, I8085 assembly-language labels are terminated with a colon, while those in M6800 assembly language are not.

The M6800 and I8085 AL representations for the simple assignment example are very similar. A form of the direct-addressing mode can be used on both processors to load the righthand side value into an accumulator and then store (assign) this value to the lefthand side value. Note that since neither processor supports memory-to-memory transfers, an accumulator must be used in both cases to hold the righthand-side value prior to assignment.

Example 2 *(Arithmetic computations)*

High-level representation

```
begin
    integer Y init (2);
    integer Z init (3);
    integer W init (1);
    integer Q;
    Q = (Y + Z) - W
end
```

M6800 representations

OS Code			AL Code			
Location	Hex code					
		*	ARITHMETIC COMPUTATIONS			
			NAM	EXAMP2		
0100			ORG	0100H		
0100	B6 01 0D		LDA	A	Y	ACCA←(Y)
0103	BB 01 0E		ADD	A	Z	ACCA←ACCA+(Z)
0106	B0 01 0F		SUB	A	W	ACCA←ACCA−(W)
0109	B7 01 10		STA	A	Q	(Q)←ACCA
010C	3F		SWI			
010D	02	Y	FCB	2		
010E	03	Z	FCB	3		
010F	01	W	FCB	1		
0110		Q	RMB	1		
			END			

I8085 representations

OS Code			AL Code		
Location	Hex code				
		;	ARITHMETIC COMPUTATIONS		
			NAME	EXAMP2	
2000			ORG	2000H	
2000	3A 0F 20		LDA	Y	; A←(Y)
2003	21 10 20		LXI	H,Z	; H,L POINT TO Z
2006	86		ADD	M	; A←A+(Z)
2007	21 11 20		LXI	H,W	; H,L POINT TO W
200A	96		SUB	M	; A←A−(W)
200B	32 12 20		STA	Q	; (Q)←A
200E	76		HLT		
200F	02	Y :	DB	2	
2010	03	Z :	DB	3	
2011	01	W:	DB	1	
2012		Q :	DS	1	
			END		

This example highlights one of the differences in the instructions available on these processors. Since the M6800 supports accumulator/memory operations in the direct-addressing mode, the M6800 representations are quite straightforward; this capability is not present on the I8085. Arithmetic operations on this processor involve the accumulator (A) and either one of the registers (A,B,C,D,E,H,L) or the memory location addressed by the H and L registers, e.g., ADD M. Since direct addressing is not available, some other technique must be used. The I8085 representations shown for this example use indirect addressing with the H and L register pair. This is not the only method that could be used (see Exercise 1 at the end of Sec. 4.2.2).

Example 3 *(Double-precision addition)*

High-level representation

```
begin
    double integer P init (1024);
    double integer Q init (753);
    double integer R;
    R = P + Q
end
```

Note that the high-level representation of the example above involves a new declaration—*double integer.* As this declaration suggests, any variable so declared will be allotted two consecutive bytes for its internal representation.

Multiple-precision arithmetic is handled so casually at the high-level representation that we tend to forget how small units must be treated collectively in order to support this construct. Since microcomputers for the most part deal with eight-bit quantities, multiple-precision routines are used often.

M6800 representations

OS Code				AL Code			
Location	Hex code						
			*		DOUBLE-PRECISION		
				NAM	EXAMP3		
0100				ORG	0100H		
0100	B6	01	14	LDA	A	P+1	$ACCA \leftarrow (P_l)$
0103	F6	01	13	LDA	B	P	$ACCB \leftarrow (P_h)$
0106	BB	01	16	ADD	A	Q+1	$ACCA \leftarrow ACCA + (Q_l)$
0109	F9	01	15	ADC	B	Q	$ACCB \leftarrow ACCB + (Q_h) + CY$
010C	B7	01	18	STA	A	R+1	$(R_l) \leftarrow ACCA$
010F	F7	01	17	STA	B	R	$(R_h) \leftarrow ACCB$
0112	3F			SWI			
0113	04	00	P	FDB	1024		
0115	02	F1	Q	FDB	753		
0117			R	RMB	2		
				END			

I8085 representations

OS Code				AL Code		
Location	Hex code					
			;	DOUBLE-PRECISION		
				NAME	EXAMP3	
2000				ORG	2000H	
2000	2A	0C	20	LHLD	P	; H,L ← (P$_h$), (P$_l$)
2003	EB			XCHG		; D,E ← H,L
2004	2A	0E	20	LHLD	Q	; H,L ← (Q$_h$), (Q$_l$)
2007	19			DAD	D	; H,L ← H,L + D,E
2008	22	10	20	SHLD	R	; (R) ← H,L
200B	76			HLT		
200C	00	04	P:	DW	1024	
200E	F1	02	Q:	DW	753	
2010			R:	DS	2	
				END		

The M6800 representations again rely on the direct-addressing capability of arithmetic operations, and make use of both accumulators A and B. Moreover, as is typical in multiple-precision arithmetic, the add-with-carry operation is used.

The I8085 handles this particular task more efficiently since it provides a special double-register add instruction (DAD), which performs double-precision addition using the H and L register pair as a 16-bit accumulator. It should be noted, however, that the I8085 method is special and does not generalize to *n*-byte operations as the M6800 method does (see Exercise 5 at the end of Sec. 4.2.2).

Note the special assembler directives used to reserve and initialize two bytes of storage: FDB (Form Double Byte) for the M6800, and DW (Define Word) for the I8085. As can be seen from the resulting storage initializations (in the OS code), the M6800 holds a word in most significant byte (MSB)/least significant byte (LSB) order, while the I8085 holds it in LSB/MSB order. This is consistent with the method of specifying addresses (in OS or CML code) in the two machines.

Example 4 (*Branching*)

High-level representation

```
                    begin
                        integer P ;
                        P = 1 ;
                        go to L1 ;
                L2 :    P = 3 ;
                        go to L3 ;
                L1 :    P = 2 ;
                        go to L2
                L3 : end
```

Note that a new high-level statement appears here—the *go to* statement. Statement labels are also introduced in conjunction with the *go to*.

M6800 representations

OS Code				AL Code			
Location	Hex code						
			*	BRANCHING			
				NAM		EXAMP4	
0100				ORG		0100H	
0100	86	01		LDA	A	#1	
0102	B7	01	16	STA	A	P	P = 1
0105	20	07		BRA		L1	
0107	86	03	L2	LDA	A	#3	
0109	B7	01	16	STA	A	P	P = 3
010C	20	07		BRA		L3	
010E	86	02	L1	LDA	A	#2	
0110	B7	01	16	STA	A	P	P = 2
0113	20	F2		BRA		L2	
0 15	3F		L3	SWI			
0116			P	RMB		1	
				END			

As indicated in this segment of AL code, the M6800 assembly language uses a "#" to denote immediate addressing.

I8085 representations

OS Code				AL Code			
Location	Hex code						
			;	BRANCHING			
				NAME		EXAMP4	
2000				ORG		2000H	
2000	3E	01		MVI		A,1	
2002	32	19	20	STA		P	; P = 1
2005	C3	10	20	JMP		L1	
2008	3E	03	L2:	MVI		A,3	
200A	32	19	20	STA		P	; P = 3
200D	C3	18	20	JMP		L3	
2010	3E	02	L1:	MVI		A,2	
2012	32	19	20	STA		P	; P = 2
2015	C3	08	20	JMP		L2	
2018	76		L3:	HLT			
2019			P:	DS		1	
				END			

The M6800 provides more options than the I8085 with respect to the implementation of branching operations. Relative addressing (branching) has been used in the M6800 representations, while direct addressing (branching) has been used for the I8085 representations. The M6800 does provide for unconditional direct branches (JMP instruction), and it would have been possible to write this example using this instruction. Since direct branches require three bytes while relative branches require two bytes, it is generally preferable to use the latter whenever the branch destination is within the range of relative addressing.

Since the M6800 provides both direct and relative branching, it would seem that, at least with respect to branching, M6800 code would require fewer bytes in general than I8085 code. This is not always the case since the M6800 permits only unconditional direct branching, whereas the I8085 supports conditional direct branching. For example, assume we wish to transfer to a point labeled L1 dependent upon a zero test. On the I8085 we can accomplish this with

```
JZ      L1
```

If L1 is accessible with relative branching, then the M6800 code would simply be

```
BEQ    L1
```

For this situation the I8085 branch requires three bytes and the Motorola two bytes. If, however, L1 is not accessible with a relative branch, then the M6800 code would be

```
        BNE    T
        JMP    L1
T       . . .
```

This requires five bytes of code.

Example 5 *Block moves (Array assignment)*

High-level representation

```
begin
    integer  P (5)  init  (1,2,3,4,5) ;
    integer  Q(5) ;
    Q = P
end
```

The declarations in this program establish P and Q as one-dimensional integer arrays of length 5. Moreover, P is initialized to the successive values 1,2,3,4,5. The purpose of the program is to move the five values held in P to the corresponding locations in the uninitialized Q array. We assume that zero-origin subscripting is used for array structures.

M6800 representations

OS Code				AL Code			
Location	Hex code						
			*	BLOCK MOVES			
				NAM		EXAMP5	
0100				ORG		0100H	
0100	C6	05		LDA	B	#5	ACCB HOLDS COUNTER
0102	CE	01	24	LDX		#P	*** SOURCE POINTS
0105	FF	01	2E	STX		SOURCE	* TO P ARRAY
0108	CE	01	29	LDX		#Q	*** DEST POINTS
010B	FF	01	30	STX		DEST	* TO Q ARRAY
010E	FE	01	2E L1	LDX		SOURCE	*** ACCA−ELEMENT
0111	A6	00		LDA	A	0,X	* OF P ARRAY
0113	08			INX			*** INCREMENT
0114	FF	01	2E	STX		SOURCE	* SOURCE POINTER
0117	FE	01	30	LDX		DEST	*** STORE ACCA
011A	A7	00		STA	A	0,X	* IN Q ARRAY
011C	08			INX			*** INCREMENT
011D	FF	01	30	STX		DEST	* DEST POINTER
0120	5A			DEC	B		*** DECREMENT COUNTER,
0121	26	EB		BNE		L1	* BRANCH IF NOT ZERO
0123	3F			SWI			
0124	01		P	FCB		1,2,3,4,5	
0125	02		Q	RMB		5	
0126	03		SOURCE	RMB		2	
0127	04		DEST	RMB		2	
0128	05			END			
0129							
012A							
012B							
012C							
012D							
012E							
012F							
0130							
0131							

The M6800 assembly language uses the form "*m*,X" to denote indexed addressing, where *m* is the specified offset. The offset must be a value that lies in the range 00–FFH and it must be an assembly-time constant.

I8085 representations

OS Code				AL Code		
Location	Hex code					
			;	BLOCK MOVES		
				NAME	EXAMP5	
2000				ORG	2000H	
2000	11	16	20	LXI	D,Q	; D,E POINTS TO Q
2003	21	11	20	LXI	H,P	; H,L POINTS TO P
2006	06	05		MVI	B,5	; B HOLDS COUNTER
2008	7E		L1:	MOV	A,M	; A←ELEMENT OF ; P ARRAY
2009	23			INX	H	; INCREMENT P POINTER
200A	12			STAX	D	; STORE A IN Q
200B	13			INX	D	; INCREMENT Q POINTER
200C	05			DCR	B	; ** DECREMENT COUNTER
200D	C2	08	20	JNZ	L1	; BRANCH IF NOT ZERO
2010	76			HLT		
2011	01		P :	DB	1,2,3,4,5	
2012	02		Q :	DS	5	
2013	03			END		
2014	04					
2015	05					
2016						
2017						
2018						
2019						
201A						

The advantage of having additional registers on the I8085 shows up rather dramatically in this example. In moving the contents of one set of contiguous locations to another set of contiguous locations, it is desirable to maintain two pointers: one pointing to the source array and second pointing to the destination array. This is handled quite easily in the I8085 representations by using the (D-E) and (H-L) register pairs.

The M6800 representations use the index register to access both the source and destination arrays. Since the M6800 has only one 16-bit register, these pointers must be alternately held in the memory locations SOURCE and DEST. This considerably lengthens the code in the M6800 representations.

Example 6 (*Subroutines*)

High-level representation

```
begin
   integer  N  init  (4) ;
   integer  SUMSQ  init  (0) ;
   integer  J ;
   integer  procedure  SQUARE  (I) ;
      integer  I ;
      begin
         return (I*I)
      end
   do  J  =  N  to  1  by  −1 ;
      SUMSQ  =  SUMSQ  +  SQUARE(J)
end
```

Note that SQUARE is declared as a *procedure* (with parameter I) which will return a value of type *integer* in this program. The iterative *do* statement specifies an initial value for J, N, a final value, 1, and a step-value, − 1, which is added to J after each iteration.

M6800 representations

OS Code				AL Code			
Location	Hex code						
			*		SUBROUTINE		
				NAM		EXAMP6	
0100				ORG		0100H	
0100	F6	01	1D L1	LDA	B	N	ACCB←(N)
0103	8D	0C		BSR		SQUARE	
0105	FB	01	1E	ADD	B	SUMSQ	*** ADD ACCB
0108	F7	01	1E	STA	B	SUBSQ	* TO RUNNING SUM
010B	7A	01	1D	DEC		N	*** DECREMENT N
010E	2E	F0		BGT		L1	* BRANCH IF NOT ZERO
0110	3F			SWI			
0111	F7	01	1F SQUARE	STA	B	I	
0114	4F			CLR	A		
0115	1B		MORE	ABA			*** ADD I
0116	7A	01	1F	DEC		I	* TO ITSELF
0119	2E	FA		BGT		MORE	* I TIMES
011B	16			TAB			*** RETURN I * I
011C	39			RTS			* IN ACCB
011D	04		N	FCB		4	
011E	00		SUMSQ	FCB		0	
011F			I	RMB		1	
				END			

I8085 representations

OS Code				AL Code		
Location	Hex code					
			;	SUBROUTINE		
				NAME	EXAMP6	
2000				ORG	2000H	
2000	21	1B	20	LXI	H,SUMSQ	; H,L POINTS TO SUMSQ
2003	3A	1A	20	LDA	N	; ** B←(N)
2006	47			MOV	B,A	;
2007	CD	11	20 L1:	CALL	SQUARE	
200A	86			ADD	M	; ** ADD A TO
200B	77			MOV	M,A	; RUNNING SUM
200C	05			DCR	B	
200D	C2	07	20	JNZ	L1	
2010	76			HLT		
2011	48		SQUARE:	MOV	C,B	
2012	3E	00		MVI	A,0	
2014	80		MORE:	ADD	B	; ADD I,(B), TO
2015	0D			DCR	C	; ITSELF I
2016	C2	14	20	JNZ	MORE	; TIMES
2019	C9			RET		
201A	04		N:	DB	04	
201B	00		SUMSQ:	DB	00	
				END		

In comparing subroutine invocation in the two instruction sets, the previous analysis of branching techniques is applicable. The M6800 offers both relative calls (BSR) and direct calls (JSR). The BSR requires two bytes and the JSR requires three. The I8085 supports only direct calls but, as with branches, it offers conditional calls, for example, CNZ. The subroutine return mechanism is much more flexible in the I8085 since it offers both conditional and unconditional returns while the M6800 has only an unconditional return.

The program shown in Example 6 is designed to calculate the sum of the squares (that is, $1 + 2^2 + 3^2 + \cdots + N^2$ for a given N). A subroutine SQUARE is used to find the square of a given number. Since neither the M6800 nor the I8085 has multiplication instructions, multiplication must be simulated. In this case the square of a number I is derived by adding I to itself I times. Note that once again the additional registers on the I8085 have resulted in shorter code.

The SQUARE subroutine in both representations expects one argument, the number that must be squared. In this example, the argument has been passed through a register—ACCB for the M6800 representations, and register B for the I8085 representations. We will consider additional methods of passing arguments in the next example.

Example 7 (*Passing parameters by value and reference*)

High-level representation

```
begin
  integer VEC(5) init (3,7,4,2,6);
  integer SUM;
  procedure TOTAL (ARRAY, DIM, COUNT);
  integer (ARRAY(*), DIM, COUNT);
  reference (ARRAY, COUNT)
  value DIM;
  begin
    integer I;
    COUNT = 0;
    do I = DIM to 0 by -1;
      COUNT = COUNT + ARRAY(I)
  end;
  CALL TOTAL (VEC, 4, SUM)
end
```

In this example, the subroutine TOTAL has three parameters. The first parameter, ARRAY, is expected to be passed by reference; i.e., an address will be passed, and this address will point to the base of an array structure. The third parameter, COUNT, is also passed by reference. In this case, the address passed will correspond to the location associated with the variable COUNT. The second parameter, DIM, is expected to be passed by value; i.e., the actual value will be passed, not the address of the location containing the value. The argument/parameter correspondence for this example is simply

```
ARRAY : VEC
DIM   : 4
COUNT : SUM
```

It is natural to pass a parameter representing an array by reference since to pass it by value would entail passing each of its individual elements. Note that when a parameter is passed by reference, an assignment to the formal parameter has the same effect as an assignment to the actual argument.

M6800 representations

OS Code			AL Code		
Location	Hex code				
		*	PASSING PARAMETERS		
			NAM	EXAMP7	
0100			ORG	0100H	
0100	8D	0C	BSR	TOTAL	
0102	01	08	FDB	VEC	***
0104	04		FCB	04	* ARGUMENT LIST
0105	01	0D	FDB	SUM	***
0107	3F		SWI		
0108	03		VEC FCB	3,7,4,2,6	

(continued)

OS Code			AL Code			
Location	Hex code					
0109	07					
010A	04					
010B	02					
010C	06					
010D			SUM	RMB		1
010E	30		TOTAL	TSX			* XR ← SP − 1
010F	EE	00		LDX		0,X	* XR ← OLD PC VALUE
0111	A6	00		LDA	A	0,X	***
0113	B7	01 5C		STA	A	ARRAY	*
0116	08			INX			* SET
0117	A6	00		LDA	A	0,X	* 1ST
0119	B7	01 5D		STA	A	ARRAY + 1	* ARGUMENT
011C	08			INX			***
011D	A6	00		LDA	A	0,X	***
011F	B7	01 5E		STA	A	DIM	* SET 2ND ARGUMENT
0122	08			INX			***
0123	A6	00		LDA	A	0,X	***
0125	B7	01 5F		STA	A	COUNT	*
0128	08			INX			* SET
0129	A6	00		LDA	A	0,X	* 3RD
012B	B7	01 60		STA		COUNT + 1	* ARGUMENT
012E	08			INX			***
012F	32			PUL		A	* DISCARD
0130	32			PUL		A	* OLD PC
0131	FF	01 61		STX		TEMP	***
0134	B6	01 61		LDA	A	TEMP	* SET NEW
0137	F6	01 62		LDA	B	TEMP + 1	* PC
013A	37			PSH		B	* FROM XR
013B	36			PSH		A	***
013C	FE	01 5F		LDX		COUNT	
013F	86	00		LDA	A	#0	SET COUNT TO ZERO
0141	A7	00		STA	A	0,X	
0143	FE	01 5F	CONT	LDX		COUNT	
0146	A6	00		LDA	A	0,X	
0148	FE	01 5C		LDX		ARRAY	
014B	AB	00		ADD	A	0,X	ADD ARRAY(I)
014D	08			INX			
014E	FF	01 5C		STX		ARRAY	
0151	FE	01 5F		LDX		COUNT	
0154	A7	00		STA	A	0,X	

(continued)

OS Code			AL Code			
Location	Hex code					
0156	7A	01	5E	DEC	DIM	*** DECREMENT DIM
0159	2C	E8		BGE	CONT	* BRANCH I< = ZERO
015B	39			RTS		
015C			ARRAY	RMB	2	
015E			DIM	RMB	1	
015F			COUNT	RMB	2	
0161			TEMP	RMB	2	
				END		

Since this example is a bit more complex than some of the earlier ones we've looked at, we'll step through it in greater detail.

The main program really consists of only one instruction, the "BSR TOTAL". Following this call, there is the list of arguments, the address of VEC (0108), the value 4, and the address of SUM (010D). This corresponds to the fact that there are two reference parameters (ARRAY and COUNT) and one value parameter (DIM) for the subroutine TOTAL.

The list of arguments following the subroutine call might appear odd. Since we normally return from a subroutine to the point immediately following the call, it looks as if we will attempt to execute our argument list when we return from TOTAL. The PC value that is stored on the stack when we make the call is 0102H; that is, this stacked PC value points to the argument list. It is quite common to use a pointer to a list of arguments as a method of passing arguments to subroutines. The method used in this example is a variation of that approach; i.e., we will use the stacked PC as our pointer to the arguments. It will be necessary to modify the stacked PC in order to avoid the problem of returning to 0102H. Note that the proper return point is 0107H.

Within the subroutine, the instructions assembled from 010EH up to and including 013BH handle the parameter linkage and adjustment of the stacked PC. The TSX instruction places in the index register a pointer to the *top* entry on the stack. With this value in the index register, LDX 0,X loads the stacked PC (0102H) into the index register; i.e., the pointer to the argument list is now in the index register. The next six instructions,

```
LDA     0,X
STA   A ARRAY
INX
LDA     0,X
STA   A ARRAY + 1
INX
```

copy the first argument, the address of VEC, into the first parameter slot, and increment the index register so that it points to the second argument. The status at this point is depicted in Fig. 4.1. Note that the stacked PC is un-

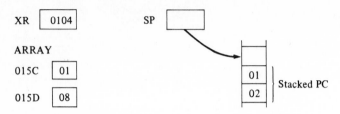

Fig. 4.1 First argument set.

changed at this point and that, in the locations assigned to ARRAY, we have a pointer to (the address of) VEC.

The next nine instructions set up the second and third arguments and again adjust the index register. The status at this point is depicted in Fig. 4.2. Note that DIM, the value parameter, is associated with a value whereas ARRAY and VEC, the reference parameters, are associated with addresses.

Now that the arguments have been associated with their respective parameters, there is one final step required to complete the linkage: updating the stacked PC. This is accomplished in the instructions assembled from 012FH to 013BH. The correct return point is held in the index register (see Fig. 4.2.) These instructions simply discard the old return point and push the correct return point onto the stack.

The actual body of the subroutine begins at the instruction assembled at 013CH. Note that, in the body, the value parameter is accessed directly while the reference parameters are accessed with the index register.

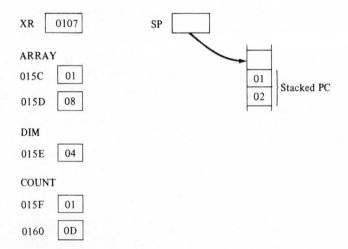

Fig. 4.2 All arguments set.

I8085 representations

OS Code				AL Code		
Location	Hex code					
			;	PASSING PARAMETERS		
				NAME	EXAMP7	
2000				ORG	2000H	
2000	CD	0F	20	CALL	TOTAL	
2003	09	20		DW	VEC	; ———
2005	04			DB	04	; ARGUMENT LIST
2006	0E	20		DW	SUM	; ———
2008	76			HLT		
2009	03		VEC:	DB	3,7,4,2,6	
200A	07					
200B	04					
200C	02					
200D	06					
200E			SUM:	DS	1	
200F	E1		TOTAL:	POP	H	; H,L—OLD PC
2010	7E			MOV	A,M	; ———
2011	32	44	20	STA	ARRAY	;
2014	23			INX	H	; SET
2015	7E			MOV	A,M	; 1ST
2016	32	45	20	STA	ARRAY + 1	; ARGUMENT
2019	23			INX	H	; ———
201A	7E			MOV	A,M	; ———
201B	32	46	20	STA	DIM	; SET 2ND ARGUMENT
201E	23			INX	H	; ———
201F	7E			MOV	A,M	;
2020	32	47	20	STA	COUNT	; SET
2023	23			INX	H	; 3RD
2024	7E			MOV	A,M	; ARGUMENT
2025	32	48	20	STA	COUNT + 1	;
2028	23			INX	H	; ———
2029	E5			PUSH	H	; PUSH NEW PC
202A	2A	47	20	LHLD	COUNT	; ———
202D	3E	00		MVI	A,0	; COUNT = 0
202F	77			MOV	M,A	; ———
2030	3A	46	20	LDA	DIM	
2033	47			MOV	B,A	
2034	EB			XCHG		
2035	2A	44	20	LHLD	ARRAY	
2038	EB			XCHG		
2039	7E		CONT:	MOV	A,M	

(continued)

OS Code		AL Code		
Location	Hex code			
203A	EB	XCHG		
203B	86	ADD	M	; ADD ARRAY(I)
203C	23	INX	H	
203D	EB	XCHG		
203E	77	MOV	M,A	
203F	05	DCR	B	
2040	F2 39 20	JP	CONT	
2043	C9	RET		
2044		ARRAY:	DS	2
2046		DIM:	DS	1
2047		COUNT:	DS	2
		END		

The use of the PC as a pointer to the argument list is also used in the I8085 representations. For this case, the code assembled from locations 200FH up to and including 2029H sets up the parameter linkage. The adjustment of the return PC is accomplished by PUSHing the contents of the H–L pair onto the stack. Note that in the I8085 representations the old return PC has actually been removed from the stack, used to access the arguments, updated, and then returned to the stack. The status after these instructions have been executed is depicted in Fig. 4.3.

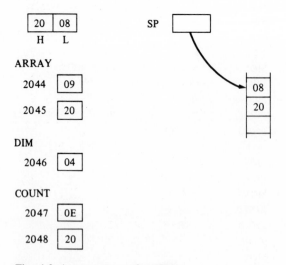

Fig. 4.3 Arguments set for I8085.

In comparing the M6800 and I8085 representations of the parameter-linkage technique, we can see that the register pairs and operations on these pairs (XCHG, POP, PUSH) provided in the I8085 have resulted in a shorter, more efficient implementation.

Example 8 (*Multiway branches*) The last programming construct we will consider is the implementation of a multiway branch. In high-level languages we often find an *if-then-else* construct that provides a mechanism for selecting one of two possible sections of code to execute. If we wish to select one of *N* possible sections of code to execute, we can use a sequence of nested *if-then-else* statements or a *case* statement. For the *case* statement

```
case  I  is
1 :         P  =  P  +  1
4 :         P  =  P  +  7
5 : 6 :     P  =  P  +  15
3 :         P  =  P  +  4
endcase
```

the intent is to:

add 1 to P   if I = 1,
add 7 to P   if I = 4,
add 15 to P if I = 5 or I = 6,
add 4 to P   if I = 3,
do none of the above if I does not equal 1 , 4 , 5 , 6 , or 3.

If we implement this with nested *if-then-else* statements, we would have:

```
if  I  = 1  then
        P  =  P  +  1
else  if  I  = 4  then
            P  =  P  +  7
    else  if  ( I  = 5  or  I  = 6)  then
                P  =  P  +  15
        else  if  I  = 3  then
                    P  =  P  +  4
```

The "case" version is much easier to read. In general, multiway branches can detract from the readability of a program. In the AL representations, we will strive for a readable implementation. Moreover, we will assume that I takes on one of the values 1 through 8.

High-level representation

```
begin
    integer  I  init  (5) ;
    integer  P ;
        case  I  is
        1 :      P  =  5 ;
        3 :      P  =  8 ;
        5 : 7 :  P  =  3 ;
        endcase
end
```

M6800 representations

Location	Hex code							
				*		MULTIWAY BRANCH		
					NAM	EXAMP8		
0100					ORG	0100H		
0100	CE	01	27		LDX	#BRTBL	XR←ADDRESS OF BRANCH TABLE	
0103	B6	01	25		LDA	A	I	*** A←I − 1
0106	4A			LOOP	DEC	A	* BRANCH IF	
0107	26	04			BNE	CONT	* NOT ZERO	
0109	EE	00			LDX	0,X	XR←BRANCH POINT	
010B	6E	00			JMP	0,X	JMP TO BRANCH POINT	
010D	08			CONT	INX		*** POINT TO NEXT	
010E	08				INX		* ENTRY IN BRANCH TABLE	
010F	20	F5			BRA	LOOP		
0111	86	05		L1	LDA	A	#5	
0113	B7	01	26		STA	A	P	P = 5
0116	20	0C			BRA	L0		
0118	86	08		L3	LDA	A	#8	
011A	B7	01	26		STA	A	P	P = 8
011D	20	05			BRA	L0		
011F	86	03		L5	LDA	A	#3	
011F				L7	EQU	L5		
0121	B7	01	26		STA	A	P	P = 3
0124	3F			L0	SWI			
0125	05			I	FCB	5		
0126				P	RMB	1		
0127	01	11		BRTBL	FDB	L1	***	
0129	01	24			FDB	L0	*	
012B	01	18			FDB	L3	*	
012D	01	24			FDB	L0	* BRANCH	
012F	01	1F			FDB	L5	* TABLE	
0131	01	24			FDB	L0	*	
0133	01	1F			FDB	L7	*	
0135	01	24			FDB	L0	***	
					END			

A label or branch-point table is being used to implement the multiway branch in the M6800 representations. The table is formed by the FDB directives listed at BRTBL. There are eight entries in the table, corresponding to the fact that I assumes one of the values 1 through 8. The entries are arranged positionally to correspond to the appropriate branch points for a given value of I, as in Table 4.1.

The EQUate directive is used to give L7 the same value as L5 so that both of these symbols refer to the address 011FH.

Transference to the proper point is accomplished as follows:

Step 1 The index register is set to point to the first entry in the branch table:

$$\text{XR} \quad \boxed{0127}$$

Step 2 The value of I is loaded into ACCA and decremented to adjust to zero origin. We then enter a loop that will decrement ACCA down to zero. For each decrement, the index register is incremented twice. This implies that each pass through the loop skips over one entry in the branch table. For our example, with I = 5, this will give us:

$$\text{XR} \quad \boxed{012F}$$

Step 3 The index register is loaded with the selected branch point,

$$\text{XR} \quad \boxed{011F}$$

Step 4 We jump in the indexed mode to the designated point:

$$\text{J MP} \qquad 0 \text{ , X}$$

with

$$\text{XR} \quad \boxed{011F}$$

takes us to 011FH.

Table 4.1

	Entry number	Value of I	Action
1	L1	1	P = 5
2	L0	2	none (SWI)
3	L3	3	P = 8
4	L0	4	none (SWI)
5	L5	5	P = 3
6	L0	6	none (SWI)
7	L7	7	P = 3
8	L0	8	none (SWI)

I8085 representations

OS Code				AL Code		
Location	Hex code					
			;	MULTIWAY BRANCH		
				NAME	EXAMP8	
2000				ORG	2000H	
2000	3A	27	20	LDA	I	
2003	3D			DCR	A	; A ← (I) − 1
2004	6F			MOV	L,A	
2005	26	00		MVI	H,0	
2007	29			DAD	H	; H,L ← H,L + H,L
2008	01	29	20	LXI	B,BRTBL	; LOAD ADDRESS OF ; BRANCH TABLE IN B,C
200B	09			DAD	B	; H,L ← ADDRESS OF ; BRANCH POINT
200C	5E			MOV	E,M	; ...
200D	23			INX	H	; move branch point into D − E
200E	56			MOV	D,M	; ...
200F	EB			XCHG		; Transfer branch point to H − L
2010	E9			PCHL		; TRANSFER TO ; BRANCH POINT
2011	3E	05	L1:	MVI	A,5	; P = 5
2013	32	28	20 STA		P	
2016	C2	26	20 JMP		L0	
2019	3E	08	L3:	MVI	A,8	; P = 8
201B	32	28	20 STA		P	
201E	C2	26	20 JMP		L0	
2021	3E	03	L5:	MVI	A,3	; P = 3
2021			L7	EQU	L5	
2023	32	28	20 STA		P	
2026	76		L0:	HLT		
2027	05		I:	DB	5	
2028			P:	DS	1	
2029	11	20	BRTBL:	DW	L1	; ———
202B	26	20		DW	L0	;
202D	19	20		DW	L3	;
202F	26	20		DW	L0	; BRANCH
2031	21	20		DW	L5	; TABLE
2033	26	20		DW	L0	;
2035	21	20		DW	L7	;
2037	26	20		DW	L0	; ———
				END		

The I8085 representations also use the branch-table technique; the difference that should be noted is the method by which the transference is effected. First, the correct entry point into the branch table is calculated directly by simply adding 2(I − 1) to the base of the table (BRTBL), using the DAD instruction. Secondly, after using this entry point to move the corresponding table entry (the branch point) into the H–L pair, the PCHL sets the PC to the branch point; i.e., it effects the jump.

The EQUate directive is again used in the I8085 representation to equate the value of L5, 2021H, with the symbol L7. Note that no colon is needed after the label in the EQU directive.

4.2 COMPARISON OF THE TWO INSTRUCTION SETS

The eight examples of the preceding section provide us with a means of making some initial comparisons of the M6800 and I8085 instruction sets. It is, of course, impossible to make an absolute statement that one of these instruction sets is "better than" the other in all cases. In Table 4.2 we list the number of object bytes used for the respective machines in each of the eight examples. Note that, for programs requiring extensive referencing of multiple contiguous sets of memory locations, the existence of multiple register pairs for nondirect addressing purposes is most helpful. On the other hand, in many instances involving arithmetic operations, the M6800's direct-addressing capabilities can result in less complex programs.

Table 4.2
Summary data for Examples 1–8.

	1 Assign- ment	2 Computa- tions	3 Double- precision add	4 Branch- ing	5 Block moves	6 Sub- routines	7 Param- eters	8 Multiway branches
M6800 Number of program object bytes	7	13	19	22	36	29	86	37
I8085 Number of program object bytes	7	15	12	25	19	26	62	39

LABORATORY ASSIGNMENT

The programs we have run thus far have all executed "instantaneously." A simple way to construct a program that takes an observable time to execute is to use nested loops. Write a M6800 (I8085) hex program that is not an infinite loop, but executes for at least five seconds. The display on your microcomputer should indicate when the program has finished executing.

EXERCISES

1. Rewrite the I8085 representations for Example 2 (arithmetic computations) without using the H and L pair for indirect addressing.

2. Write the OS and AL representations for Example 2 in I8085 specifications such that fewer object bytes are needed than are required for the M6800 representations shown for Example 2.

3. Write a M6800 (I8085) segment in hex code that will count the number of 1's in an arbitrary memory location. Store this count in ACCA. Sketch out the solution in AL code and then hand-convert the AL code to hex code.

4. Write a M6800 (I8085) segment in hex code that will perform double-precision subtraction.

5. Write a M6800 (I8085) segment in hex code that will perform triple-precision addition.

6. Write a M6800 (I8085) program in hex code that will find and save in ACCA the largest of the numbers in locations 0100H, 0101H, . . . , 0120H. You are to view the contents of these locations as unsigned binary numbers in the range 00H–FFH.

7. Write a M6800 (I8085) program in hex code to find and store in consecutive bytes the prime numbers between 3 and 119. Your program should use a subroutine that will test whether a given number is prime. (A number n is *prime* if the only numbers that divide it evenly are 1 and n.)

8. In Example 7 the PC was used to point to the parameter list. Another method of passing parameters is to arrange the definitions of the arguments in a suitable fashion and then use a pointer other than the PC to point to the arguments, for example,

M6800		I8085	
LDX	LIST	LXI	H,LIST
CALL	TOTAL	CALL	TOTAL
SWI		HLT	
.		.	
.		.	
.		.	

(continued)

	M6800			I8085	
LIST	FDB	VEC	LIST:	DW	VEC
	FCB	04		DB	04
	FDB	SUM		DW	SUM
	.			.	
	.			.	
	.			.	
	END			END	

Discuss the advantages and disadvantages of both these methods of passing parameters.

9. The use of a branch table to implement a multiway branch may appear confusing when seen for the first time. Rewrite the M6800 and I8085 representations for Example 8 without using this feature; i.e., use a sequence of tests on the value of I. If you had to implement a *case* that selected 1 of 50 sections of code, which method would you use?

10. Suppose that the M6800 had two additional instructions that could be used to Push (Pull) the contents of the index register on (off) the stack. Discuss the advantages of having these two instructions available for the M6800 representation of Example 7.

4.3 PROGRAM DEVELOPMENT TECHNIQUES

The normal method for program development has been very primitive up to this point. In general the process has involved:

1. Coding algorithms in hex code. (This step may have been preceded by sketching out an AL program, but the AL code has been hand-assembled, i.e., transformed to hex code by hand.)

2. Hand-loading the hex code into the microcomputer's memory.

3. Debugging the algorithm with the use of breakpoints, examination of registers and memory locations, etc.

As we begin this section of the text we will modify our program-development process by switching our emphasis away from hex code and toward AL programming. This of course involves the use of an *assembler*, which will translate AL programs to OS-level programs. Since microcomputers normally have only a small memory capacity, one cannot usually run an assembler on the microcomputer for which the assembler is producing code. In this situation, a *cross assembler* is used. A cross assembler differs from resident assemblers in that it runs on one machine but produces code for another.

In making use of cross assemblers for the M6800 and the I8085 the program-development process will involve:

1. Coding the algorithm in assembly language.

2. Using a cross assembler to convert the assembly-language representation to hex code.

3. Making use of the hex-code listing produced by the cross assembler to hand-load the code into the microcomputer's memory.

4. Debugging the algorithm. In this regard, it is very useful to set "breakpoints" or establish locations in the program where control is returned to the monitor, so that the status of the system may be examined.

Note that the new procedure has automated the process of translating from AL to hex code and that this automation requires the existence of an assembler. Hand-loading is still required. As we proceed through the text, we will continually modify the program-development process, gradually evolving toward a more sophisticated, fully automated process.

The reader is referred to Appendixes D and E for full details on the Motorola 6800 Cross Assembler and the Intel 8080/8085 Assembler. Note that the symbols A, B, C, D, E, H, L, and M are *reserved* on the Intel assembler; i.e., they may not be defined as user symbols. The same is true for the symbols A, B, and X on the M6800 cross assembler.

One additional anomaly on the M6800 concerns the use of direct addressing, i.e., the use of symbols for which location values will be in the range 00H–FFH. These symbols must be defined before their first use in the program. This implies that the program listed in Fig. 4.4(a) is illegal, since P is used before it is defined and P is directly addressable. There are two ways to avoid this problem:

1. Force the symbol to be accessed via extended addressing by suitable ORGing the program (Fig. 4.4(b)); or

2. Move the definitions for directly addressable symbols to the beginning of the program (Fig. 4.4(c)).

LABORATORY ASSIGNMENTS

1. Write the M6800 (I8085) AL solution to Exercise 6, following Sec. 4.2. Assemble the AL program using the appropriate cross assembler. Hand-load the generated object code and verify its correctness.

2. Rewrite the M6800 AL representation for Example 2, Sec. 4.1, but ORG the program at 0000H. Use the M6800 cross assembler to assemble the program.

```
              NAM      DA1
              ORG      0000H
              LDA   A  P             Use of P
              ADD   A  #5
              SWI
        P     FCB      02            Definition of P
              END
```

(a) Illegal use of a directly addressable symbol.

```
              NAM      EXT
              ORG      0100H
              LDA   A  P             Use of P
              ADD   A  #5
              SWI
        P     FCB      02            Definition of P
              END
```

(b) P is now accessible only with extended addressing, so use may precede definition.

```
              NAM      DA2
              ORG      0000H
              BRA      L1
        P     FCB      02            Definition of P
        L1    LDA   A  P             Use of P
              ADD   A  #5
              SWI
              END
```

(c) Legal: definition precedes use.

Figure 4.4 Using directly addressable symbols.

REFERENCES AND SUPPORTIVE MATERIAL

Section 4.1. Complete specifications for the Motorola and Intel assembly languages can be found in Motorola (1976) and Intel (1977), respectively. Leventhal (1978) is an additional source of information on the M6800 assembly language.

A discussion of programming considerations for these processors can be found in Osborne (1976a) and Osborne (1976b).

1. Intel [1977]. "8080/8085 Assembly-Language Programming Manual," Intel Corporation, 3065 Bowers Ave., Santa Clara, California.

2. Leventhal, L. A. [1978], *6800 Assembly-Language Programming,* Adam Osborne and Associates, Inc.

3. Motorola [1976]. "M6800 Cross-Assembler Reference Manual," Motorola Semiconductor Products, Incorporated, Box 20912, Phoenix, Arizona.

4. Osborne, A. [1976a], *8080 Programming for Logic Design.* Adam Osborne and Associates, Inc., Berkeley, California.

5. Osborne, A. [1976b], *6800 Programming for Logic Design.* Adam Osborne and Associates, Inc., Berkeley, California.

CHAPTER FIVE

INTRODUCTION TO MICROCOMPUTER ARCHITECTURE

5.1 BASIC CIRCUITS

At their lowest level, computers consist of logical circuits. The building blocks for these circuits are *gates*. We can think of gates as the physical (electronic) counterparts of logical operations AND, OR, COMP(NOT), and others. Recall from Sec. 1.2.4 that logical AND and OR are binary (two-operand) operations, while COMP is a unary (one-operand) operation; and these can be defined by the following table:

X	Y	X AND Y	X OR Y	COMP X
0	0	0	0	1
0	1	0	1	1
1	0	0	1	0
1	1	1	1	0

Thus we might say, for example, that the AND operation *outputs* 0 on *inputs* X = 1, Y = 0. An AND gate then is a physical two-input, one-output device. Its inputs and output can be either 1 (that is, a high voltage—for example, +5 volts) or 0 (that is, a low voltage—for example, 0 volts). Moreover (see above table), an AND gate outputs a 1 if and only if both inputs are 1. The standard symbol for an AND gate is:

97

Similarly, an OR gate outputs a 0 if and only if both inputs are 0; its usual symbolic representation is:

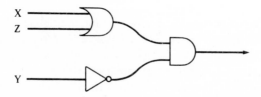

X OR Y

As indicated by the table above, the gate for COMP (usually called an *invertor*) outputs a 0 if and only if the input is 1. An invertor is symbolized as:

X ————————▷∘———— COMP (X)

These gates (and there are others as well) can be combined in various ways; for example,

Note that with each such combination we can naturally associate a corresponding expression. For the combination above, the expression is

$$(X \text{ OR } Z) \text{ AND } COMP(Y).$$

The various combinations that can be formed in this fashion (including single gates) are referred to as *logical circuits*. A second example of a logical circuit and its corresponding expression appears in Fig. 5.1.

It is not difficult to see that logical circuits are uniquely determined by their corresponding expressions. The following important basic fact about logical circuits underlies their ubiquity in computing systems: Suppose one has

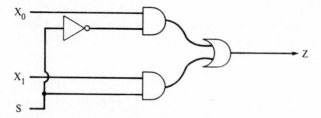

$$Z = (X_0 \text{ AND } COMP(S)) \text{ OR } (X_1 \text{ AND } S)$$

Fig. 5.1 A 2-1 selector/multiplexor.

a certain number of inputs, and for each combination of input values (0's and 1's) a certain output value is desired. Then one can effectively construct a logical circuit with this specified behavior.

Circuits such as the selector/multiplexor of Fig. 5.1 are important for directing the flow of data through a computing system. In this particular circuit, the selector line S determines whether data from X_0 (S = 0) or data from X_1 (S = 1) is passed through to Z. As another example of a logical circuit that appears in computing systems, we examine the *half-adder* shown in Fig. 5.2.

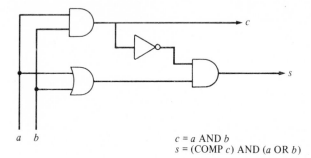

$c = a$ AND b
$s = (COMP\ c)$ AND $(a$ OR $b)$

Fig. 5.2 Half-adder.

The half-adder has two input lines, a and b (regarded as binary digits). The outputs are the binary sum s of the values a and b and the carry-out value c. Thus the half-adder represents the hardware realization of the arithmetic operation of binary addition. Half-adders are important components of a computer's arithmetic logic unit.

In all of the circuits we have considered in this section, the data flows directly through from one side to the other; i.e., there is no *feedback*. Logical circuits that do not involve feedback are called *combinational* circuits.

By incorporating feedback in a logical circuit, one can introduce the possibility of a circuit that "remembers." The basic circuits of this type are usually called *"flip-flops."* A variety of different kinds of flip-flop are available, but for our purposes we can think of a flip-flop as a kind of basic memory element, which might be pictured as follows (after suppressing the particular internal configuration of gates):

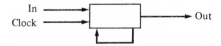

The behavior of such a device might simply be that, following a particular input (0 or 1), the output will take and hold that value until such time as the next input occurs. At any given time the output value is referred to as the present *state* of the device. Memory devices such as this are often operated in *synchronous fashion,* i.e., a clock is present in the system, and an input can be acknowledged (state changes can occur) only during a clock pulse. Logical circuits that contain these basic memory elements—that is, involve feedback —are referred to as *sequential circuits.* Again, the following important fact can be established: Given any sequential task (certain specified output sequences desired in response to given input sequences) that involves a finite number of different internal configurations or "states," one can effectively construct a sequential circuit that realizes (performs) this task.

These memory devices form important building blocks in computing systems. We can, for example, think of a register as a sequence of these devices. Thus an eight-bit register might be viewed as follows:

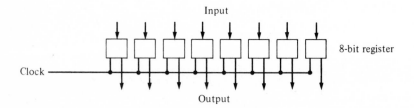

In this case the devices operate in unison and can, upon signal, accept at the input and hold at the output any eight-bit word. An accumulator is also essentially just a register of the sort described above. By constructing arrays of these basic memory elements, we form more general memory units. For example, a 64-word-by-eight-bit (64 × 8) memory might be viewed as a matrix of 512 of these devices arranged in 64 rows each eight units long.

As a specific example of an important kind of sequential circuit, we consider the following four-bit *shift register.*

In Fig. 5.3, each of the boxes again represents a basic memory element or flip-flop. In one kind of application of a shift register, data entering serially on the input is collected and made available for parallel output by the shift register. If data d_0, d_1, d_2, d_3 arrive serially at successive clock times t_0, t_1, t_2, t_3, then after time t_3, the data d_0, d_1, d_2, d_3 are available at the (parallel) outputs z_0, z_1, z_2, z_3, respectively.

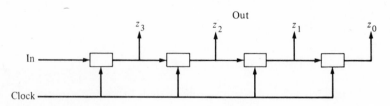

Fig. 5.3 Shift register.

EXERCISES

1. Draw the logical circuit corresponding to the expression (X AND (COMP Y)) OR (COMP(Z AND (COMP X))).

2. For which input combinations (values of X, Y, Z) will the circuit of Exercise 1 output a 0?

3. Find a circuit with inputs X and Y that will output a 1 if and only if exactly one of X, Y has the value 1.

4. Find the expression corresponding to the following logical circuit.

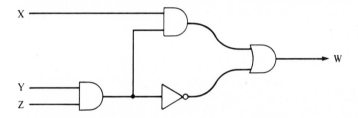

5. Microcomputers serve nicely as general-purpose circuits that can be programmed to simulate any given circuit (programmed logic). Write an M6800 program to simulate the circuit of Exercise 4. Your program should involve four logical operations corresponding directly to the four gates in the circuit. Choose three consecutive memory locations, and let X, Y, and Z be the low-order bits of these three locations, respectively; the output W is the low-order bit of accumulator A.

6. Do Exercise 5 for the I8085 microcomputer.

7. Consider the circuit diagram given in Fig. 5.4. Explain why *w* can never be 1.

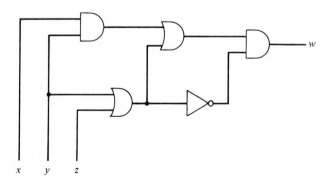

Figure 5.4

5.2 MICROPROCESSORS AND ASSOCIATED COMPONENTS

We now consider the structure of the microcomputer in somewhat greater detail and examine some specific products.

As indicated earlier, the heart of any microcomputer system is the *microprocessor*. The microprocessor is a central processing unit, which, through the use of the latest techniques in electronic circuit miniaturization, is typically contained on a 40-pin package known as a DIP (*d*ual *i*nline *p*ins). The "chip" or portion of the DIP that contains the circuitry may be less than one square centimeter in size and contain more than 20,000 transistors (the building blocks from which gates are formed).

We shall consider both the M6800 and I8085 microprocessors noting common elements as well as some of the differences.

5.2.1 The M6800 System

The Motorola M6800 microprocessor is described in the block diagram in Fig. 5.5. The various buffers indicated in the diagram can be viewed as registers for holding data until it can be read by the appropriate source. Lines A_0-A_{15} are address lines by which the microprocessor addresses memory and other external devices. Lines D_0-D_7 are bidirectional data lines. The remaining lines are for processor and bus control. In particular, the read/write (R/W) line indicates whether the microprocessor is in a Read or Write state and the Valid Memory Address line (VMA) signals to memory (and peripherals) that the address lines contain a valid address. A bar over the label on a line (e.g., $\overline{\text{HALT}}$ in Fig. 5.5) indicates that the line is low (or 0) active as opposed to the normal high (or 1) active.

The microprocessor operates in a synchronous manner; its operations are synchronized by the cycles of a clock (actually two phases of the clock are required). The minimal clock-cycle time for the M6800 is one microsecond (1 μs). As we shall see, relative to the execution of a given instruction, the processor must perform a specific series of subinstructions or *microinstructions,* which consist of the most basic acts the processor can perform. (This is exactly the passage from Level 2 to Level 1 in Fig. 1.1.) One or more microinstructions can be performed per clock cycle, and thus each instruction involves a number of cycles.

Before considering the details of instruction execution, we must regard the microprocessor as a component in a larger system. A typical small microcomputer system is displayed in Fig. 5.6.

In Fig. 5.6, the RAM is a *Random Access Memory*—a memory unit that can be both written into and read from. RAMs are constructed from basic memory elements (flip-flops), as indicated in Sec. 5.1, and are *volatile*, so that when the power to a RAM is turned off, its contents are lost. A RAM might typically be organized as 128 (K/8) eight-bit words and be placed on a single

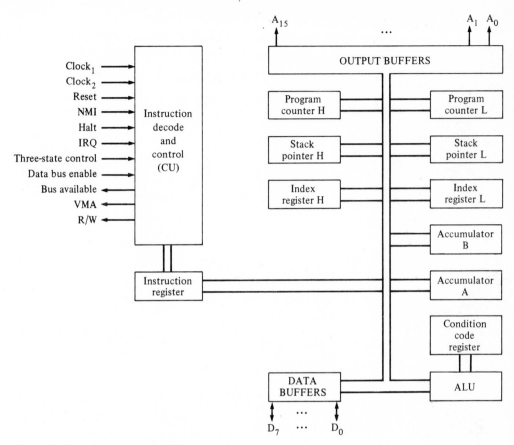

Fig. 5.5 Block diagram for M6800.

24-pin DIP (or it might occur as one of several components on a DIP). The individual storage cells of a RAM may be either *static* or *dynamic*. If static, the device need only be addressed when data is read or written. However, in dynamic RAMs the data must constantly be refreshed (read out and written back in) to preserve the quality of the data.

In the M6800-based system, lines A_{14}, A_{15} are used as RAM-select lines. Lines $A_0, \ldots, A_6$ select a particular word within the RAM and lines $A_7, \ldots, A_{13}$ select one from among several RAMs. The R/W control line selects the Read or Write mode within the RAM.

The ROM of Fig. 5.6 is a *Read Only Memory*. A ROM is essentially a combinational circuit that is written into once and may then be repeatedly read from. ROMs are nonvolatile and are consequently used to hold programs that are needed repeatedly in a computing system. For example, monitor programs

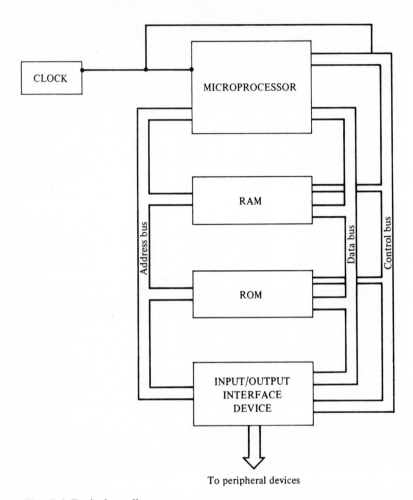

Fig. 5.6 Typical small system.

for microcomputers are generally stored in ROMs. Although ROMs are often "mask-programmed" at the factory, Programmable ROMs (PROMs) are somewhat easier and less expensive to program on a low-volume basis. Some PROMs are erasable: EPROMs can be erased by exposure to ultraviolet light.

In the M6800-based system, lines A_{14}, A_{15} are again used as ROM-select lines. $A_{10}, \ldots , A_{13}$ select one of several ROMs and $A_0, \ldots , A_9$ select a particular word within a ROM.

In general, the instructions of a program are stored in consecutive locations in a RAM or ROM. Prior to execution of the program, the address of the first instruction of the program is loaded into the microcomputer's program counter (PC).

Relative to the fetching (from memory) and execution of an instruction in the M6800, the following microinstructions are typical. During the first cycle, the contents of PC are put on the address bus and, using this address, the instruction's opcode is brought to the instruction register via the data bus. The PC is incremented by 1. The control unit (CU) issues the signals that enable these actions.

The successive microinstructions depend on the opcode now held in the instruction register. If, for example, the opcode were 1BH (add accumulators), the contents of accumulators A and B would be added by the arithmetic logic unit and the sum placed in accumulator A during the second, and final, cycle. If the opcode were A6H (load accumulator A in the indexed addressing mode), the second cycle would involve fetching the second byte (index offset) of the instruction and the PC would be incremented once more. During the third cycle, the ALU is used to add the index offset to the low-order byte of the index register (XR). The carry is added to XR's high-order byte during cycle 4. During cycle 5, the contents of XR is applied to the address bus and, using this address, the operand is brought to accumulator A. Again, the microcomputer would then be read to process the next instruction. We note again also that in each case, the signals that enable the various microinstructions are issued by the control unit in response to the opcode, the cycle number, or other signal.

5.2.2 The I8085 System

The I8085 microprocessor is described in the block diagram of Fig. 5.7 next. The I8085 is a somewhat more recent processor than the M6800 and represents movement in the direction of a single chip computer. For example, the I8085 DIP includes a clock generator, on-board serial I/O capability, and other features not found on the M6800 DIP. One consequence is that the I8085 must make more efficient use of its pins.

This more efficient use of pins is achieved in part by using pins $AD_7, \ldots, AD_0$ for data as well as for the low-order address values (see Fig. 5.7). During the execution of an instruction, $AD_7, \ldots, AD_0$ contain low-order address values during the first clock cycle and data during the next clock cycles. This process is referred to as *multiplexing* and is facilitated by the use of multiplexors such as that described in Fig. 5.1.

This double use of pins and bus lines is further facilitated by the use of *three-state* devices. For example, the address outputs from the I8085 chip to the bus can be, in addition to the usual high or low (1 or 0), driven to a "high-impedance mode" or high-resistance state. In this latter condition, the address outputs are effectively detached from the address bus. Three-stating is used to ensure that at most one signal is applied to the bus at any one time.

Once again, the remaining lines on the I8085 are for processor and interrupt control, serial I/O, and other purposes.

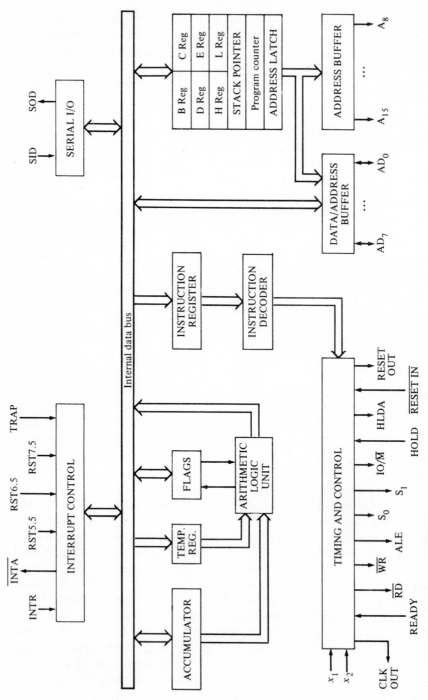

Fig. 5.7 Block diagram for I8085.

A typical computing system built around the I8085 might again follow the general pattern depicted in Fig. 5.6. Some RAM and ROM DIPs available in the I8085 family of components include on-board, parallel I/O capability. The RAMs and ROMs and their respective internal locations are accessed via the address bus in a manner similar to that discussed previously for the M6800 system.

Each I8085 instruction is composed entirely of a sequence of READ and WRITE operations. These operations form the only communication between the I8085 and the other components and each involves a transfer of one byte of data. Each READ and WRITE operation is referred to as a *machine cycle* and each machine cycle consists of from three to six clock cycles. A clock cycle in the I8085 is roughly 330 nanoseconds. This particular technique of organizing microinstructions into machine cycles facilitates the process of multiplexing data over the lines AD_7–AD_0.

Each I8085 instruction consists of a series of from one to five machine cycles. The Store Accumulator Direct (STA) instruction is typical; its decomposition into machine cycles and clock cycles is illustrated below in Fig. 5.8.

As indicated in Fig. 5.8, machine cycle 1 (M_1) is a READ cycle—the opcode fetch cycle. During the first clock cycle (T_1) of M_1, AD_7–AD_0 contain the lower-order byte of the program counter and A_{15}–A_8 contain the high-order byte of the program counter. During clock cycles T_2 and T_3 of M_1, the opcode is brought (via AD_7–AD_0) to the instruction register (see Fig. 5.7).

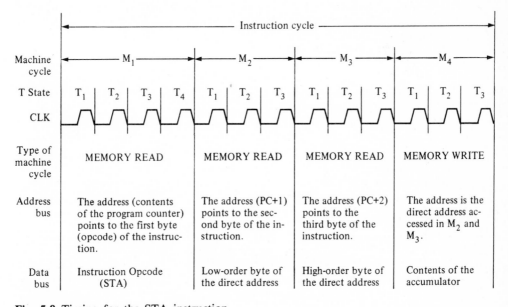

Fig. 5.8 Timing for the STA instruction.

During T_4, the opcode is recognized. The program counter is incremented and now points to the second byte of the instruction, which is the low-order byte of the direct address. During machine cycle 2 (M_2), this low-order byte is brought to the CPU and held in temporary storage. Similarly, M_3 is a READ cycle during which the high-order byte of the direct address is fetched. During the WRITE cycle M_4, the fetched direct address is placed on the address bus and then the contents of the accumulator are placed on the data bus. A memory-write signal completes execution of the instruction.

In an instruction such as DCX (decrement register pair), there is only one machine cycle—the opcode fetch cycle. In this particular case, after the opcode is decoded during T_4, the CPU continues with clock cycles T_5 and T_6 of M_1 and decrements the register pair rather than beginning a new machine cycle.

EXERCISES

1. Exercises 5 and 6 of Sec. 5.1 involved the simulation of combinational circuits on microcomputers. Here you are asked to simulate a sequential circuit. Choose a sequence of consecutive memory locations. The "inputs" are to be the low-order bits in these locations. The "output" is identified with the low-order bit of accumulator A. The inputs are to be considered sequentially, with a new input read in approximately every five seconds (see Laboratory assignment at end of Sec. 4.2.2).

   At any time, the output should be 1 if and only if the number of 1's that have been input to that point in time is evenly divisible by 3. The output should be constantly displayed. In order to display the output (contents of accumulator A), you should utilize the display routine provided as part of the monitor program of your microcomputer.

   Write an M6800 program to accomplish this task.

2. Do Exercise 1 above for the I8085 microcomputer.

3. We have noted that the I8085 clock cycle is roughly three times faster than that for the M6800 (330 nanoseconds vs. 1 microsecond). By referring to the tables in Chapters 2 and 3, determine the amount of time it takes for each of the processors to execute a "STORE ACCUMULATOR" instruction. (Use the direct-addressing mode on the I8085, the extended-addressing mode on the M6800.) How do you account for the fact that the amount of time it takes the M6800 to execute this instruction is much less than three times the amount of time taken by the I8085?

5.3 HARDWARE SUPPORT FOR INPUT/OUTPUT FUNCTIONS

Thus far our discussion of microprocessor systems has centered on activities that are essentially "internal." Since the usefulness of a microsystem is measured not only by what it can do but also by its ability to communicate its "answers," we must have an I/O capability on the system. In this section we will concentrate on the hardware support for I/O. Programmer interaction with this hardware—i.e., the hardware-software interface—will be elaborated on in subsequent chapters.

5.3.1 Data Transmission Techniques

Assume that we have an eight-bit pattern in some register or memory cell that we wish to output. If we are dealing with a peripheral that is capable of receiving all eight bits at one time (has eight lines that can be used for input), we could use a Peripheral Interface Device (PD) that transmits data in a parallel fashion (has eight lines, so that all bits can be transmitted at one time). This technique, known as *parallel* I/O, is illustrated in Fig. 5.9.

A similar statement can be made with respect to input. If a peripheral is capable of transmitting eight bits in parallel to the microsystem, we can use a parallel input device to capture this bit pattern and then transfer it to memory or a register.

Some peripherals are not capable of receiving or transmitting more than one bit of information at any given time. Most terminals fall into this category. If we are dealing with such a peripheral, and again wish to output an eight-bit quantity, the bits must be sent serially (i.e., one bit at a time). This would necessitate the use of a serial PD to effect *serial* I/O. The actual serialization of the data (breaking it up into individual bits) may be performed by the software so that only one bit at a time is sent to the PD, or it may be performed by the PD itself. In the latter case, the eight-bit quantity is sent at one time to the PD. The PD then serializes the data, perhaps with a shift register, and transmits one bit at a time. Both situations are depicted in Fig. 5.10. In 5.10(b) the first bit, b_0, is being sent. The serial PD would then send b_1, b_2, etc., at subsequent time intervals.

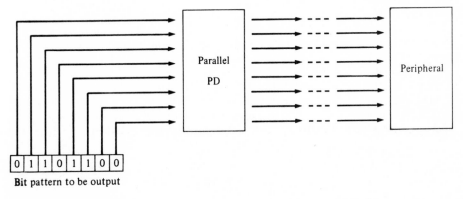

| 0 | 1 | 1 | 0 | 1 | 1 | 0 | 0 |

Bit pattern to be output

Fig. 5.9 Parallel I/O.

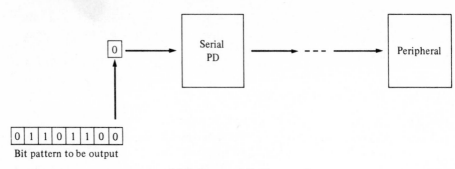

(a) Software serialization

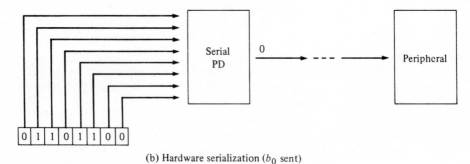

(b) Hardware serialization (b_0 sent)

Fig. 5.10 Serial I/O.

Once again, we should note that a similar discussion would apply to receiving from a serial peripheral. In this case the PD may wait until all eight bits have been captured and then make this pattern available (hardware parallelization) or bits may be made available individually and thus require merging by the software.

5.3.2 Connecting the PD to the Computing System

The manner in which the PD is connected with the microprocessor determines how it may be accessed from the software. There are two possibilities: connecting to the address and data busses, so that PD's have "memory" addresses that the microprocessor can access (*memory-mapped* I/O), or connecting the PD as a separate I/O device, so the I/O address space is separated from the memory address space (*isolated* I/O).

If memory-mapped I/O is used, the programmer may access the PD with the normal memory reference instructions provided in the instruction set. In particular, instructions that read from memory (LDA, ADDA, etc.) can be used to pass information from the PD to the microprocessor while instructions that write into memory (STA, CLR, etc.) can be used to pass information from the microprocessor to the PD. Selection of a PD is indicated by the use of the memory addresses that have been associated with the unit.

If PDs are connected separate from the memory space, I/O port numbers are associated with them and they are then accessed via special I/O instructions that must be present in the instruction set. Under this scheme the PD may *not* be accessed by any memory reference instruction. It is accessible only through the special I/O instructions.

We will clarify this discussion with a few specific examples of PD connections typically found in the I8085 and M6800 microcomputer systems.

Example 1 The Intel 8155 RAM DIP is commonly used in I8085-based systems. In addition to 256 bytes of RAM, this DIP contains two eight-bit parallel I/O ports (Ports A and B) and one six-bit parallel I/O port (Port C). A block diagram for the I8155 is shown in Fig. 5.11. Ports A and B are "programmable" in that their specific functions (e.g, input or output) are determined by the setting of an internal command/status register, and the three I/O ports are accessible through the IN and OUT instructions provided in the I8085 instruction set. Port C serves a dual role in that it can be used as an I/O port or to provide control/status signals for the A and B ports.

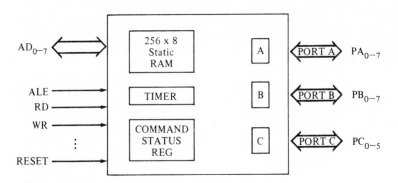

Fig. 5.11 Intel 8155 block diagram.

Example 2 Another Intel memory DIP, the 8355, contains 2K bytes of ROM and two eight-bit I/O ports. Again, these ports can be set for either input or output. The 8355's I/O section can be used in either a memory-mapped or isolated configuration.

Example 3 The I8085 itself provides an I/O capability in that a serial I/O port is available on the I8085 CPU DIP. The SID (serial input data) and SOD (serial output data) lines (see Fig. 5.7) can be used in conjunction with the RIM and SIM instructions to provide isolated I/O. In this special case, the SIM and RIM instructions serve as the specialized I/O instructions that must be used with isolated I/O. In particular, the data in the SID line is loaded into accumulator bit 7 when a RIM instruction is executed, and the SOD line is set from accumulator bit 7 when a SIM instruction is executed. The RIM and SIM instructions can perform other functions as well; their specific role is determined by the setting of bit 6 in the accumulator.

Although the I8085 does provide for serial I/O, the interface requires that the serialization be performed by the software. Most systems allow for the connection of dedicated Serial Interface Adaptors (SIA) that support hardware serialization. We consider a generalized SIA in the next example.

Example 4 Both the M6800 and the I8085 provide SIA DIPs that can be connected to the microprocessor. These DIPs must be connected in a memory-mapped fashion for the M6800, but isolated or memory-mapped connections are available for the I8085. A generalized SIA that is representative of both the Intel and Motorola SIAs is illustrated in Fig. 5.12. Note that shift registers are used to serialize the data within the SIA itself. The SIA can function as either an input or output device depending on the control-line settings. The transmit buffer supports the output function while the receiver buffer supports the input function. The transmit buffer will hold an eight-bit quantity that has been written by the CPU, serialize that quantity, and output it one bit at a time using the transmit shift register. The receive buffer will hold an eight-bit quantity that has been input and collected in parallel from the receive shift register. This quantity can be read by the CPU.

The status and control registers found on the SIA can be used to specify what action will be performed by the SIA and to determine the status of the device. The control register (CR) will hold information that has been written by the CPU and controls the activities of the SIA. This information might include:

a) An indication whether the data is to be transmitted synchronously or asynchronously. In the synchronous case, bits are sent in accordance with the cycles of some clock. In the asynchronous case, a unit of data is sent only when the transmitter is ready to send such a unit.

b) In the case of synchronous transmission, timing information that indicates the relationship between the CPU's clock rate and the rate at which bits are being transmitted.*

---

*Peripherals are generally much slower than the CPU. The data transfer rate must be set to match the speed of the CPU to the peripheral.

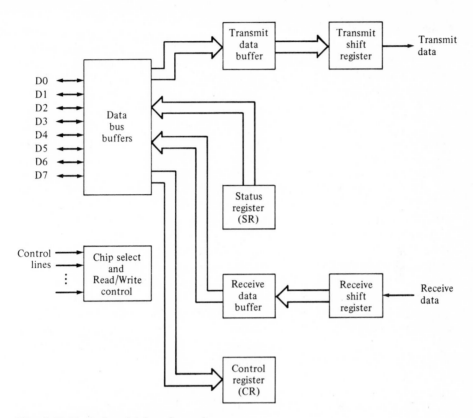

Fig. 5.12 Typical serial interface adaptor.

c) In the case of synchronous transmission, a specification of the number
    of SYNCH characters. (SYNCH characters are used so that the receiv-
    ing device can synchronize on data unit boundaries.)

d) In the asynchronous case, an indication of the particular "framing"
    used so that the receiving device can identify the different data units.
    This framing might, for example, consist of a "start" bit and one or
    more "stop" bits.

The status register (SR) will hold information concerning the status of the SIA
and can be read by the CPU. This information might indicate (1) whether the
buffers are empty or full, and (2) whether or not errors have occurred in transmission.

  In the subsequent discussion we will assume that the SIA has been set up
as a memory-mapped device and is associated with consecutive memory locations i and $i + 1$. The specific assignment of the addresses and the interaction
between the CPU and the SIA's buffers and registers is noted in Fig. 5–13.

	Location	CPU Interaction
Status Register	i	Reads from
Control Register	i	Writes into
Transmit Buffer	$i + 1$	Writes into
Receive buffer	$i + 1$	Reads from

Fig. 5.13 CPU–SIA interaction

In a memory-mapped configuration, the specific action that takes place depends on the type of instruction that references the memory-mapped address. In general, memory reference instructions that read from memory will pass information from the SIA to the CPU while memory reference instructions that write into memory will pass information from the CPU to the SIA. Under the specifications we've assumed, this would imply that, for the M6800,

LDA	A	i	reads from the status register to ACCA
LDA	A	$i + 1$	reads from the receive buffer register to ACCA
STA	A	i	writes the contents of ACCA to the control register
STA	A	$i + 1$	writes the contents of ACCA to the transmit buffer
LDA	B	i	reads from the status register to ACCB
ADD	A	$i + 1$	adds the contents of the receive buffer to ACCA

etc.

Similar manipulations would be available on a memory-mapped SIA on the I8085. For example,

LDA		reads from the status register to the accumulator
LDA	$i + 1$	reads from the receive buffer register to the accumulator
STA	i	writes the contents of the accumulator to the control register
STA	$i + 1$	writes the contents of the accumulator to the transmit buffer
LXI	H,$i + 1$	sets the H–L pair to point to the buffer address and then adds the contents
ADD	M	of the receive buffer to the accumulator

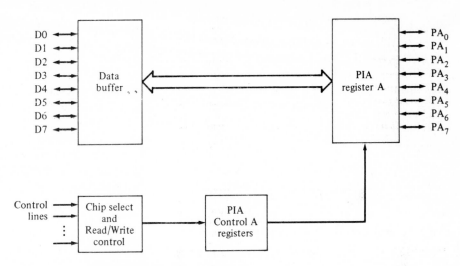

Fig. 5.14 Typical parallel interface adaptor.

Example 5 Dedicated Parallel Interface Adaptors (PIA) are also available on most systems including the M6800 and I8085. As before, the M6800 supports only memory-mapped PIA DIP connections, while the I8085 provides both isolated and memory-mapped PIA connections. Figure 5.14 illustrates a generalized PIA DIP and indicates what one might expect to find on such a DIP for either the M6800 or the I8085. Although only one peripheral register (PIA register A) is shown, a PIA may contain one or more such registers together with a set of dedicated control registers. Software interaction with a PIA is quite similar to that described for SIA interaction. In particular, if we again assume a memory-mapped configuration, a programmer may use write-memory reference instructions to output data or set control information, and use read-memory reference instructions to input data or determine the status of a given peripheral register. A detailed analysis of specific PIAs used with the M6800 and I8085 systems is made in subsequent chapters.

5.3.3 Programming Considerations

As noted earlier, a basic problem in dealing with I/O is that peripherals that send or receive data from the CPU are generally much slower than the CPU. There are various standard techniques for dealing with this problem. A relatively easy (but inefficient and often impractical) method is to write a program that processes a particular input/output unit and then loops (waits) for the next input or output unit. This process is repeated until all units have been processed. This is referred to as *busy-wait I/O*. The inefficiency of this technique stems from the fact that CPU cycles are being wasted while waiting for the I/O to occur.

A more efficient technique is to have the peripheral signal to the CPU when it is ready to transmit or receive data. This signal or *interrupt* causes the microprocessor to save its current status, process the data, and then return to the original task. This is referred to as *interrupt I/O*. The increased efficiency possible through the use of interrupt I/O can be seen quite easily if we consider a multiuser system. Assume we have two user programs (U1 and U2) that are being processed by the CPU on a time-slicing basis (i.e., the CPU switches back and forth, at a given time frequency, in processing these programs). Let us further assume that U1 wishes to output *n* data units. For this analysis, we will also assume that there is enough time in a given time slice to process all units of output data. If busy-wait I/O is used, the following sequence of activities will take place during U1's time slice:

1. Set control information for the appropriate PD.

2. Send data unit 1 to the PD register.

3. Enter a busy wait loop and wait until the PD can receive another data unit.

4. Send data unit 2 to the PD register.

5. Enter a busy wait loop and wait until the PD can receive another data unit.

   etc.

Using this scheme, the CPU will spend most of the time it has dedicated to processing U1's time slice in nonproductive busy wait loops. This time can be reclaimed and put to good use if interrupt I/O is used. If this technique is used, we would have the following sequence of activities during U1's time slice:

1. Set control information including the enabling of interrupts on the appropriate PD (enabling interrupts indicates our intent to use interrupts on the PD and permits the interrupt signal to interrupt the CPU).

2. Send data unit 1 to the PD register.

3. Permit CPU to switch from processing U1 and start processing U2.

4. When an interrupt is generated, the CPU saves its current status (U2's status) and processes the interrupt (in this case an interrupt would mean that the PD is ready to accept another data unit, so data unit 2 would be sent to the PD). The CPU then restores U2's status and continues processing U2. This last step is repeated until all of U1's data has been output. The time that was wasted in the busy wait process has been used here to productively process the U2 program.

It should be noted that busy-wait I/O is essentially a synchronized method of data transfer, whereas interrupt I/O is asynchronous. The loop cycle in busy wait I/O forms the basis of the synchronization time unit. With interrupt I/O, transmission may take place at any time, whereas transmission is limited to a particular point in the loop for busy-wait I/O.

Relative to the interrupt I/O discussed above, the M6800 has basically two (hardware) interrupt lines: $\overline{NMI}$ (nonmaskable interrupt) and $\overline{IRQ}$ (interrupt request). When a signal occurs on $\overline{IRQ}$, the microprocessor will complete execution of the current instruction. Then if the interrupt mask bit (I) of the Condition Code Register (CCR) is not set, the microprocessor will begin an interrupt sequence. This involves stacking the index register, program counter accumulators, and condition code register, and setting the interrupt mask bit so that no further interrupts can occur. Finally, the PC is loaded with the two bytes obtained from memory locations FFF8H, FFF9H. Thus the address stored in these two locations is taken as the address of a routine to service the interrupt. This technique of indirect addressing is referred to as *vectoring*. With respect to our previous interrupt example, the address of a routine that sends the data units U1 is processing would have been placed in FFF8H and FFF9H by the software in order to direct what activity would take place when an interrupt occurred.

The M6800 has a Return from Interrupt (RTI) instruction that is used to terminate an interrupt service routine. This instruction restores the values of the index register, program counter, accumulators, and condition code registers. In restoring the old PC, the CPU returns to processing whatever it was doing prior to the interrupt. Note that restoring the CCR will reset the interrupt mask bit and therefore permit interrupts once again.

A signal on $\overline{NMI}$ will cause similar action to that described above; however, the setting of the interrupt mask bit is ignored in this case.

The I8085 provides a more elaborate interrupt capability. There are four hardware interrupt lines on the I8085 that we will consider: TRAP, RST 5.5, RST 6.5, and RST 7.5.

The RST 7.5, RST 6.5, and RST 5.5 lines are very similar in their behavior. When a signal occurs on one of these lines, the microprocessor completes execution of the current instruction and then initiates the following activities. First a check is made to determine whether the entire interrupt system is enabled or disabled. The system is enabled with an EI instruction and it remains enabled until either an interrupt occurs or a DI instruction is executed. If the interrupt system is enabled, then a check is made to determine whether interrupts on this particular line are enabled. Interrupts on each of these three lines can be independently enabled or disabled via the use of a SIM instruction, which sets or resets the masks on the basis of the contents of the accumulator (see Fig. 5.15). Assuming that interrupts are enabled for the given line, one additional check is made: The priority of the given interrupt line is compared

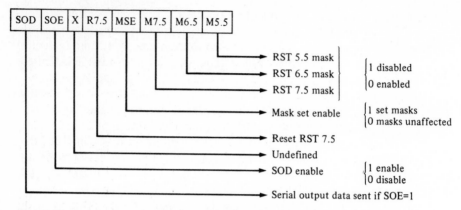

Fig. 5.15 Accumulator format for a SIM instruction.

with the priorities of other interrupts that may be pending. The lines are arranged in a fixed priority that determines which will be serviced if more than one is pending. The priority settings are:

TRAP   (highest)
RST 7.5
RST 6.5
RST 5.5   (lowest)

These priorities are used only in breaking ties on interrupt signals that occur simultaneously.

Assuming that all conditions are satisfied for the interrupt (i.e., the interrupt system is enabled), the interrupt mask for the given interrupt is reset ($=0$), and the priority of the given interrupt is higher than any other pending interrupt, then the microprocessor initiates an interrupt sequence during which the following events take place.

1. The current PC value is pushed onto the stack.

2. The interrupt system is disabled and will remain disabled until another EI instruction is executed.

3. The PC is loaded with the address assigned to the interrupt line. For the RST interrupts the addresses are:

002CH   for RST 5.5
0034H   for RST 6.5
003CH   for RST 7.5

The code found at these locations must then accommodate transferral to the appropriate interrupt handler.

There are some differences between the Intel interrupt sequence and the Motorola interrupt sequence that should be noted. First of all, only the PC is saved by the I8085 whereas all registers are saved on the M6800. Secondly, the interrupt system is automatically disabled and re-enabled on the M6800 but only automatically disabled on the I8085; that is, the system must be re-enabled with an EI instruction on the I8085. Finally, transference to the interrupt handler is slightly different on the two systems. The address of the handler is expected to be held in certain locations on the M6800, and this address is loaded in as the new PC. On the I8085, the PC is always loaded with a hardware-designated address (assigned to that interrupt line) and the code found starting at the address is responsible for then transferring to the handler.

Returning from an interrupt handler is accomplished by one of the normal return instructions found on the I8085. This restores the old PC and thereby permits the CPU to resume its interrupted activity.

A signal on the TRAP line will result in similar activities with the following exceptions:

1. TRAPs cannot be disabled; i.e., an interrupt sequence will be performed independently of the mask bits and whether the interrupt system is enabled or disabled.

2. Since the TRAP signal has highest priority, it will always proceed.

3. The new PC for a TRAP interrupt is 0024H.

EXERCISES

1. Why does the M6800 have to provide a special RTI instruction while the I8085 uses normal return instructions to return from interrupts?

2. Write an I8085 program segment that will serially output the contents of register B through the I8085's serial I/O port. The bits of register B are to be output in order from right to left. You may assume that the SIM instruction serves as an output instruction when bit 6 of the accumulator is set to 1.

3. Assume that an M6800 program sets accumulator A to 0 and then remains in an infinite loop as long as accumulator A remains 0. If accumulator A is changed from 0 while the program is in the infinite loop, the program should halt. Devise an interrupt routine (and specify the linkage) so that when an interrupt occurs, accumulator A is changed to 1 and hence execution halts up on return to the program.

REFERENCES AND SUPPORTIVE MATERIAL

Section 5.1. Bartee (1974) contains a more detailed discussion of basic computer hardware concepts. Other more advanced reference texts on logical design and circuits include Nagle, Carroll, and Irwin (1975), and Hill and Peterson (1974).

Section 5.2. The architecture of the M6800 and its supporting components is covered in Motorola (1976a) and, in greater detail, in Motorola (1975). Intel (1977a) covers the technical and architectural aspects of the various components of the I8085 system. Osborne, Jacobson, and Kane (1977) contains chapters on the design and operation of the M6800, the I8085, and several other microcomputer systems. Finally, both Hilburn and Julich (1976) and Leventhal (1978) include sections on microcomputer architecture.

Section 5.3. Osborne (1976) and Leventhal (1978) are recommended as references for the general topic of microcomputer I/O. Specific details on the I/O interface devices discussed in Sec. 5.3 can be found in Motorola (1976a) and Intel (1977a).

1. Bartee, T.C. [1974], *Digital Computer Fundamentals.* New York: McGraw-Hill.

2. Hilburn, J.L., and P.M. Julich, [1976], *Microcomputers/Microprocessors.* Englewood Cliffs, N.J.: Prentice-Hall.

3. Hill, F.J., and G.R. Peterson, [1974], *Introduction to Switching Theory and Logical Design.* New York: Wiley.

4. Intel [1977a], "MCS-85 User's Manual." Intel Corporation, 3065 Bowers Ave., Santa Clara, California.

5. Leventhal, L.A. [1978], *Introduction to Microprocessors: Software, Hardware, Programming,* Englewood Cliffs, N.J.: Prentice-Hall.

6. Motorola [1976a], "M6800 Microcomputer: System Design Data." Motorola Semiconductor Products, Inc. Box 20912, Phoenix, Arizona.

7. Motorola [1975], "M6800 Microprocessor Applications Manual." Motorola Semiconductor Products, Inc. Box 20912, Phoenix, Arizona.

8. Osborne, A. [1976], *An Introduction to Microcomputers. Volume I: Basic Concepts.* Berkeley, California: Adam Osborne and Associates, Inc.

9. Osborne, Jacobson, and Kane [1977], *An Introduction to Microcomputers. Volume II: Some Real Products.* Berkeley, California: Adam Osborne and Associates, Inc.

CHAPTER SIX

AUTOMATING THE LOADING PROCESS

6.1 MICROCOMPUTER DEVELOPMENT SYSTEMS AND SYSTEMS PROGRAMS

It should be apparent at this point that the development of our microcomputer systems is proceeding within a much larger computing environment. For example, the cross assemblers that have been utilized until now reside, by definition, on another (presumably larger) computer. As we continue to expand our microcomputer systems, our dependence on this supporting equipment will become even more obvious.

The development of a microcomputer system and its associated software does not usually take place entirely within the system itself.* Among other things, there generally isn't enough memory to support the necessary software packages such as cross assemblers, compilers, text editors, etc.

Thus we come to the concept of a Microcomputer Development System (MDS)—a system that can provide this support. The exact composition of this MDS can vary widely; and in the most restricted sense, the MDS might be based on the particular microprocessor for which the applications are being developed. For our present purposes, we assume the existence of such a support system based around a computer large enough to handle our software development packages and including at least a terminal and a hardware link between the system and our microcomputers' I/O interface devices.

In the first five chapters we became familiar with the organization and instruction sets of the M6800 and the I8085. Programming was carried out at

---

*There are exceptions to this statement; i.e., there exist large systems based on microcomputers that are used to develop microcomputer systems software.

two levels: the conventional machine level and the assembly-language level. For the most part, the programs that have been written up to this point fall into the applications area. In this module we will turn our attention to what are known as *systems programs* or programs that facilitate our use of the computer, as opposed to programs that are directed toward the solution of external problems. This is a vital step toward our goal of converting our microcomputers into functional computing systems. Eventually, we wish to be able to enter an assembly-language source program through a terminal linked to a microcomputer, assemble the program with a resident assembler (i.e., an assembler residing in the memory of the microcomputer), and finally execute it. All of this will be made possible by the systems programs that will be described in this and subsequent chapters and which can be implemented by the reader.

Our first step will be to establish links with external devices to facilitate the process of loading programs. Recall that even though the use of cross assemblers has (to some degree) facilitated the process of programming the microcomputers, we are still forced to manually load the object code. Since the cross assemblers reside in the development system external to the microcomputer, we need some means of transferring data from the development system to the microcomputer by way of a hardware link, if we are to automate the loading process.

Rather than jump directly into this, we will first study another link that already exists on many microcomputers—a cassette link (or interface). Supporting a cassette link is one means of providing an auxiliary storage facility.* With this feature a programmer can save (and later recover) large segments of memory on a cassette tape. Consequently, any program can be saved on tape and need not be manually loaded each time it is required.

6.2 A TYPICAL CASSETTE INTERFACE

Support for a cassette link is frequently provided as a function of a *monitor* program. A monitor, which might be viewed as a kind of simple operating system, is often included with a microcomputer to facilitate its use. In order to better understand the general environment of the cassette interface function, we will briefly examine the characteristics of a monitor. The following discussion is based on the monitor routines used on Motorola's MEK6800D2 evaluation kit (Motorola, 1977).

---

*A paper tape link is another common method of providing auxiliary storage on microcomputer systems.

6.2.1 An Overview of a Monitor

Among the features included in a monitor, one would expect to find some kind of I/O support allowing the programmer to input programs and data and determine the results of program execution. In this regard, we shall assume an elementary, but common capability: Input is made through a keypad including monitor *command* keys and hexadecimal data keys; output occurs, as hexadecimal digits, through seven-segment light-emitting diode (LED) displays. As usual, the hexadecimal digits abbreviate groups of four binary digits.

The monitor operates as a nonterminating program that constantly waits for a signal from the keypad. As indicated above, such a signal might be a command to the monitor or it might be data. Typical monitor commands include Display and Change memory, Display and change registers, Execute (starting at specified location), and Reset (or abort current operation). The hexadecimal data keys would be used to specify addresses and, for example, to write into memory following a Display and change memory command. An overview of a sample monitor appears as a flowchart in Fig. 6.1.

As this figure shows, the monitor program performs various initialization functions following entry through a reset or restart. In particular, a "prompt" signal might be displayed indicating that the monitor is ready for a command. Typically, the monitor will utilize a nested loop structure in which an interior loop cycles once for each of the LED displays. The actual display of a particular LED will involve moving the contents of the corresponding buffer (where the digital encoding of the display configuration is held) to the LED itself.

After all LED's have been refreshed, the monitor checks to see whether any of the keys on the keypad have been depressed. If not, the monitor resumes the task of refreshing the displays. When a key is depressed, the monitor determines whether a command or data entry has been signalled. With each monitor command, there is a corresponding routine for servicing the command. Thus when a command is signalled, control is transferred to the associated routine. When data is appropriately entered, the data is stored in the proper display buffer and displayed on the next refresh cycle.

With this overview of a monitor, we return to the matter of the cassette interface. The software portion of the cassette interface can be divided naturally into two components as follows: an output or punch routine to transfer data from memory to the tape, and an input or load routine to transfer data from the tape to memory. In those instances where a microcomputer monitor includes such Punch and Load routines, we normally find associated Punch and Load commands on the keypad.

Both the hardware and software portions of the interface can be facilitated very naturally by the use of a Serial Interface Adaptor (SIA) of the sort considered in Sec. 5.3.2. In our subsequent discussion, we assume the use of a SIA.

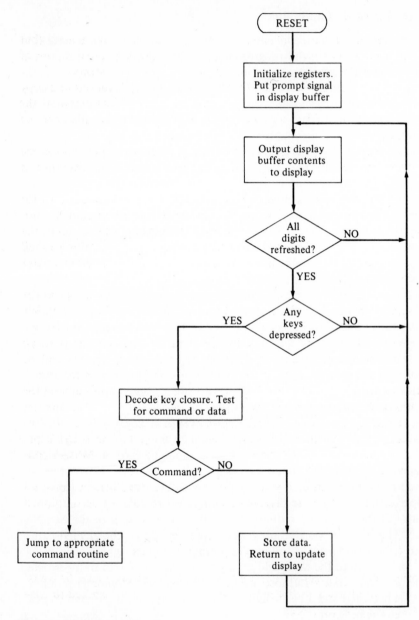

Fig. 6.1 Typical monitor flow.

6.2.2 The Punch Routine

In our discussion of the Punch routine, we first make certain general (but typical) assumptions about the overall context and then suggest realizations of key segments of the routine for both the M6800 and I8085 systems.

The routine will take some set of contiguous memory locations and copy the contents of these locations onto the cassette tape. We assume that the addresses of the first and last bytes of these locations are made available to the Punch routine.

After the recorder has been started in its record mode, the Punch routine is called. A flowchart for the routine and its supporting subroutine appears in Fig. 6.2.

Since we are interested in eventually establishing a link of our own (to load our assembled programs), we shall examine the code that actually supports this algorithm. A first important step in the routine is the set up of the SIA. The action taken here depends on the particular SIA used, and we shall discuss this step in detail for both the Motorola and the Intel microcomputer systems.

In the case of the Motorola system, the SIA normally used would be the M6850 Asynchronous Communications Interface Adapter, a 24-pin DIP. We shall refer to this particular SIA as the MSIA. Like the generalized SIA discussed in Sec. 5.3.2, the MSIA includes an eight-bit control register (CREG) and an eight-bit status register (SREG). Recall that both registers will be accessed with the same address. As noted above, the first step in the Punch routine is to set up the SIA, that is, to appropriately select from among the various options available. These options include the selection of the number of bits per second to be sent (*Baud rate*) as a function of the system clock, the format and size of the groups (words) to be transmitted, and the interrupt capabilities to be utilized. Figure 6.3 associates the various bits of the MSIA's control register with these options.

The first step that should be taken in "setting up" the MSIA is to issue a *master reset,* i.e., $b_1 b_0 = 11$. In M6800 code, this would be accomplished with:

```
PNCH    LDA    A    #0000011B    * * INITIALIZE
        STA    A    CREG         * MSIA
```

The Master Reset clears SREG and initializes both the receiver and the transmitter functions. Having initialized the device, we may now proceed to configure it for the intended usage.

A Baud rate of 300 is rather common in serial transferrals of data to and from cassette recorders (and terminals as well). If we assume a frequency of 4800 Hz (cycles per second) available to the MSIA from the system clock, we can obtain the 300-Baud rate by dividing the clock signal by 16. According to

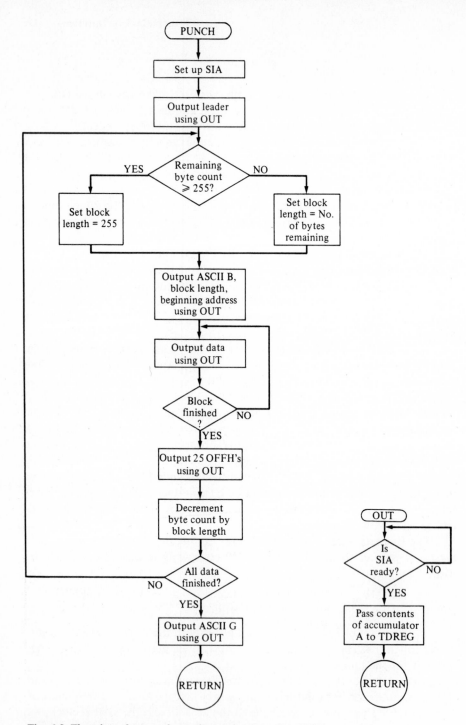

Fig. 6.2 Flowchart for punch routine and subroutine OUT.

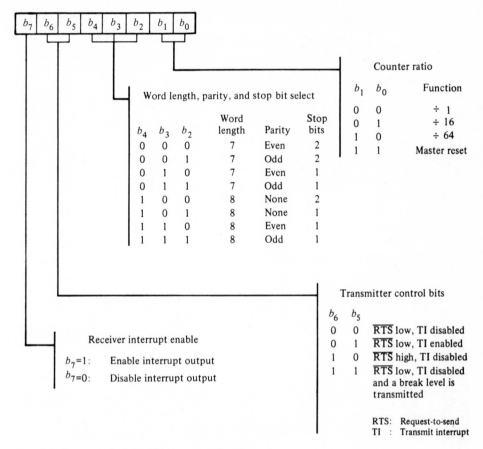

Fig. 6.3 Format of the MSIA's control register.

Fig. 6.3, this requires that $b_1 b_0$ be set to 01. For the word format, a word length of eight with no parity bit and two stop bits is selected. These stop bits serve as "frames" for the consecutive bytes being placed on the tape (see Sec. 5.3.2). Again, according to Fig. 6.3, $b_4 b_3 b_2$ should therefore be set to 100. In this particular interface problem, we will utilize busy-wait I/O rather than interrupt I/O. Thus we wish to disable all interrupts and set $b_7 b_6 b_5 = 000$.

Now that the desired control register bit pattern has been identified, the MSIA setup that begins the Punch routine might take the following form in M6800 code:

```
LDA    A    #00010001B        * * CONFIGURE MSIA
STA    A    CREG              * FOR TRANSMISSION
```

The next step in our Punch routine of Fig. 6.2 begins the actual output process. The initial output consists of a "leader" of 1024 OFFH's, which might be viewed as a "fudge factor" to allow for synchronizaton between the recorder and the microcomputer.

Transmitting the leader involves repeated invocation of the subroutine OUT that accomplishes the actual output (of the single byte in accumulator A). In fact, OUT is used for all the output to the tape in the Punch routine. The flowchart for OUT appears in Fig. 6.2. Prior to passing data to the SIA, OUT repeatedly polls the SIA's status register to determine whether the SIA is ready to receive data. Once again, we will examine this key segment of code in detail. In the Motorola System's MSIA, the format of the status register is as described in Fig. 6.4.

The MSIA can receive a new byte of data whenever its transmit data register is empty (cf. Sec. 5.3). As can be seen from Fig. 6.4, this condition is indicated by a $b_1 = 1$ in the status register. Thus if we identify SREG with the address of the status register, the following segment of M6800 code will make the desired test:

OUT	LDA	B	SREG	MOVE	SREG TO ACCB
	ASR	B		* *	MOVE
	ASR	B		*	b_1 TO CY
	BCC		OUT	WAIT IF $b_1 = 0$

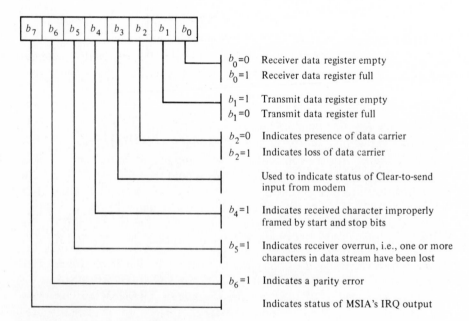

Fig. 6.4 Format of the MSIA's status register.

Note that this loop constitutes the busy-wait that characterizes the particular kind of I/O being used here. Once the condition $b_1 = 1$ is satisfied (i.e., the transmit data register is empty), a byte of data can be moved from accumulator A to the transmit data register (TDREG) with the instruction:

$$\text{STA}\qquad\text{A}\qquad\text{TDREG}$$

Returning once again to the original problem, we have then that the leader is transmitted by making 1024 calls to the subroutine OUT. The Punch routine continues with the calculation of the BYTE COUNT as a function of the specified beginning and ending addresses. The output is made in terms of successive blocks, each of which is at most 255 bytes long. If at any time, the amount of data remaining to be transmitted exceeds 255 bytes, the next block length is set to 255. An individual block has the following format:

'B'	Block length	beginning address	data bytes	25FF's

Here 'B' denotes the ASCII character B (42 hex) and signals the beginning of a new block. Note that each block includes information about the number of data bytes in that block and the starting address of this data.

In transmitting a region of memory, we will be moving one or more blocks of memory to the tape. These will be preceded by the leader and followed by the single ASCII 'G' that signals the end of the data stream. As a result, memory, as output on the tape, will assume the following configuration:

1024 FF's	BL	BL	. . .	BL	'G'

In this scheme, each BL represents a block with the previously specified format. The Load routine, which we consider in the next section, will presuppose this particular tape format.

Before moving to a discussion of the Load routine, we wish to review two key aspects of the Punch routine for the I8085 system. The Serial Interface Device typically used in this system would be the 8251 Programmable Communications Interface—a 28-pin DIP, which we refer to as an ISIA. The programming of the ISIA is divided into two phases. After a reset, the first byte of data written into the control register defines the mode (synchronous or asynchronous) and the characteristics of the particular mode selected. The second byte of data written into the control register serves as a command that controls the actual operation of the ISIA. The formats of the ISIA's register, relative to each of these functions, are given in Fig. 6.5. Since we shall be transmitting asynchronously, the mode instruction format is given only for this mode.

As noted above, the first byte of data written into the ISIA's control register is determined relative to the mode instruction format. Apart from the fact that the ISIA contains no provision for programmable interrupt control, it is

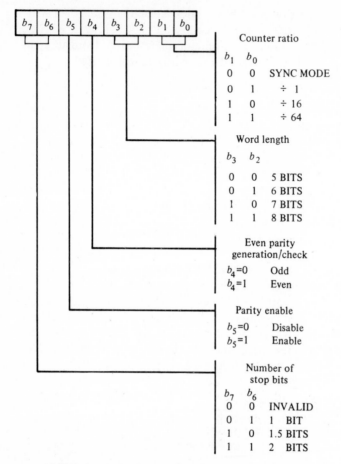

(a) Mode instruction format, Asynchronous mode

Fig. 6.5 ISIA control register formats.

quite similar to the MSIA and, insofar as possible, we shall set the ISIA up in a similar fashion. Thus we again choose to transmit at $\frac{1}{16}$ clock rate, word length of eight, no parity, and two stop bits. From Fig. 6.5(a), it can be seen that the mode instruction should set the ISIA's control register to 11001110B to achieve this.

The second byte of data (the command instruction) is determined according to the Command Instruction Format, as described in Fig. 6.5(c). Here we want in particular to enable the transmit function of the ISIA and reset all error flags. This is a achieved by sending 00110111B to the control register. (Since this particular byte of data will also serve as the command in later I/O applications involving the ISIA, we have enabled a greater capability than required in the present instance.)

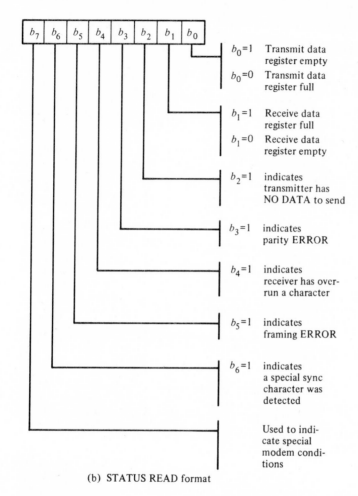

$b_0=1$ Transmit data
register empty

$b_0=0$ Transmit data
register full

$b_1=1$ Receive data
register full

$b_1=0$ Receive data
register empty

$b_2=1$ indicates
transmitter has
NO DATA to send

$b_3=1$ indicates
parity ERROR

$b_4=1$ indicates
receiver has over-
run a character

$b_5=1$ indicates
framing ERROR

$b_6=1$ indicates
a special sync
character was
detected

Used to indi-
cate special
modem condi-
tions

(b) STATUS READ format

Fig. 6.5 continued

Consequently, in the case of the I8085, the Punch routine can begin with the following segment of code:

```
PNCH:    MVI    A, 11001110B        ; *    MODE
         STA    CREG                ;      DEFINITION
         MVI    A, 00110111B        ; *    COMMAND
         STA    CREG                ;      DEFINITION
```

where CREG has as its value the address of the ISIA control register.

Note that the above segment assumes that the ISIA is being used in a memory-mapped configuration. We conclude our discussion of the Punch routine with a brief look at the subroutine OUT in the case of I8085 code.

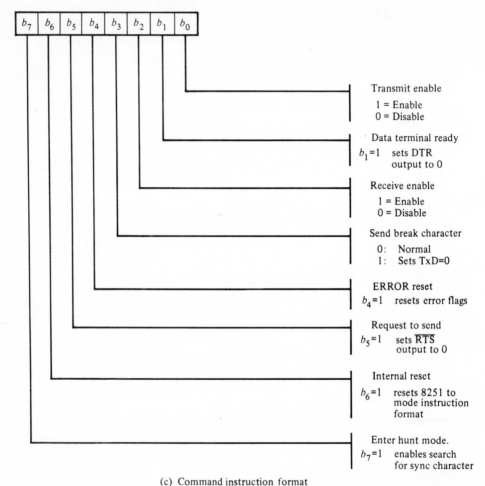

(c) Command instruction format

Fig. 6.5 continued

From Fig. 6.5(b), we see that, when reflecting the status of the ISIA, the low-order bit of the control register signals when the Transmit Data Register is ready to receive data. Accordingly, in a manner that is quite similar to the earlier case with the MSIA, we can use the following segment for OUT's busy-wait loop:

```
OUT:    LDA     SREG    ;   MOVE STATUS TO ACCUMULATOR
        RAR             ;   SHIFT b_0 TO CY
        JNC     OUT     ;   WAIT IF b_0 = 0
```

where SREG, which has the same value as CREG, is used to access the ISIA status register.

6.2.3 The Load Routine

The Load routine presupposes that the tape has been rewound and that the recorder is operating in its playback mode. A flowchart for this routine is given in Fig. 6.6.

As might be expected, the structure of Load routine is determined in large part by the format of the output produced by the Punch routine. When the initial test for the start of a block ('B') is successful, there is the subsequent retrieval of block length and starting address. This information enables the CPU to load the blocks of data in the proper memory locations. Since these aspects of the Load routine are fairly straightforward, we will simply consider the interaction between the routine and the SIA and do this only for the case of the M6800 system and its MSIA.

Relative to initializing the MSIA's control register, we refer again to Fig. 6.3. In the process of transferring data to the tape, it is customary to impose a clock signal on the tape along with the data from memory. This signal can then

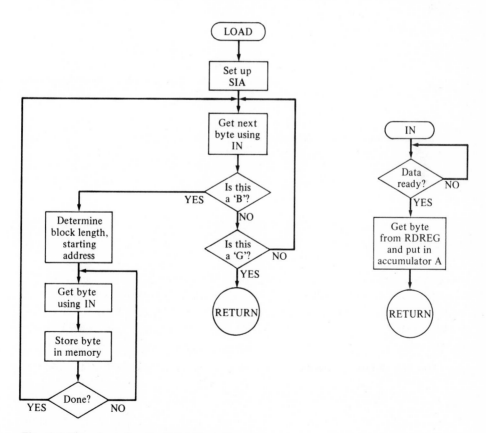

Fig. 6.6 Flowchart for the LOAD routine.

be used by the MSIA during the Load routine. With this assumption, we would want to receive at the 300-Baud rate (since we transmitted at this rate) and hence divide the signal by 1 (that is, set $b_1 b_0 = 00$). As in the output case, the words are of length eight with no parity and two stop bits, so that $b_4 b_3 b_2 = 100$, and all interrupts are disabled, so that $b_7 b_6 b_5 = 000$. As a result the following M6800 segment will properly initialize the MSIA.

```
LDA   A   #00000011B        * *    INITIALIZE
STA   A   CREG              *          MSIA
LDA   A   #00010000B        * *    CONFIGURE MSIA
STA   A   CREG              *      FOR TRANSMISSION
```

The actual receiving function is carried out by the subroutine IN. Note that IN involves a busy-wait loop since we are again operating in a noninterrupt mode. Data can be read in from the MSIA when its Receive Data Register (RDREG) is full—a condition indicated by $b_0 = 1$ in the status register (see Fig. 6.4). Consequently, in the case of the M6800, we can take the subroutine IN to be as follows:

```
IN    LDA   A   SREG      MOVE SREG TO ACCA
      ASR   A             SHIFT b_0 = 0
      BCC       IN        WAIT IF b_0 = 0
      LDA   A   RDREG     MOVE DATA TO ACCA
      RTS
```

Although the ideas behind these routines are ultimately quite straightforward, we will see that they also serve as a basis for the more general loaders considered in the next chapter.

LABORATORY ASSIGNMENTS

1. Use the Punch and Load routines available on your microcomputer to transfer a program to tape. Subsequently retrieve the program from tape and verify that it has been correctly recovered.

2. The various components of this experiment are designed to give you a better feel for the differences between CPU speeds and peripheral speeds. This is done by relating CPU cycles to Baud rates.

    i) This part of the experiment involves the M6800 and its MSIA. Following setup for a given Baud rate, a byte of data (the contents of accumulator A) is to be placed in the MSIA's transmit data register (TDREG). The M6800 is to then enter a busy-wait loop until the MSIA's status register indicates that TDREG is empty. At this time the program is to halt. The index register XR is to be initialized to zero and incremented each time through the loop. One can then use the final XR value, the number of CPU cycles in the loop, and the Baud rate, to determine the number of CPU cycles executed per bit transmitted.

After determining the addresses of the MSIA's CREG, SREG, and TDREG in your system, write a program to perform the task described above. Run your program five times at each of the Baud rates 75, 300, and 4800 and determine the average number of CPU cycles per bit transferred at each rate.

ii) Repeat part (i) above for the I8085 and its ISIA.

iii) This part of the experiment, to be carried out with the M6800 system, is again designed to relate CPU cycles to Baud rates, but here we use interrupt I/O. Instead of testing for an empty TDREG in a busy-wait loop, we arrange to have an empty TDREG cause an interrupt to the M6800.

Your program should begin by clearing the interrupt mask (CLI) and setting the interrupt vector in your system to point to your interrupt routine. Set CREG to 00001000B indicating noninterrupt mode (TDREG has not yet been loaded) and 4800 Baud (see Fig. 6.3). After initializing XR to zero and storing the contents of accumulator A in TDREG, reset CREG to 00110000B to enable interrupts. The subsequent loop should merely increment XR (the program should halt when XR returns to zero). Your interrupt routine should simply ensure that the program halts upon return from interrupt (with the value in XR still available). Once again, run the program five times at each of the Baud rates and determine the average number of CPU cycles per bit transferred at each Baud rate. Compare these results with the results of part (i).

EXERCISES

1. Relative to the Load routine, discuss the setting of the control register and write the subroutine IN for the I8085 system.

2. In general, an I8085 program (including data) that is intended to be placed in locations M, $M + 1$, . . . , $M + r$ will not execute properly if it is placed in locations N, $N + 1$, . . . , $N + r$, where $M \neq N$. What restrictions would have to be placed on the program if we wish to do this and obtain correct results?

3. Repeat Exercise 2 for the case of the M6800.

4. Assuming the Punch routine discussed in this chapter, describe the tape format we would get if we Punched from locations 0000H to 0120H (indicate proper values for beginning addresses, byte counts, etc.).

REFERENCES AND SUPPORTIVE MATERIAL

Sections 6.2 and Laboratory Assignments. Complete specifications for Motorola's M6850 Asynchronous Communications Interface Adapter can be found in Motorola (1976a). The Intel 8251 Programmable Communications Interface device is detailed in Intel (1977a).

1. Intel [1977a], "MCS-85 User's Manual." Intel Corporation, 3065 Bowers Ave., Santa Clara, California.

2. Motorola [1976a], "M6800 Microcomputer: System Design Data." Motorola Semiconductor Products Inc., Box 20912, Phoenix, Arizona.

3. Motorola [1977], "MEK6800D2 Evaluation Kit Manual." Motorola Semiconductor Products Inc., 3501 Ed Bluestein Blvd., Austin, Texas.

CHAPTER SEVEN

SYSTEM INTERFACE PROGRAMS

7.1 BOOTSTRAP AND ABSOLUTE LOADERS

In the broadest sense, the function of a loader is to take the object code produced by an assembler (or compiler) and place it in memory for subsequent execution. There are several different types of loaders and they vary in the manner in which they perform this basic loading function.

The loading situation relative to our own developing computing system is improving, but still quite limited. After using a cross assembler to produce object code, we still must perform the loading function ourselves. Assuming the existence of the cassette Punch and Load routines as described in Chapter 6, we can automatically save on tape, and later recover from the tape, a program that has already been loaded into memory. However, this procedure still requires that a program be hand-loaded at least once. This is reasonable for the small programs that have been written thus far, but as we encounter much larger programs, such as an assembler, we will want more efficient techniques to move the object code from the supporting development system to the microcomputer's memory.

We will assume that the object code is made available to the microcomputer's Serial Interface Adaptor (SIA). Generally, the data is presented in a manner that includes information about the amount of data and where it is to be placed in memory. For present purposes, we will assume that the data arrives in consecutive *records,* each having the following format:

No. of bytes of data	Starting address	Data	...	Data

Each record consists of a series of fields, and each field except the second field will eventually yield one byte of information. The second field (starting address) will produce two bytes of information. The first field holds a count of the number of bytes of data in the record. The last record consists of only the first field (number of bytes), which will contain zero. Note that all of the information in a record can be represented by hexadecimal digits.

Since data is frequently transmitted in an encoded form, we make one final assumption regarding the information present in the records. The information is assumed to arrive encoded in its ASCII representation (and hence is not directly usable as presented). To illustrate, we consider the following transmission:

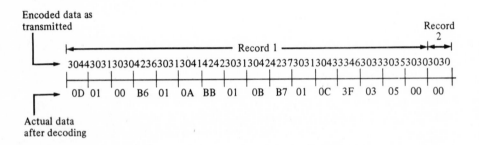

Here we see that the information has a total length of 34 bytes. To decipher this we must convert it from the ASCII to the hexadecimal data that is being represented. Note that this implies a compression of the information to one-half of its initial length since the ASCII representation of one hexadecimal digit is one byte (2 hexadecimal digits) long.

Decoding the first two bytes in the first record above, we produce OD and so we now know that "OD" or 13 bytes of data are present in this record. Continuing the decoding process, the next four bytes of the record (30313030) produce 0100—the starting address for the 13 bytes of data (26 ASCII characters) that follow.

After decoding the ASCII representations for these thirteen bytes of data, we see that the second record consists of a single field containing 3030 ("00") and hence this is the last record. The 13 bytes of data in this case produce the object code listed in Fig. 7.1, which also contains a possible corresponding M6800 AL program. Note that the last byte of the first record is "00". This value will be loaded into the storage cell reserved for SUM.

Assuming that we are working with a particular Serial Interface Adaptor and using our knowledge of the object form produced by the supporting Microcomputer Development System (MDS), it is not difficult to write a program that will accept input from the MDS and load the object program into the proper memory locations. We will refer to such a loader as a System Inter-

M6800 CML Code			M6800 AL Code		
Location	Hex code				
			NAM		EXAMP
			ORG		0100H
0100	B6	010A	LDA	A	FNUM
0103	BB	010B	ADD	A	SNUM
0106	B7	010C	STA	A	SUM
0109	3F		SWI		
010A	03	FNUM	FCB	3	
010B	05	SNUM	FCB	5	
010C		SUM	RMB	1	
			END		

Fig. 7.1 Object and AL code from sample record.

face or SI loader. Having such a SI loader, our method of operation will be as follows:

1. Use the cross assembler to assemble the AL program and produce the object code. (This code, when prepared for transmission by the MDS, will appear in the format of the records as indicated above.)

2. Hand-load the SI loader into the microcomputer.

3. Execute the loader as the MDS is sending the object form.

We have then eliminated the need to hand-load the program the first time, but we must still hand-load the loader each time we need to use it. This last manual step can of course be eliminated by storing the SI loader on a cassette tape. Step 2 above can then be replaced with 2', as follows:

2'. Use the Load routine to load the SI loader from the tape.

At this point we have taken a major step toward our goal of turning our microcomputers into functional systems. It is no longer necessary to hand-load any programs.

The Load routine supporting the cassette interface is an example of a *bootstrap loader.* Bootstrap loaders either are found in the ROM of a machine or are hand-loaded as an initial step in bringing up a system. The major role performed by the bootstrap loader is to load a more powerful loader such as an absolute loader. The SI loader is the absolute loader for our system.

An *absolute loader* is a system program that can input and load machine-language instructions that are bound to absolute locations. For our SI loader, these "absolute" locations are determined from the starting address present in a record.

Although we will not need to produce loaders more powerful than the SI loader for the system we are building, some systems also utilize *relocating* loaders and *linking* loaders. In the next two sections of this chapter we consider the functions performed by these loaders.

LABORATORY ASSIGNMENT

Write a System Interface (SI) loader for your microcomputer. Assume a record format as indicated in the text.

7.2 RELOCATING LOADERS

In Exercises 2 and 3 at the end of Chapter 6, we considered the problems involved with moving a program from one area of memory to another, and noted that, in general, a program functions correctly only when placed in those locations in which it is intended to reside. In other words, programs are *location-dependent.*

There are many situations in which a program cannot be tied to specific memory locations until just prior to execution of the ML code. In fact, it is common to have a program execute repeatedly and have it placed in different memory slots for each run. This is the case, for example, with an external subroutine that may be assembled independently of, and invoked by, various calling programs. There is no reason to expect that the subroutine will reside in exactly the same locations each time it is used. Figure 7.2 illustrates this.

Relative to the situation depicted in this diagram, one could insist that SR be loaded into the same locations each time it is used, but this would entail

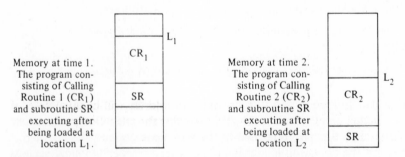

Memory at time 1. The program consisting of Calling Routine 1 (CR$_1$) and subroutine SR executing after being loaded at location L$_1$.

Memory at time 2. The program consisting of Calling Routine 2 (CR$_2$) and subroutine SR executing after being loaded at location L$_2$

Figure 7.2

allocating a considerable amount of time to moving programs around and would constitute an inefficient use of CPU time.

Another example of a situation in which it is necessary to move programs around is a time-slicing multiprogramming environment. In a system of this type, a program is allowed to execute for a while (its time slice) and then the program is swapped out to a disk so that some other program can have its turn. After a while, the original program will get another time slice and will have to be reloaded. Again, there is no reason to expect that the program will be loaded into its original memory slot. Thus the basic problem facing us is how to get a program to function properly after it has been set up to work one area of memory and is then shifted to another area of memory. Two possible solutions suggest themselves:

1. Reassemble the program with its new origin set at the beginning of the new area. This is a very expensive solution, both in terms of CPU time (the program will have to be assembled many times) and space (the AL file must be saved).

2. Find some way to delay the time at which symbolic names are bound to physical locations (*binding time*); i.e., find a way to have location-dependent information fixed only when the program is loaded into memory and not when it is assembled.

Pursuing option 2, we find that some possible times for binding are:

1. When the program is written (in the case of CML programming);

2. When the program is translated (in the case of AL programming);

3. When the routines constituting the program are linked, but before the program is loaded;

4. When the program is loaded;

5. When the base register is loaded (in the case of a base/displacement addressing system);

6. When the instruction containing the address is executed.

An instruction containing a direct memory address will be invalidated if the data it references is relocated. In order to solve the relocation problem, we need to delay binding time at least until the program is loaded (4, above). We now consider how this can be accomplished with a relocating loader. Let us recall the program of Fig. 7.1.

M6800 AL Code			M6800 CML Code	
			Location	Hex code
NAM		EXAMP		
ORG		0100H		
LDA	A	FNUM	0100	B6 010A
ADD	A	SNUM	0103	BB 010B
STA	A	SUM	0106	B7 010C
SWI			0109	3F
FNUM FCB	3		010A	03
SNUM FCB	5		010B	05
SUM RMB	1		010C	
END				

If we want to load and execute this program at 0210H the CML code would have to be changed as follows:

M6800 CML Code

Location	Hex code	
0210	B6	021A
0213	BB	021B
0216	B7	021C
0219	3F	
021A	03	
021B	05	
021C		

In this program, the bytes of data that have to be changed are those that are underlined. In general for the case of the M6800, the only bytes we need to worry about are memory references in the direct or extended mode. A fairly common way of handling this is to associate relocation information with each byte. For example, we might associate one bit with each byte using a 0 to indicate that the byte does not need to be relocated and a 1 to indicate that it does require relocation. We might then form a load module that begins with two bytes indicating the assembled ORG point and one byte containing a count of the number of bytes of object code in the program. This would be followed by the relocation bits grouped into successive bytes (the last such byte may be filled out with redundant data). Finally, the bytes of object code would com-

plete the load module. Using these conventions, the resulting load module relative to the example above would include the following:

01 00 0D 6D 80 B6 01 0A BB 01 0B B7 01 0C 3F 03 05 00

The first two bytes, 0100, indicate that the module was assembled relative
to ORG point 0100. The third byte, 0D, indicates that the module includes
0DH or 13 bytes of object code. Note that it is now apparent that there will be
two bytes of relocation information (since the 13 bits of relocation information will be rounded off to two bytes). The first byte of relocation information, 6DH = 01101101B, indicates that the second, third, fifth, sixth, and
eighth bytes of object code require relocation. Similarly, the second byte of
relocation information, 80H = 10000000B, indicates that the ninth byte of
object code must be relocated.

Now if the object form indicates that an extended address requires relocation, the new address value can be found by adding a relocation constant to the
given address. This relocation constant is simply the difference between the
new start address and the original ORG point (0210–0100 in the case of the
above example).

A relocating loader, then, is a loader that accepts as input an object form
including relocation information, computes the relocation constant, and loads
the relocated code.

Processors that rely heavily on direct addressing are subject to relocation
problems when instructions and the data referenced by these instructions are
moved to new locations. One method of avoiding this problem at the processor
level is to make use of relative addressing in referencing data and thereby produce position-independent code, that is, code that can be repositioned without
requiring adjustment.

7.2.1 Exercise

Discuss and compare the problems associated with building relocating loaders
for the M6800 and the I8085. In particular for the case of the M6800, consider
the matter of relocating an old direct address to a new extended address and
an old extended address to a new direct address.

7.3 LINKING LOADERS

In addition to being able to relocate an appropriate object form, a loader may
be required to perform other functions as well. In Sec. 7.2 we indicated that it
is common to have a routine assembled independently and then invoked by
various calling routines. This suggests the need for a loader which, when presented with a group of independently assembled modules, can combine or link

them into a single functioning module. Such a loader is referred to as a *linking loader*. We now consider briefly how such a loader can be constructed. In an environment involving independently assembled modules, we would expect to find additional directives, for example PUBLIC and EXTRN, where

PUBLIC   namelist

signals that each entry in namelist is defined in this module, but accessible to other modules, and

EXTRN   namelist

signals that each entry in namelist can be used in this module, but is defined elsewhere.

The use of these directives is illustrated in the following example:

```
            NAME      MAIN
            EXTRN     INCHAR
            PUBLIC    INBUF,SREG,RDREG
CREG        EQU       xy01
SREG        EQU       xy01
RDREG       EQU       xy00
            ORG       0000H
            MVI       A,01111010B
            STA       CREG              ; MODE DEFINITION
            MVI       A,00110111B
            STA       CREG              ; COMMAND DEFINITION
            LDA       BCNT              ; STORE COUNT IN
            MOV       D,A               ; REG D
            CALL      INCHAR
            HLT
INBUF:      DS        20
BCNT:       DB        20
            END

            NAME      SUB
            EXTRN     INBUF,SREG,RDREG
            PUBLIC    INCHAR
            ORG       0000H
```

```
INCHAR:    LXI        H, INBUF
L1:        LDA        SREG
           RAR
           RAR
           JNC        L1
           LDA        RDREG
           MOV        M,A
           INX        H
           DCR        D
           JNZ        L1
           RET
           END
```

In these two modules, the MAIN routine sets up a buffer (of size 20 bytes), initializes the Serial Interface Adapter and then calls SUB. SUB inputs and stores characters in the buffer set up by MAIN. In this example, xy is used to represent the most significant byte of the SIA's register addresses. The specific value of xy would depend on the particular system.

In the present context, we wish to understand how it might be possible to assemble MAIN and SUB separately and then place both in memory so that they can communicate during execution. Relative to this, several problems should be noted:

1. When MAIN is assembled, the value of INCHAR will be unknown so that CALL INCHAR can't be fully assembled.

2. Similarly when SUB is assembled, the value of INBUF, CREG, and RDREG cannot be known.

3. Both MAIN and SUB are ORG'ed at 0000H. Obviously they cannot both be placed at this location and at least one of them will need to be relocated.

One solution to these problems is to have an assembler produce specialized object modules that are the input to a linking loader. The linking loader then produces one absolute (or relocatable) load module. This process is depicted in Fig. 7.3.

The specialized object module must contain enough information to make linking possible. A sample object-module format that will suit our present pur-

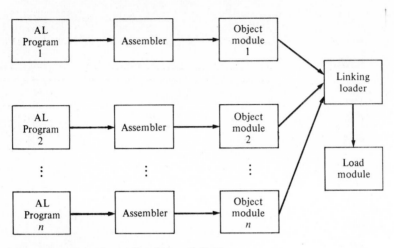

Fig. 7.3 Independent assembly and linking.

pose is shown in Fig. 7.4. The role of each of the fields in this object module format is as follows:

Identification: Name of module and length (in bytes)

Public entry table: A list of symbols (defined in this module) that may be referenced in other modules (PUBLIC's) together with their assigned locations.

External reference table: A list of symbols used in this module but defined in another (EXTRN's) together with a list of reference locations.

Machine instructions and constants: This part gets loaded into memory; the other parts are used by the linker to complete this part prior to a load.

Relocation directory: The directory tells the linker which addresses need to be relocated in this module. Each symbol not associated with an absolute address is listed along with the addresses of its occurrences (if any) in the module.

End of module: Symbol table for local variables. These are the variables that are referenced in this module only. They don't appear in either the public entry table or the external reference table.

Identification
Public entry table
External reference table
Machine instructions and constants
Relocation directory
End of module

Fig. 7.4 Linking object module format.

Using this format, assembly of our previous modules should produce the object modules shown in Fig. 7.5. Note that the memory reserved for INBUF in MAIN does not appear in the machine instructions and constant area, but these bytes are reflected in the module length.

Object module for MAIN

MAIN	27H	
INBUF	0012	
SREG	xy01	
RDREG	xy00	
INCHAR	000F	

0000	3E	7A	
0002	32	01	xy
0005	3E	37	
0007	32	01	xy
000A	3A	26	00
000D	57		
000E	CD	--	--
0011	76		
0026	14		

BCNT	000B
INBUF	

CREG	xy01
BCNT	0026

Object module for SUB

SUB	15H	
INCHAR	0000	
INBUF	0001	
SREG	0004	
RDREG	000C	

0000	21	--	--
0003	3A	--	--
0006	1F		
0007	1F		
0008	D2	03	00
000B	3A	--	--
000E	77		
000F	23		
0010	15		
0011	C2	03	00
0014	C9		

LI	0009, 0012
INCHAR	
LI	0003

Figure 7.5

These object modules constitute the input to the linking loader. Assume, for purposes of discussion, that the linking loader is to combine these (MAIN followed by SUB) into a single load module, which is to begin at 0100. The resulting load module should appear as follows:

0100	3E	7A	
0102	32	01	*xy*
0105	3E	37	
0107	32	01	*xy*
010A	3A	26	01
010D	57		
010E	CD	27	01
0111	76		
0112	00		
0113	00		
.	.		
.	.		
.	.		
0125	00		
0126	14		
0127	21	12	01
012A	3A	01	*xy*
012D	1F		
012E	1F		
012F	D2	2A	01
0132	3A	00	*xy*
0135	77		
0136	23		
0137	15		
0138	C2	2A	01
013B	C9		

It is important to note here how the linker can use the information provided in the original object modules to form this relocated composite. The relocation constant for MAIN is 100H and for SUB, the relocation constant is the constant for MAIN plus the length of MAIN—that is, 100H + 27H = 0127H. MAIN is loaded starting at 0100H. As MAIN is being loaded, the linking loader must appropriately adjust those addresses listed in MAIN's relocation directory. In addition, the loader must fill in those addresses omitted in the object modules such as the address of INCHAR required in MAIN (locations 010FH, 0110H). This address is 0127H as computed above, and so the linking loader inserts 27H in location 010FH and 01H in 0110H. Continuing the loading process with SUB, the loader selects 21 from SUB's machine instruction section and inserts it in location 0127H. To determine what is to be loaded into locations 0128H and 0129H, the linking loader finds from SUB's External Reference Table that the proper value of INBUF is required here. Tracing back to MAIN's public entry table, the loader finds that INBUF is at 0012H. However, since INBUF is also in MAIN's relocation directory, the value 0012H must be augmented by MAIN's relocation constant of 0100H. Hence starting at location 0128H, the loader will load 1201H (0112H = 0012H + 0100H).

Continuing in this way, we see that a final complete load module can be generated using only the original object modules and the knowledge of where the composite module is to begin.

EXERCISES

1. Using the conventions set out in the text for linking loaders, indicate the object modules that would be created for the routines below. (Recall that initialized data goes into the fourth field of the object module.)

	NAM		O1		NAM		O2
	PUBLIC		SUM		PUBLIC		ADDR
	EXTRN		ADDR		EXTRN		SUM
	ORG		0100H		ORG		0104H
	LDA	A	ONE	ADDR	ABA		
	LDA	B	TWO		STA	A	SUM
	JSR		ADDR		RTS		
	SWI				END		
ONE	FCB		1				
TWO	FCB		2				
SUM	RMB		1				
	END						

2. Indicate the composite load module, assuming you load in the order (O1-O2) and start loading at 0300H.

7.4 TEXT EDITORS

As our final example of a system interface program, we consider a kind of generalization of a loader known as a *text editor*. A text editor is a program that typically accepts input from a terminal and places it into the appropriate memory locations. Text editors usually include the ability to "echo" the input data back to the terminal so that it may be examined and possibly altered (edited). Thus a basic text editor would include both INPUT and EDIT modes. Data could be input (and examined) during the INPUT mode; the complete file could be examined and edited while in the EDIT mode. Typical EDIT functions might include the ability to modify, delete, or insert a character string, modify, delete, or insert a line, and arrange a file in a specific format.

We shall briefly discuss the structure of the INPUT mode of a typical text editor. A flow diagram for our INPUT routine appears in Fig. 7.6.

This routine utilizes two addresses, MEM and LINE, which are maintained in memory. At any given time MEM contains the address of the byte into which the next character will be placed. LINE always holds the address of the beginning byte of the line currently being entered. These and the SIA are initialized in the first steps of the routine.

The reading of characters from the terminal can be achieved by utilizing the SIA and a busy-wait loop, as was done in the cassette tape Load routine of Chapter 6. Likewise, the subsequent output or "echoing" for the display of a character that has been stored, or of a command signal to the terminal utilizes the SIA in a manner similar to that of the Punch routine of Chapter 6.

Like the sample monitor program discussed in Sect. 6.2.1, an input character sent to the INPUT routine can be either a command signal or data to be stored in memory. The command signals acknowledged by the routine of Fig. 7.4 include the carriage return (CR) that causes the beginning of a new line, a rubout signal that causes the pointer MEM to be decremented, and a shift-o signal (←) that causes MEM to be reset to LINE. Thus the rubout and shift-o give the INPUT mode of the text editor a limited error-correcting capability: Rubout causes a character-delete signal to be echoed to the terminal and shift-o effectively erases the line currently being entered. As noted above, a text editor's EDIT mode would normally include further error-correcting capabilities.

As can be seen from Fig. 7.6, following the input of a character from the terminal, the routine tests to see if the character constitutes a command. Upon detecting a carriage return, the routine stores CR (0DH) and LF (Line Feed or 0AH) in MEM. (These values are stored in memory so that, when the file is subsequently printed back to the terminal, it will automatically be displayed as a series of lines as entered.) Following this, MEM and LINE are updated and CR and LF are echoed back to the terminal.

Upon detecting a rubout command, the routine simply decrements MEM and issues a character-delete signal back to the terminal. Following a shift-o signal, MEM is reset back to LINE, and CR and LF signals are sent back to the terminal.

Termination of input is indicated by a period at the beginning of a line (MEM = LINE); a period elsewhere is ignored. All other input characters are stored as data in memory; and in each case, the corresponding character is echoed back for display at the terminal. Following the final period (which is also stored), a DISPLAY routine can be invoked to display the entire file. The stored period can be used to signal the end of text to this DISPLAY routine.

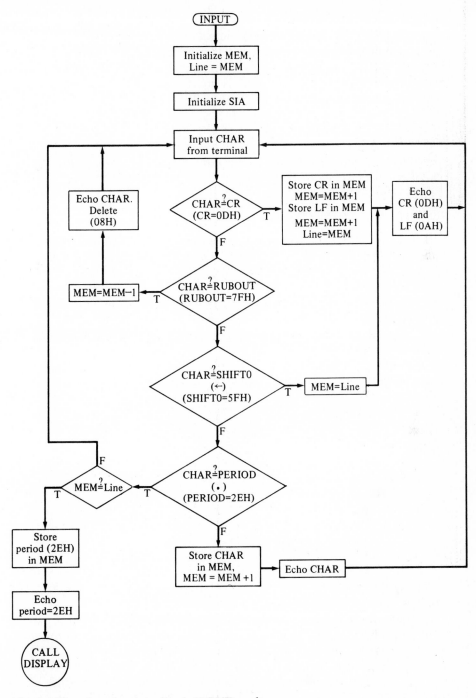

Fig. 7.6 Flowchart for text editor's INPUT mode.

In a typical system configuration, there will be some provision for saving files created by the text editor and, subsequently, retrieving them. For the primitive system we are developing, we will not provide this capability. For our purposes, the text editor will simply create a core image of an assembly-language program that will be accessed as input by a resident assembler. This topic is discussed in more detail in Chapter 9.

EXERCISE

Write a text editor for your microcomputer system following the flowchart of Fig. 7.6.

REFERENCES AND SUPPORTIVE MATERIAL

Sections 7.1 and 7.2. The reader should consult Barron (1969), Donovan (1972), and Graham (1975) for additional information on system loaders. The relocation and linkage capabilities of the Intel 8085 Assembly Language are discussed in Intel (1977).

1. Barron, D. W. [1969], *Assemblers and Loaders*. New York American Elsevier.

2. Donovan, J. J. [1972], *Systems Programming*. New York: McGraw-Hill.

3. Graham, R. M. [1975], *Principles of Systems Programming*. New York: John Wiley & Sons.

4. Intel [1977], "8080/8085 Assembly Language Programming Manual." Intel Corporation, 3065 Bowers Ave., Santa Clara, California.

CHAPTER EIGHT

HIGH-LEVEL LANGUAGE PROGRAMMING

In the previous chapters, assembly-language and machine-language programming have been emphasized for all programming tasks. From this point on, the emphasis will be placed on programming in a high-level language—the highest level depicted in Fig. 1.1. PL/M®, a high-level language developed by Intel, will be used as the language vehicle in this discussion.

8.1 THE PL/M PROGRAMMING LANGUAGE

PL/M was developed by Intel to support software development for their microcomputers. Intel has created several compilers for PL/M; for example, PL/M80 is a compiler that accepts a PL/M program as its source or input language and produces 8080* object code as its target language. Since PL/M was introduced by Intel, additional compilers have been produced for other machines. Intermetrics (Intermetrics, 1975) implemented PL/M6800, a PL/M compiler that produces M6800 object code. PL/M STAR, a retargetable compiler that generates either I8085 assembler code or M6800 assembler code, has been implemented at Southern Illinois University at Carbondale (Smith and Tondo, 1978). A user of the PL/M STAR system can specify which target language is desired.

PL/M is a PL/I-like language. It contains only a subset of the constructs found in a complete PL/I compiler, but it has been augmented with other constructs that make it suitable for writing systems programs. PL/M allows the

---

® PL/M is a registered trademark of Intel Corporation.

*Intel's 8080 microprocesor was a predecessor of the I8085. The 8080 and I8085 are very similar. At the instruction level, the only significant difference is that the I8085 supports two additional instructions: RIM and SIM.

advantages of a high-level language without sacrificing access to the hardware features available in the target machine. Figure 8.1 contains a listing of the language features found in PL/M. The PL/M grammar that specifies the syntax of the language is listed in Appendix F.

Data types:
   BYTE ~ 8 bit quantity
   ADDRESS ~ 16 bit quantity

Arithmetic operators:
   + Addition   MOD   Modulo
   − Subtraction   PLUS   Add with carry
   * Multiplication   MINUS   Subtract with carry
   / Division

Logical operators (bitwise operators):
   NOT One's complement   OR   Logical or
   AND Logical and   XOR   Logical exclusive or

Relational operators (unsigned compares):
   < Less than   < = Less than or equal to
   > Greater than   > = Greater than or equal to
   = Equal to   < > Not equal to

Statements:
   Assignment   DO CASE   REPEAT-UNTIL
   Compound   DO WHILE
   IF-THEN-ELSE   Iterative DO

Declarations:
   All variables must be declared in PL/M. PL/M supports declarations for data types (BYTE or ADDRESS), arrays, structures, and initialization of variables. Variables may also be addressed indirectly *via* the BASED declaration attribute. Communication between independently compiled modules is supported with PUBLIC and EXTERNAL attributes.

Built-in functions:
   The built-in functions provided by PL/M support a wide variety of operations, e.g., condition code testing, time delays, size attributes, rotation, shifting and byte isolation functions.

Procedures:
   PL/M supports both subroutine and function type procedures. Subroutines are invoked with the CALL statement. All parameters are passed by value. Recursive procedures are permitted.

Fig. 8.1 PL/M language features.

8.1.1 Data Types and Constants

PL/M supports two basic data types: BYTE and ADDRESS. An object of type BYTE is eight bits in length; an object of type ADDRESS is 16 bits in length. Type distinction is based only on the size of the object, eight or 16 bits, and not on the computational interpretation of that object. For example, an object of type BYTE may represent a numeric or an ASCII character value.

PL/M supports both numeric and character-string constants. Numeric constants may be specified in hexadecimal (denoted by a trailing H*), octal (denoted by a trailing O or Q), binary (denoted by a trailing B), or decimal (the default case, optionally followed by a trailing D). String constants are delimited by opening and closing quotes. The length (L) of a string constant must lie in the range $1 \le L \le 255$.

Examples

```
12
1AFH
01111010B
177Q
'STRING CONSTANT'
```

To aid in readability, a dollar sign ($) may be used in numeric constants, for example, 0101$1111$0000$1010B. The dollar sign is ignored by the compiler.

8.1.2 Declarations

PL/M requires that all variables used in a program be declared. A variable name (identifier) must start with a letter, consist of only letters, digits, and the dollar sign, and be less than or equal to 31 characters in length. The dollar sign is used for readability and has no significance otherwise; it is not counted in the 31-character-limit total. LAB6 and LAB$6, for example, represent the same identifier.

The simplest form of declaration is the basic type declaration that is used to define BYTE or ADDRESS variables. For example,

```
DECLARE   A   BYTE;
DECLARE   C   ADDRESS;
DECLARE   Q   BYTE;
```

establishes A and Q as BYTE variables and C as an ADDRESS variable. Declarations of common types may be grouped so the declarations given above could be written as

```
DECLARE   (A,Q)   BYTE;
DECLARE   C   ADDRESS;
```

---

*Hexadecimal numbers must start with one of the digits 0–9.

It is even possible to declare several items of different types in the same declaration, thus:

```
DECLARE   (A,Q)   BYTE,
           C   ADDRESS;
```

PL/M supports two forms of data aggregates: arrays and structures. Only one-dimensional arrays are permitted and zero origin subscripting is used. An array of 10 ADDRESS elements, B(0), B(1), . . . , B(9) would be delcared as

```
DECLARE   B(10)   ADDRESS;
```

Structures, or nonhomogeneous arrays, permit the grouping of nonsimilar data types in a single data structure. For example,

```
DECLARE   VALUE   STRUCTURE(
          PART$1  ADDRESS,
          PART$2  BYTE);
```

defines a data structure VALUE that consists of two distinct subcomponents. The subcomponents of a structure are referenced as

```
structure name. component  name
```

For the structure definition given above, VALUE.PART$1 references an ADDRESS quantity while VALUE.PART$2 references a BYTE quantity.

The subcomponents of a structure may themselves be arrays, but they cannot be structures. The declaration given below defines a structure called TABLE that has three subcomponents. TABLE.NAME is a BYTE array with five elements. TABLE.CODE is a simple BYTE variable and TABLE.NB is a simple ADDRESS variable.

```
DECLARE   TABLE   STRUCTURE(
          NAME(5)   BYTE,
          CODE   BYTE,
          NB    ADDRESS);
```

Note that in the context of this declaration, TABLE.NAME(2) references the third element of the NAME subcomponent of TABLE.

Arrays of structures are also permitted; for example,

```
DECLARE   NODE(100)   STRUCTURE(
          L$PTR   ADDRESS,
          DATA$PART(5)BYTE,
          R$PTR   ADDRESS);
```

In the context of this declaration, NODE(1).DATA$PART(2) references the third element of the DATA$PART subcomponent of second element of the NODE structure array.

PL/M supports indirect references to quantities by means of BASED declarations. A based variable does not have storage allocated for it. The storage cell it references is determined by the current value of its base. Consider, for example, the declarations given below:

```
DECLARE      MEM$PTR    ADDRESS,
            (MEM BASED MEM$PTR)  BYTE;
```

MEM has been defined as a based byte variable with MEM$PTR as its base. Since the base must determine a storage cell, the base must be of type ADDRESS. If MEM$PTR has the value 0100H, then an attempt to assign the value 0AH to MEM would store the value 0AH in memory location 0100H. If the value of MEM$PTR changes, then so does the storage cell referenced by MEM.

In using based variables, the following restrictions should be noted:

1. The base must be of type ADDRESS.

2. The base may not be subscripted.

3. The base may not be a based variable itself.

4. The keyword BASED must immediately follow the name of the variable in the declaration, e.g.,

> DECLARE (A BASED B) (100) ADDRESS;

declares a 100-element ADDRESS array called A. The storage region denoted by A is determined by the value of B, the base. If B has the value 2000H, then A(2) references the ADDRESS quantity held in memory locations 2004H and 2005H.

With the exception of based variables, variable declarations result in the allocation of storage. Using the facilities discussed so far, the PL/M programmer can cause storage to be allocated but not at a specified memory location. For example, in response to

```
DECLARE   ALPHA BYTE;
```

the PL/M compiler will allocate one byte of storage at some arbitrary memory location. If the programmer wants the storage cell allocated for ALPHA to be at some specific point in memory, the AT attribute may be included in the declaration; for example,

```
DECLARE   ALPHA   BYTE   AT (2000H);
```

allocates one byte of storage for ALPHA at memory location 2000H. The AT attribute may be used with simple types, arrays, and structures; it may not be used in a based declaration.

PL/M provides two mechanisms for associating initial values with variables at compile time: INITIAL† and DATA. The DATA attribute is used to assign values to variables that will not be updated during program execution; for example,

```
DECLARE  Z  ADDRESS  DATA  (1024);
```

will associate the value 1024 with Z at compile time. Furthermore, since Z's value has been set with the DATA attribute, any attempt to change this value during execution will be flagged as an error or it may have a null effect.‡

Variables whose compile-time values are set by the INITIAL attribute may have their values updated during execution, thus:

```
DECLARE  Y  BYTE  INITIAL  ('A');
```

DATA and INITIAL attributes may be used with simple type, array, and structure declarations, as is noted in the following examples:

a) `DECLARE  A(100)  BYTE  INITIAL (5,7,10);`

This declaration initializes A(0) to 5, A(1) to 7 and A(2) to 10. A(3) through A(99) are left undefined. While it is permissible to specify fewer initial values than are required for the array, it is not possible to list more initial values than are required by the declaration.

b) `DECLARE  Q(5)  BYTE  DATA ('ABCDE');`

This declaration establishes the following initial values:

Q(0) ~ 'A'   Q(3) ~ 'D'
Q(1) ~ 'B'   Q(4) ~ 'E'
Q(2) ~ 'C'

In each case, the internal stored value is the ASCII representation of the character.

c) `DECLARE  TABLE(5)  STRUCTURE (`
    `SYMBOL(5)  BYTE,`
    `CODE  BYTE)`
    `INITIAL (`
    `'STAøø' , 32H,`
    `'LDAøø' , 3AH);`

---

†Variables initialized with the DATA attribute may have their storage allocated in ROM rather than RAM.

‡There are restrictions on where the INITIAL attribute can be used in a PL/M program. These restrictions are discussed in Sec. 8.1.7.

The following initial values are established by this declaration:

TABLE(0).SYMBOL(0) ~ 'S'	TABLE(1).SYMBOL(0) ~ 'L'
TABLE(0).SYMBOL(1) ~ 'T'	TABLE(1).SYMBOL(1) ~ 'D'
TABLE(0).SYMBOL(2) ~ 'A'	TABLE(1).SYMBOL(2) ~ 'A'
TABLE(0).SYMBOL(3) ~ 'b'	TABLE(1).SYMBOL(3) ~ 'b'
TABLE(0).SYMBOL(4) ~ 'b'	TABLE(1).SYMBOL(4) ~ 'b'
TABLE(0).CODE ~ 32H	TABLE(1).CODE ~ 3AH

All other entries of the structure are left undefined. Note that the symbol 'b' is being used in this example to represent a blank.

PL/M also provides a compile-time macro substitution facility with the LITERALLY attribute. With a LITERALLY declaration, an identifier is associated with a character string. Subsequently, whenever the identifier is recognized by the compiler, the corresponding character string is substituted. For example,

```
DECLARE  EOS  LITERALLY  'OFFH' ;
```

associates EOS with the character string 'OFFH'. In any PL/M statement that follows this declaration and uses the identifier EOS, 'OFFH' will be substituted for EOS. If the statement

```
DECLARE  NAME(20)  BYTE  INITIAL  ('JOHN BROWN',EOS) ;
```

follows the LITERALLY definition, the compiler will read it as

```
DECLARE  NAME(20)  BYTE  INITIAL ('JOHN BROWN',OFFH) ;
```

8.1.3 Expressions

At the expression level, PL/M provides arithmetic, logical, and relational operators. The arithmetic operators include + (addition), − (subtraction or unary minus), * (multiplication), and / (integer division). A module operator (MOD) is also provided; for example,

```
X   MOD   8
```

returns as its result the remainder of X/8. PLUS and MINUS are special addition and subtraction operations that take into account the current setting of the CY (Carry/Borrow) flag. These functions mirror the add-with-carry and subtract-with-borrow hardware instructions.

In addition to determining a result value, each of the arithmetic operations determines a resultant type. For PLUS, MINUS, binary + , and binary − , the resultant type is BYTE only if both operands were of type BYTE. In all other cases the resultant type is ADDRESS. MOD, /, and * always yield a resultant type of ADDRESS independent of the type of the operands involved. The resultant type of the unary minus operation is the same as the type of its operand.

The evaluation of arithmetic expressions normally proceeds left to right. The left-to-right evaluation may be overridden by the use of parentheses or the precedence relations of the operations, as below:

> Unary minus   (Highest precedence)
> / * MOD
> + − PLUS MINUS   (Lowest precedence)

PL/M supports the four logical operations that are found in both the M6800 and the I8085 instruction sets, that is, AND, OR, XOR (exclusive or), and NOT (one's complement). These operations perform bitwise logical operations. The binary logicals, AND, OR, and XOR determine a resultant type of BYTE only if both operands were of type BYTE; ADDRESS is the resultant type otherwise. The resultant type of the unary NOT operation is the same as the type of its operand.

The precedence relations of the logical operations are as follows:

> NOT   (Highest precedence)
> AND
> OR, XOR   (Lowest precedence)

As with the arithmetic operators, evaluation of logical expressions usually proceeds left to right but is overridden by the precedence relations or parentheses. Expressions containing both arithmetic and logical operators are permitted. The arithmetic operators have higher precedence than the logical operations.

Six relational operators are supported in PL/M. They are:

> <   Less than
> >   Greater than
> < =   Less than or equal to
> > =   Greater than or equal to
> < >   Not equal to
> =   Equal to

The relational operators always yield a resultant type of BYTE. The value that results from evaluating a relational operation will either be OFFH (*true*) or 00H (*false*). The relational operators have equal precedence. They take precedence over the logical operators, but have a lower precedence than the arithmetic operators.

The relational operators always treat their operands as unsigned integers, and the comparisons are made on this basis. Since the two's complement system is used in representing negative numbers, this implies that a negative number is always "larger than" a positive number.

One additional operator supported by PL/M is the location reference or dot operator.† This is a unary operator which, upon evaluation, yields the actual memory address of its operand. For example,

$$@SUM$$

when evaluated, determines a value that is the memory address at which SUM is stored. The dot operator may also be applied to arrays and structures; for example;

@VEC(4)	→	The address of the fifth element of the VEC array.
@VEC @VEC(0)	→	Both yield the address of the first element of VEC.

Given the declaration

```
        DECLARE    NODE(10)    STRUCTURE (
                   PART(5)     BYTE,
                   PTR     ADDRESS);
```

@NODE	→	The address of the first element of the structure array, i.e., the address of NODE(0). PART(0)
@NODE(5)	→	The address of the first element of NODE(5), i.e., the address of NODE(5). PART(0)
@NODE(9).PTR	→	The address of the last element in the structure.

The dot operator may also be used with PL/M's constant list, which has the form

$$(constant\ list)$$

The constant list, which is a list of constants separated by commas, causes the constants in the list to be stored in successive memory locations. When the dot operator is applied to this construct, the resulting value is the address where the first constant in the list is stored; for example,

$$@('STRING',\ 0DH,\ 0AH)$$

stores the ASCII representation of 'STRING', 0DH, and 0AH in successive memory locations and returns the address of the memory location where the 'S' is stored.

---

†In early PL/M compilers, ' • ' was used as the symbol for the dot operator. PL/M STAR uses either ' • ' or '@', but the latter is preferred, to avoid confusion with structure references.

8.1.4 Statements

In addition to the usual assignment statement, which has the form,

```
variable reference = expression;
```

PL/M also supports a multiple assignment statement, for example,

$$A, B, C = M + N;\qquad\qquad(1)$$

and an embedded assignment, such as:

$$A = B + (X := Y + Z);\qquad\qquad(2)$$

For (1), the value of M + N is calculated and then this value is assigned to each of the variables C, B, and A. In (2), the value of Y + Z is calculated and this value is assigned to X. The value is then added to B and the result is assigned to A. In other words, (2) is equivalent to

```
X = Y + Z;
A = B + X;
```

Conversions may be performed in evaluating an assignment statement if the types of the lefthand side and righthand side do not agree. If the lefthand side is of type BYTE and the resultant righthand-side type is ADDRESS, only the low byte of the righthand side is assigned. If the lefthand side of the assignment statement is of type ADDRESS and the righthand side yields a value of type BYTE, then the lefthand side is assigned the ADDRESS value, which is formed by using 00H as the high byte and the righthand-side value as the low byte.

PL/M supports a number of control structures: IF-THEN-ELSE, DO CASE, DO WHILE, iterative DO, REPEAT-UNTIL,† and a GOTO statement. Compound statements may be formed by grouping statements within a DO; . . . END; construct. The program segments given below illustrate the PL/M interpretation of these constructs.

Example 1

```
IF (A<>B) THEN
Z=X+Y ;
```

The assignment statement is executed only if A is not equal to B.

Example 2

```
IF (C+D>=E) THEN
    X=1 ;
ELSE
    X=2 ;
```

---

†REPEAT-UNTIL is only supported in PL/M STAR.

X is set to 1 if the sum of C and D is greater than or equal to E; X is set to 2 otherwise.

Example 3

```
IF ((Y AND Z)<Q) THEN
    DO;
    A=1 ;
    B=2 ;
    END;
ELSE
    DO;
    A=3 ;
    B=4 ;
    END;
```

A and B are set to 1 and 2, respectively, if the logical AND of Y and Z is less than Q; A is set to 3 and B to 4 otherwise.

Example 4

```
DO CASE I ;
    A=0 ;        / * I =0 * /
    ;            / * I =1 * /
    DO;          / * I =2 * /
    B=0 ;
    C=0 ;
    END;
    D=0 ;        / * I =3 * /
END;
```

In the DO CASE construct, PL/M first evaluates the expression in the heading (I in Example 4). The value of the expression determines which of the statements listed in the CASE is executed; that is, if the value of the expression is 0, the first statement in the list is executed; if the value is 1, then the second statement is executed, etc. If the value of the expression is N and there are fewer than N + 1 statements in the CASE statement, then none of the listed statements are executed. A null statement (;) is used to specify that no action will be taken for a particular CASE.

In Example 4, A is set to 0 if I = 0, B and C are set to 0 if I = 2, D is set to 0 if I = 3, and no action is taken if I = 1 or if I is greater than 3.

Example 5

```
I =0 ;
DO WHILE ( I< =4 ) ;
    VEC( I ) =0 ;
    I =I +1 ;
END;
```

The first five elements of the VEC array are set to 0 in this segment.

Example 6

```
DO  J =0  TO  6  BY  2 ;
   VEC( J ) =0 ;

END ;
```

This segment sets VEC(0), VEC(2), VEC(4), and VEC(6) to 0; the index variable J is initialized to 0 and then incremented by 2 each time through the loop. The loop is executed as long as the value of the index variable is less than or equal to the TO-value (6, in Example 6).

Example 7

```
DO  Q=0  TO  5 ;
   VEC1 ( Q) =0 ;
   VEC2 ( Q) =0 ;
END ;
```

The BY-value of the iterative DO is optional. An increment of 1 is used if the BY-value is not specified. In Example 7, the first six elements of arrays VEC1 and VEC2 are set to 0.

The BY-value of the iterative DO must be positive; i.e., negative increments are not permitted. Since PL/M does not support signed comparisons, a negative increment would be meaningless. This restriction causes some problems. Consider the following DO WHILE segment.

```
J =5 ;
DO  WHILE  ( J> =0 ) ;
   VEC( J ) =0 ;
   J  =  J  - 1 ;
END ;
```

This rather harmless-looking segment is actually an infinite loop. During execution, J will take on the values 5, 4, 3, 2, 1, 0, 255 (OFFH), etc., and in fact J will never take on a value for which (J >= 0) is *false*.

Stepping backwards through an array is a common programming technique, but it is a difficult to implement in PL/M. To overcome this drawback, PL/M STAR has augmented PL/M by adding the REPEAT-UNTIL control construct. This construct has the form

```
REPEAT ;
_____

_____
_____  list of statements
  .
  .
  .
UNTIL  ( e x p r e s s i o n ) ;
```

With the REPEAT-UNTIL, the expression is evaluated at the bottom of the loop and the list of statements is executed until the expression is *false*. Note that this implies that the list of statements will always be executed at least once.

Since the test is performed at the bottom of the loop, the REPEAT-UNTIL can be used to step backwards through an array. For example,

```
J =6 ;
REPEAT ;
   J =J −1 ;
   VEC( J ) =0 ;
   UNTIL  ( J =0 ) ;
```

PL/M supports label definitions in the form

```
label:statement
```

The rules for forming labels are the same as for variable names (see Sec. 8.1.2). Unconditional transfer to a labelled statement is accomplished with the GOTO statement:

```
GOTO  label ;
```

Additional rules concerning the use of GOTO statements in PL/M programs are discussed in Sec. 8.1.7.

The undisciplined use of GOTO's is discouraged since they may cloud the logic of code segments. Fortunately, PL/M provides reasonable control structures (IF-THEN-ELSE, DO WHILE, etc.) so the use of GOTO transfers is seldom necessary.

8.1.5 Built-in Functions

So far, our discussion of PL/M has existed at a machine-independent level; the concepts discussed have semantic interpretations that are independent of the target machine on which the programs will be run. Since the built-in functions available in PL/M take us much closer to the hardware level, some machine-dependent constructs will be encountered.

A list of the PL/M built-ins appears in Fig. 8.2. A description of the functions provided by the built-ins may be found in Appendix G.

As noted in Fig. 8-2, the OVERFLOW built-in is available only if the M6800 is the target machine. OVERFLOW returns *true* (OFFH) or *false* (OOH) depending on the setting of the V bit in the M6800. Since the I8085 doesn't have a V bit, this function is not supported for the I8085. Similarly, the PARITY function, which returns *true* or *false* depending on the value of the I8085 parity bit, is not supported on the M6800.

LENGTH	STACKPTR
LAST	SCL
LOW	SCR
HIGH	CARRY
DOUBLE	ZERO
ROL	SIGN
ROR	PARITY[1]
SHL	INPUT[1]
SHR	OUTPUT[1]
MEMORY	RIM[1]
TIME	SIM[1]
	OVERFLOW[2]

[1]Available on I8085 only.
[2]Available on M6800 only.

Fig. 8.2 PL/M built-in functions.

The INPUT and OUTPUT functions are supported only on the I8085 system. These functions have the following formats:

```
INPUT( number )
OUTPUT( number ) = expression ;
```

In both cases, number refers to an I/O port used in Intel's isolated I/O system. INPUT may be used in an expression. Its value is the byte quantity input from the specified port. OUTPUT is used on the lefthand side of an assignment statement. The value of the expression on the righthand side is output to the specified port. If the resultant type of the righthand side is ADDRESS, only the low byte is output.

Since the M6800 uses memory-mapped I/O, INPUT and OUTPUT are not necessary in supporting I/O for the M6800. Using the AT attribute or based variables and assignment statements, memory-mapped I/O for either the M6800 or the I8085 can be accommodated.

The RIM and SIM bulit-ins are also available only on the I8085. Their format is

```
CALL SIM(expression) ;
RIM
```

RIM is a function routine that can be used in expressions. It returns a BYTE value corresponding to the current setting of the interrupt mask on the I8085. SIM is a subroutine that accepts one BYTE argument. The value of this argument is assigned to the interrupt mask.

8.1.6 Procedures

PL/M supports both function-type and subroutine-type procedures. The parameter call mechanism is call-by-value; that is, assignments to a formal parameter have only a local effect and do not change the value of the corresponding actual parameter.

The procedure heading for a subroutine-type procedure has the following format:

```
<procedure name>:PROCEDURE[ (<formal  parameter  list>] ;
```

The square brackets are used to signify that the formal parameter list is optional; the procedure may not have *any* parameters. For example,

```
F :PROCEDURE( X ,Y ,Z ) ;
```

would be the procedure heading for a subroutine called F that has three formal parameters X, Y, and Z.

For function type procedures, the type of value that will be returned must be included in the procedure heading. The format for a function-type procedure is

```
<procedure  name>:PROCEDURE[(<format  parameter  list>)]<procedure type>;
```

For example,

```
Q :PROCEDURE ( A ,B) ADDRESS ;
```

would be the procedure heading for a function called Q that has two formal parameters A and B and returns a value of type ADDRESS.

Procedure definitions are declarations for the procedure name. A definition consists of the procedure heading followed by the body of the procedure. The body includes declarations for the formal parameters, declarations for local variables that will be used by the procedure, and the executable statements that define the action that will be performed by the procedure when it is invoked. Function-type procedures must contain at least one executable statement of the form

```
RETURN<expression> ;
```

This statement will return the value of the expression as the result of the function call. Subroutine procedures use the simple return statement,

```
RETURN ;
```

as their exit mechanism.

Subroutine procedures are invoked with a call statement;

```
CALL  F( P ,Q ,R) ;
```

whereas function procedures are invoked whenever the function name appears in an expression, for example,

```
SUM = P + Q( M ,N) ;
```

Although PL/M supports only call-by-value, the FORTRAN or PL/I-like parameter mechanism, call-by-reference, can be effected by passing addresses with the dot operator. For example,

```
CALL  SUB(X) ;
```

invokes SUB passing in the *value* of X, whereas

```
CALL  SUB( @X) ;
```

invokes SUB passing in the *address* of X. In the latter case, the value of X can be updated in SUB by using a based variable that is based on X. To illustrate this point, consider the definitions of P1 and P2 given below:

```
P1 :PROCEDURE(PARM) ;       P2 :PROCEDURE(PARM) ;
    DECLARE  PARM BYTE;         DECLARE  PARM ADDRESS,
    PARM=PARM+1 ;                  A BASED PARM BYTE;
    END  P1 ;                   A =A +1 ;
                                END  P2 ;
```

In calling P1 with the sequence

```
X  =  1 ;
CALL  P1 ( X) ;
```

P1 has access to only the value of X, not its address. As a result, the increment of PARM in P1 has no effect on X; that is, X will still have the value 1 when we return to the calling routine.

On the other hand, if P2 is invoked with the sequence

```
X =1 ;
CALL  P2 ( @X) ;
```

P2 has access to the address of X that is associated with PARM. Since A is based on PARM, incrementing A actually increments X, so that X will have the value 2 upon return to the calling routine. The reader is referred to Sec. 4.1, Example 7, for a discussion of the realization of call-by-value and call-by-reference at the assembly-language level.

8.1.7 Programming Examples

The previous sections of this chapter have concentrated on the individual constructs found in PL/M. In this section we will "put the pieces together" and look at some PL/M programs. Our discussions will be limited to a single main module. External routines are discussed in Sec. 8.2.

A PL/M program has the following format:

```
<identifier>:DO;
              <declarations>
              <executable statements>
              END[<identifier>] ;
              [ EOF]
```

Any internal procedures defined for the program should be included in the declaration section. The keyword EOF (End Of File) may optionally be used to mark the end of the program.

Figure 8.3 illustrates the use of this format in defining an exchange sort program. In particular, this program sorts the initialized array A into ascending order. The built-in function LAST, which returns as its value the last legal subscript of its array argument, is used to calculate the upper bounds on the iterative DO's. Note the use of / * . . . * / to write comments in PL/M.

```
MAIN: DO;/ *  INLINE EXCHANGE SORT */
   DECLARE A(10) BYTE INITIAL(17,15,2,3,8,12,20,97,27,32);
   DECLARE (I,J,TEMP) BYTE;
   DO I=0 TO LAST(A)-1;
     DO J=I+1 TO LAST(A);
       IF A(I)>A(J) THEN
         DO;
         TEMP=A(I);        / *  EXCHANGE */
         A(I)=A(J);        / *  UNORDERED */
         A(J)=TEMP;        / *  ELEMENTS */
         END;
       END;
     END;
   END MAIN;
   EOF
```

Fig. 8.3 Inline sort program.

Since sorting is a very common programming tool that is useful in several contexts, a sort subroutine is more appropriate than an in-line, main-routine sort. A sort subroutine is illustrated in Fig. 8.4. This SORT routine expects two parameters: the address of the array to be sorted and the value of the last legal subscript of the array.

Note that the SORT routine contains declarations for the local variables PTR, DIM, ARRAY, I, J, and TEMP. PL/M is a block-structured language; this implies the capability to define program segments (blocks) whose local variables have meaning only in that segment. A procedure is treated as a block in PL/M so, for SORT, I, J, TEMP, ARRAY, PTR, and DIM are defined to be local and therefore have no significance outside of SORT.

In a block-structured language, it is important to distinguish between the use of local and global variables. A variable that is declared to be local to a block may be referenced globally within an enclosed block as long as the enclosed block does not have a local declaration for the variable name. This situation is illustrated in Fig. 8.5. In this figure, BLOCK#1 has two local variables: A and B; BLOCK#2 has B and C; and BLOCK#3 has A and D. The BYTE variable A that is declared in BLOCK#1 may be referenced (used) in the region of the program that is exclusively labelled BLOCK#1 and, since A is not

```
MAIN: DO;
  DECLARE A(10) BYTE INITIAL(17,15,2,3,8,12,20,97,27,32);
  DECLARE B(8) BYTE INITIAL(27,16,34,88,92,17,1,15);
  SORT :PROCEDURE(PTR,DIM);
    /* EXCHANGE SORT */
    DECLARE PTR ADDRESS; /* POINTER TO THE ARRAY */
    DECLARE DIM BYTE; /* LAST LEGAL SUBSCRIPT OF THE ARRAY */
    DECLARE (ARRAY BASED PTR) BYTE;
    DECLARE (I,J,TEMP) BYTE;
    DO I =0 TO DIM-1;
      DO J =I+1 TO DIM;
        IF ARRAY(I)>ARRAY(J) THEN
          DO;
          TEMP =ARRAY(I);           /* EXCHANGE */
          ARRAY(I) =ARRAY(J);       /* UNORDERED */
          ARRAY(J) =TEMP;           /* ELEMENTS */
          END;
        END;
      END;
    END SORT;
  /* MAIN PROGRAM */
  CALL SORT (@A,LAST(A));
  CALL SORT (@B,LAST(B));
  END MAIN;
  EOF
```

Fig. 8.4 Sort procedure.

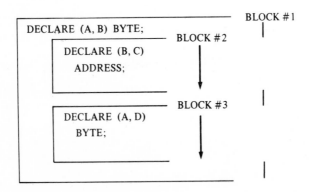

Fig. 8.5 Nested block structure.

declared in BLOCK#2, it may be referenced globally in BLOCK#2. Any use of A in BLOCK#2 would be called a global reference to A, and A would be termed a global variable with respect to BLOCK#2. Note that the concept of a local variable is defined with respect to declarations, whereas global variables are defined with respect to their usage. In general, a variable is termed global with respect to BLOCK$_i$ if it is used in that block but not declared there. The rule for determining which declaration binds a global variable is quite simple; a global variable is bound to the nearest statically enclosing declaration. In other words, in determining which declaration is associated with a use of an identifier, one first searches the current block, then the enclosing block, etc.

Once again referring to Fig. 8.5, the reader should note that the variable B declared in BLOCK#1 can be referenced locally in BLOCK#1 or globally in BLOCK#3. The variables B and C declared in BLOCK#2 can only be referenced locally in BLOCK#2 and the variables A and D declared in BLOCK#3 can only be referenced locally in BLOCK#3.

As noted previously, PL/M procedures are defined to be blocks. In addition, the main program and any compound statements, *which include declarations,* are also defined to be blocks. The previous discussion applies to all forms of blocks.

Given the definition of a block, we can now point out restrictions with respect to the usage of INITIAL attributes and GOTO statements in PL/M programs. The INITIAL attribute can be used only on declarations in the outermost module or block of the program. It cannot be used in internal procedures or nested blocks. This restriction does not apply to the DATA attribute.

The use of labelled statements and GOTO's has some interesting ramifications in a block-structured language such as PL/M. In particular, a "GOTO label;" statement is legal only if label is known at the point the statement is executed. A label is declared by using it on a statement. That label is then known in the block where the declaration occurs and in any enclosing blocks that do not redeclare the identifier. In referencing a label it is perfectly legal to use a label before it has been declared. The following examples will illustrate these points.

Example 1

```
                                    BLOCK # 1
   N:   statement;
   ⋮
   GO TO M:
   ⋮
   M:   statement;
   GO TO N;
```

Both of the transfers listed in this example are legal. The labels M and N are known throughout BLOCK#1.

Example 2

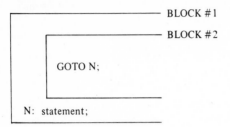

This is also a legal transfer since N is declared in BLOCK#1 and accessed globally from BLOCK#2.

Example 3

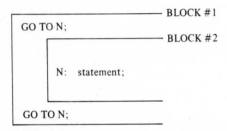

Both of these transfers are illegal since N is declared and known only in BLOCK#2.

Example 4

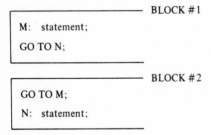

These transfers are also illegal since M is known only in BLOCK#1 and N is known only in BLOCK#2.

The next programming example we will consider is a searching routine. The program shown in Fig. 8.6 uses a linear search to find one particular element of an array. If the element is found, its index in the array is returned; a 0FFH is returned otherwise. For the invocation shown, the number 22 will be found in the seventh position in the array, so J will be assigned the value 7.

```
MAIN : DO ;
  DECLARE A(10) BYTE INITIAL (7,6,8,15,4,3,12,22,39,50) ;
  SEARCH : PROCEDURE( PTR , DIM , ITEM ) BYTE ;
    / • LINEAR SEARCH • /
    DECLARE (DIM) BYTE ; / • LAST LEGAL SUBSCRIPT OF THE ARRAY • /
    DECLARE (ITEM) BYTE ; / • GOAL VALUE FOR THE SEARCH • /
    DECLARE PTR ADDRESS ; / • POINTER TO THE ARRAY • /
    DECLARE (ARRAY BASED PTR) BYTE ;
    DECLARE (I, POSITION, MORE) BYTE ;
    I = 0 ;  POSITION = 0FFH ;  MORE = 0FFH ;
    DO WHILE ((I<=DIM) AND MORE) ;
      IF ARRAY (I) = ITEM THEN
        DO ;
        POSITION = I ;
        MORE = 00H ; / • SIGNAL ITEM FOUND • /
        END ;
      ELSE
        I = I + 1 ;
      END ;
    RETURN POSITION ;
    END SEARCH ;
  DECLARE J BYTE ;
  J = SEARCH ( @A, LAST (A), 22 ) ;
  END MAIN ;
EOF
```

Fig. 8.6 Linear search.

PL/M does not support any constructs to facilitate the processing of character data (tests for string equality, pattern-search routines, concatenation operations, etc.). It is fairly easy, however, for a programmer to define these routines as procedures. For example, EQUAL, a function procedure that tests for two character strings being equal, is defined in Fig. 8.7. EQUAL has two parameters, which are expected to be pointers to (addresses of) character strings. It will return *true* (0FFH) if the strings are equal and *false* (00H) other-

```
/ • TEST FOR THE EQUALITY OF TWO STRINGS • /
EQUAL : PROCEDURE (STR1$PTR, STR2$PTR) BYTE ;
  DECLARE EOS LITERALLY ' 0FFH' ;
  DECLARE (STR1$PTR, STR2$PTR) ADDRESS ;
  DECLARE (STR1 BASED STR1$PTR) BYTE,
    (STR2 BASED STR2$PTR) BYTE ;
  DECLARE I BYTE ;
  I = 0 ;
  DO WHILE (STR1(I) = STR2(I) AND STR1(I) <> EOS) ;
    I = I + 1 ;
    END ;
  IF STR1(I) = STR2(I) THEN
    RETURN 0FFH ;        / • TRUE • /
  ELSE
    RETURN 00H ;         / • FALSE • /
END EQUAL ;
```

Fig. 8.7 String equality testing.

```
EDIT:DO;
        /.             TEXT EDITOR           ./
   TEXT$SLOT ADDRESS INITIAL (8000H),     /. TEXT WILL BE STORED
                                             AT 8000H./

   MEMPTR ADDRESS,
   LINEPTR ADDRESS,
   (MEM BASED MEMPTR) BYTE,               /. NEXT AVAILABLE SLOT
                                             FOR TEXT ./

   CHAR BYTE,
   MORE$TO$COME BYTE INITIAL(0FFH),       /.FLAG USED TO TERMINATE
                                             EDITOR ./

   CR LITERALLY '0DH',
   RUBOUT LITERALLY '7FH',
   SHIFTO LITERALLY '5FH',
   PERIOD LITERALLY '2EH',
   DELETE LITERALLY '08H',
   LF LITERALLY '0AH',
   REGISTER ADDRESS INITIAL (3801H),
   BUFFER ADDRESS INITIAL (3800H),
   (CREG BASED REGISTER) BYTE,            /.USED TO REFERENCE
                                             CONTROL REGISTER./
   (SREG BASED REGISTER) BYTE,            /.USED TO REFERENCE
                                             STATUS REGISTER./
   (INBUF BASED BUFFER) BYTE,             /.USED TO REFERENCE IN-
                                             PUT BUFFER./
   (OUTBUF BASED BUFFER) BYTE;            /.USED TO REFERENCE
                                             OUTPUT BUFFER./

GETCHAR:PROCEDURE BYTE;
/...READS ONE CHARACTER FROM THE TERMINAL.../
   /.BUSY WAIT LOOP./
   DO WHILE ((SREG AND 00000010B)=0);
       END;
   RETURN INBUF;
END GETCHAR;

PUTCHAR:PROCEDURE(CHAR);
/...WRITES ONE CHARACTER TO THE TERMINAL .../
   DECLARE CHAR BYTE;
   /.BUSY WAIT LOOP./
   DO WHILE ((SREG AND 00000001B)=0);
       END;
   OUTBUF=CHAR;
END PUTCHAR;

DISPLAY:PROCEDURE(TEXTPTR);
/...MESSAGE OR TEXT PRINTER.../
/...PERIOD MARKS END OF TEXT.../
   DECLARE
       TEXTPTR ADDRESS,
   CHAR BASED TEXTPTR BYTE;
   CALL PUTCHAR(CR);
   CALL PUTCHAR(LF);
   DO WHILE (CHAR<>PERIOD);
       CALL PUTCHAR(CHAR);
       TEXTPTR=TEXTPTR + 1;
       END;
END DISPLAY;
```

```
MEMPTR , LINEPTR=TEXT$SLOT ;
CREG=01111010B ;                                    / •  MODE  DEFINITION·/
CREG=00110111B ;                                    / •  COMMAND  DEFINITION  •/
DO  WHILE  ( MORE$TO$COME ) ;
   CHAR=GETCHAR ;
    IF  (CHAR=CR)  THEN                              / •  CARRIAGE  RETURN?  •/
        DO ;
        MEM=CHAR ;                                   / •  STORE  CR  •/

        MEMPTR=MEMPTR+1 ;
        MEM=LF ;                                     / •  STORE  LF  •/
        MEMPTR=MEMPTR  +  1 ;
        LINEPTR=MEMPTR ;
        CALL  PUTCHAR(CR) ;
        CALL  PUTCHAR(LF) ;
        END ;
    ELSE  IF  (CHAR=RUBOUT)  THEN                    / •  CHARACTER  DELETE?  •/
        DO ;
        MEMPTR=MEMPTR−1 ;                            / •  BACK  UP  •/
        CALL  PUTCHAR( DELETE) ;
        END ;
    ELSE  IF  (CHAR=SHIFTO)  THEN                    / •  LINE  DELETE?  •/

        DO ;
        MEMPTR=LINEPTR ;                             / •  RESET  TO  START  OF  LINE
                                                     •/
        CALL  PUTCHAR  (CR) ;
        CALL  PUTCHAR(LF) ;
        END ;
    ELSE  IF  (CHAR=PERIOD  AND  LINEPTR=MEMPTR)  THEN
        MORE$TO$COME =0 ;                            / •  FINISHED!  •/
    ELSE  IF  (CHAR<>PERIOD)THEN                     / •  ORDINARY  CHARACTER
                                                        SO  STORE  IT  */

        DO ;
        MEM=CHAR ;
        CALL  PUTCHAR( CHAR) ;
        MEMPTR=MEMPTR  +  1 ;
        END ;
    END ;                                           / •  END  OF  WHILE  •/
MEM  =  CHAR ;                                       / •  STORE  THE  PERIOD  •/
CALL  DISPLAY  ( @( ' ••TEXT•• ' ,CR,LF ,PERIOD) ) ;
CALL  DISPLAY  ( TEXT$SLOT ) ;
END  EDIT ;
EOF
```

Fig. 8.8 Text editor program.

wise. One further assumption is made: It is assumed that character strings are terminated with a special *End Of String* marker 0FFH. This avoids the problem of having to determine the lengths of the strings.

We conclude this section with the presentation of a PL/M program that implements the text editor that was described in Sec. 7.4. A listing of this program appears in Fig. 8.8. The editor uses a function procedure GETCHAR for input and a subroutine procedure PUTCHAR for output. Busy-wait I/O is used in both cases.

If you examine the busy-wait loop tests, you will note that the editor has been set up to function on the I8085. The bit tests conform to the bit settings described for the ISIA in Sec. 6.2.2. In addition, 3801H is assumed to be the memory-mapped address of the control/status register while 3800H is used for the data buffer. The mode definition initializes the ISIA for 300 Baud, a seven-bit word, one stop bit, and even parity. Note that both input and output functions are enabled in the command definition (see Sec. 6.2.2).

The editor is a straightforward implementation of the flowchart depicted in Fig. 7.4. The reader is encouraged to compare the program and flowchart and note the programming techniques that have been used to implement the algorithm.

8.1.8 Laboratory Assignment

Rewrite Exercise 6 following Sec. 4.2 using PL/M. Download the generated code to a microcomputer using the loader you implemented in Chapter 7. Verify the correctness of the program by executing it on the microcomputer.

EXERCISES

1. Assume that the following variables have been declared with the indicated type and initial values:

Name	Type	Value
A	BYTE	01H
B	BYTE	0FAH
C	ADDRESS	1234H

   Indicate the effect of evaluating the following PL/M expressions by filling in the resulting value and type of that value.

	Expression	Type	Value
a)	B − A		
b)	B + B		
c)	A + C		
d)	− B		
e)	A ˙ B		

2. Indicate how the PLUS operator could be used to implement 32-bit integer addition.

3. In the following program, will C be given the value of 1 or 2?

```
MAIN : DO ;
   DECLARE  ( A , B , C )  BYTE ;
   A = 5 ;
   B = -A ;
   IF  B<A  THEN
      C = 1 ;
   ELSE
      C = 2 ;
   END  MAIN ;
   EOF
```

4. Rewrite the following program fragment, using the DO WHILE construct:

```
DO  I = A  TO  B  BY  C ;
   X = Y + Z ( I ) ;
   END ;
```

5. Rewrite the following program fragment, using a DO CASE construct:

```
IF  ( I = 0 )  THEN
   DO ;
   X = 1 ;
   Y = 2 ;
   Z = 3 ;
   END ;
ELSE  IF  ( I = 3 )  THEN
   DO ;
   X = 2 ;
   Y = 3 ;
   Z = 1 ;
   END ;
ELSE  IF  ( I = 1 )  THEN
   DO ;
   X = 3 ;
   Y = 1 ;
   Z = 2 ;
   END ;
```

6. PL/M is highly oriented toward a zero-origin system. For instance,

```
DECLARE  X ( 50 )  BYTE ;
```

declares a BYTE array with 50 elements, where the first element is accessed by
X(0), not X(1). Another example of zero-origin is found in the DO CASE construct, where the first possible selection is termed the 0th case as opposed to the
first case.

Indicate why the PL/M designers selected a zero-origin system by comparing the M6800 assembler code needed to load the value of X(I) into the A register (assuming X and I are byte variables and I has a value that is a legal subscript for X),

a) If a one-origin system is used, and

b) If a zero-origin system is used.

7. Indicate what compile-time identifier-value associations are established by the following declarations.

a) `DECLARE (Y(5),A,B) BYTE INITIAL (0,1,2);`

b) `DECLARE Z(6) BYTE DATA ('LIQ', 54H,17);`

c) `DECLARE NODE(2) STRUCTURE(`
```
        ITEM(2) BYTE,
        PTR ADDRESS) INITIAL(0,1,2,3,4);
```

8. a) Given the following, fill in the definition of MAX so that MAX will return the value of the largest element in the array A.

```
MAIN:DO;
    DECLARE A(6) ADDRESS INITIAL(15,27,32,53,16,4);
    DECLARE DIM BYTE INITIAL(6);
    DECLARE LARGE ADDRESS;
    MAX:PROCEDURE(SIZE) ADDRESS;
        /* fill this in */
        END;
    LARGE=MAX(DIM);
    END MAIN;
    EOF
```

b) How could you change MAX so it would work for any array?

9. List the outputs of this program in the order in which they are generated. (Assume OUTPUT(1) = exp outputs the value of "exp" to port 1.)

```
L:DO;
        DECLARE A BYTE;
        TRICKY:PROCEDURE(X);
            DECLARE X BYTE;
            OUTPUT(1)=X;
            X=10;
            OUTPUT(1)=X;
            END;
        A=5;
        CALL TRICKY(A);
        OUTPUT(1)=A;
        END L;
        EOF
```

10. Same as Problem 9 but for the following program.

```
L:DO;
      DECLARE A BYTE;
TRICKIER:PROCEDURE(XPTR);
        DECLARE XPTR ADDRESS;
        DECLARE X BASED XPTR BYTE;
        OUTPUT(1)=X;
        X=10;
        OUTPUT(1)=X;
        END;
      A=5;
      CALL TRICKIER(@A);
      OUTPUT(1)=A;
      END L;
      EOF
```

11. List the output of the following program:

```
L :DO ;
   DECLARE  (A,B,C)  BYTE  INITIAL(2,4,6),
        POINTER ADDRESS,
        X BASED POINTER BYTE;
     POINTER=@A;  OUTPUT(1)=X;
     POINTER=@B;  OUTPUT(1)=X;
     POINTER=@C;  OUTPUT(1)=X;
END  L;
EOF
```

12. Write a PL/M procedure called SWAP that will interchange the values of parameters. For example, if we have

```
DECLARE  (A,B)  BYTE  INITIAL(1,2),
   X(2)  BYTE  INITIAL(3,4);
```

we could pass @A and @B to SWAP and end up, after returning from the call, with

    A   2

    B   1

SWAP should work for any BYTE values, so if we pass @X(0) and @X(1) to SWAP, we end up with

    X(0)   4

    X(1)   3

13. Indicate the scope of the variable names declared in this program by listing the lines over which each name is known.

Line

```
    0    M:DO;
    1       DECLARE  (A,B,C,D)  BYTE;
    2          A=1;
    3          B=2;
    4          C=3;
    5          D=4;
    6          DO;
    7             DECLARE  (B,C,D)  BYTE;
    8                B=5;
    9                C=6;
   10                D=7;
   11                DO;
   12                   DECLARE  (A)  BYTE;
   13                      A=8;
   14                      B=9;
   15                      C=10;
   16                      D=11;
   17                   END;
   18             END;
   19    END  M;
   20    EOF
```

(continued)

Variable		Scope (inlines)
A	declared in line 1	1–10, 18–19
A	declared in line 12	
B	declared in line 1	
B	declared in line 7	
C	declared in line 1	
C	declared in line 7	
D	declared in line 1	
D	declared in line 7	

14. Indicate the values of all accessible variables in the program listed in Problem 13 at:

    a) line 5   b) line 10   c) line 16   d) line 17   e) line 18

    List values for only those values that exist at the given point of execution.

15. What value is printed by the following PL/M program?

```
X : DO ;
   DECLARE A BYTE ;
   BUMP : PROCEDURE ;
     A = A + 1 ;
     RETURN ;
     END ;
   A = 1 ;
     DO ;
        DECLARE A BYTE ;
        A = 2 1 ;
        CALL BUMP ;
        OUTPUT ( 1 ) = A ;
     END ;
   END X ;
   EOF
```

16. Rewrite GETCHAR and PUTCHAR (Fig. 8.8) so they will function as busy-wait I/O routines for the M6800.

8.2 STRUCTURED PROGRAMMING AND SOFTWARE ENGINEERING

Successful software systems do not just happen; they are carefully designed and implemented, and a great deal of forethought goes into each phase of the development. The terms *structured programming* and *software engineering* are often used in defining the design techniques that are used by professional software developers. *Structured programming* is normally defined to be the production of programming systems based on a restricted set of control structures. These include:

a)   Sequencing

     A ; B

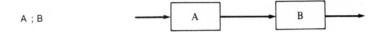

b)   Selection

     I F (e) T H E N
        A
     E L S E
        B

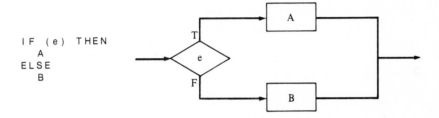

c)   Iteration

     DO WH I L E (e) ;
        S
        END ;

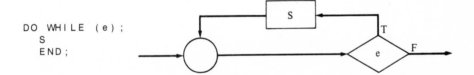

It has been shown (Böhm, Jacopini, 1966) that these three control structures are sufficient for representing all algorithms. In addition, the one input–one output control-line flow of these structures supports the construction of readable programs. In some programming environments, these three structures, together with a procedure definition and call statement, are the only constructs used in producing software. The DO CASE is sometimes included in the set of permitted control structures as a mechanism for implementing the selection of 1 of N possible actions.

Software engineering is a more general term that is used to denote the application of engineering principles to the design of software systems. It implies a great number of techniques, some of which we will discuss in the following paragraphs. In designing and implementing large software systems, one should adhere to the following principles. The investment made in acquiring these habits returns enormous benefits.

1. Declare all variables. PL/M makes this an easy rule to follow since it requires declarations, but the rule should be adopted even for languages that permit default declarations. Every time a default is used, problems may occur, such as a FORTRAN IF test that is never true because the programmer forgot a declaration and is inadvertently comparing a REAL quantity with an INTEGER QUANTITY. It may seem like a waste of time to have to add a declaration for each variable, but the debugging time that is recovered is well worth the effort. In addition, it also makes the program readable both for other programmers and for yourself, should you find it necessary to work with the program at a later date.

Techniques that seem to work on 20-line, 100-line, or even 1000-line programs do not always work on large-scale systems. There is a difference between programming-in-the-small versus programming-in-the-large. The complexity of large-scale systems forces the adoption of a disciplined style that will reduce the complexity factor. Declaration of variables is one method of achieving a more disciplined use of names.

2. Use compile-time initializations to establish values for all variables that are used to denote constants, and do not use them for variables that will change their values during execution.

The DATA, INITIAL, and LITERALLY attributes supported by PL/M can be used to realize this technique. The DATA attribute is most useful in this regard since the use of this attribute implies that the variables associated value will not be changed during execution. Since the use of the DATA attribute expresses this intent, the compiler can take certain liberties with DATA initialized variables. In particular, the compiler can guarantee that it will be impossible to change the values of such variables during execution and thereby prevent an erroneous use of the variable.

Compile-time initializations can be used to create programs that are relatively easy to modify when certain parameters of the program are changed. Suppose, for example, that in a given program the hex constant 0FFH is used to denote an end-of-string marker. This marker may be used in several different places in the program:

a)   in declarations:

```
DECLARE STR$1(5)BYTE
   DATA('ABCD', 0FFH);
```

b)   in tests for finding the end of a string:

```
DO WHILE (STR$1(I)<>0FFH);
```

c)   in constant lists:

```
@('MESSAGE', 0FFH)
```

The use of the constant 0FFH in several sections of the program could create a problem if for some reason the program must be modified so that 00H denotes the end-of-string marker. In particular, each use of 0FFH would have to be located and changed. This problem could have been avoided if the declaration

```
DECLARE EOS LITERALLY 'OFFH' ;
```

had been included in the program and the sections of code that made reference to the end-of-string marker used the EOS LITERALLY variable, i.e.,

```
DO WHILE (STR$1(I)<>EOS) ;
```

Having used this technique, we could now easily solve the problem of changing the program so that 00H would denote the end-of-string marker. All that is necessary is to change the EOS declaration to

```
DECLARE EOS LITERALLY '00H' ;
```

3. Declarations should precede executable code within a block and they should be laid out in a 'human readable' format.

One must keep in mind the fact that programs must be read by people as well as machines. Statements that are perfectly legal as far as the compiler is concerned may be completely unintelligible to a programmer who is not familiar with the program. For example, the compiler has no objections to the following declaration:

```
DECLARE (CHAR, COUNT) BYTE, (NODE,
    L$PTR) ADDRESS DATA (8000H, 9000H),
T$SIZE BYTE DATA (20), EOS
LITERALLY 'OFFH', CR LITERALLY
'00H', L BASED LPTR BYTE;
```

A programmer, on the other hand, would have a difficult time trying to decipher information concerning the attributes of a variable if this format is used. When several variables are declared in a block, it is preferable to use some standard format for ordering the declarations, e.g., alphabetic ordering. In procedures it is very common to see the declarations for the parameters listed before the local variable declarations. No matter what ordering is used, it is advisable to list only one declaration per line. This avoids cluttering and makes the declaration section much easier to read and/or modify.

4. Flow of control should be expressed in terms of the structured-programming control constructs: sequencing, selection, and iteration. The unconditional jump (GOTO) should be used sparingly since it tends to make the logical flow of an algorithm more difficult to detect (Dijkstra, 1968).

PL/M supports a reasonable set of control structures for expressing flow of control. Selection is available in the form of the IF-THEN-ELSE statement and the DO CASE statement. The DO WHILE and iterative DO are available for expressing iteration. In addition the procedure definition and CALL statement can be used to support modular programming. In using these basic control structures, the programmer will find that GOTO statements are seldom necessary.

The structure imparted to a program by the basic control structures should be highlighted by proper indentation. A suggested indentation format for the PL/M constructs is illustrated below. The actual indentation format that is used is not as important as the fact that the selected format should be applied consistently throughout the program.

a)   I F- THEN- ELSE
       I F (expression) THEN
          DO ;

          ————— ⎫
          ————— ⎬ THEN clause
          ————— ⎭
          END ;
       ELSE
          DO ;

          ————— ⎫
          ————— ⎬ ELSE clause
          ————— ⎭

          END ;

b)   DO CASE
     DO CASE expression ;
          —————   / • CASE   0 • /
          —————   / • CASE   1 • /
          —————   / • CASE   2 • /
          —————   / • CASE   3 • /
             •   •
             •   •
             •   •
             •   •
             •   •
          —————   / • CASE   N • /
          END ;

c)   DO WHILE
     DO WHILE (expression) ;
          —————
          —————
          —————
     END ;

d)   DO index =start TO finish BY increment ;
          —————
          —————
          —————
     END ;

e)   procedure definition
     name : PROCEDURE [(parameters)] [attributes] ;

          ————— ⎫
          ————— ⎬ declarations and
          ————— ⎭ procedure body
          —————
     END name ;

5. Subdivision of the task. One of the most critical aspects of defining successful software systems is the subdivision of the overall task into subtasks that will actually solve the problem. In defining these subtasks or modules, one must carefully specify how these modules will communicate with each other. Interfaces between modules are frequently the source of software errors, so they should be clearly laid out.

A natural approach to module specification, and the approach advocated here, is called Topdown Design. In adopting a Topdown approach, one first assumes the existence of a high-level module (A) that solves the given problem. Then assuming that this module exists, one can simply invoke it and be done with the job.

Depending on the complexity of the original problem and the expressive power of the implementation language, A may be fairly close to a language specification or quite removed from it. For example, if we are dealing with a sorting problem, we are fairly close to a COBOL solution since COBOL provides a built-in sorting routine. This capability is not available in some other languages (such as FORTRAN or PL/M). For these languages, A would be far removed from an expression of the sorting algorithm.

In the following topdown approach, one starts with this initial step and then works toward a stepwise refinement of the solution. At each step, we get closer and closer to a language expression of the algorithm.

Continuing with the sorting example, we would start with a first step that would assume the existence of a SORT module.

```
┌─────────────┐
│  SORT       │
│             │
└─────────────┘
```

At this point, SORT itself could be divided into three substeps:

INPUT$ELEMENTS,

REARRANGE$ELEMENTS,

and

OUTPUT$ELEMENTS

—thus giving us

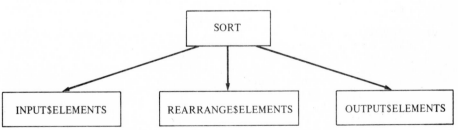

Assuming the existence of these three submodules, the SORT module can now be encoded as

    CALL INPUT$ELEMENTS(arguments);

    CALL REARRANGE$ELEMENTS(arguments);

    CALL OUTPUT$ELEMENTS(arguments);

The original problem of expressing the sorting algorithm is now replaced by the problem of expressing the three submodules and the linkages between the SORT module and the submodules.

The SORT example is rather simplistic, but we can use this example to illustrate the benefits of Topdown decomposition of a problem. In general, the stepwise refinement process should be iteratively applied to each submodule until the entire solution structure is expressed in terms of single-function modules that are capable of being clearly expressed in the implementation language. In Chapter 9 we will return to this topic and discuss a more complex example: the topdown design of an assembler.

One of the benefits of a topdown approach is that the designer is forced to deal with the interfaces between separate modules at an early point in the design. In specifying interfaces, the designer should attempt to make communication lines specific and should isolate modules from one another whenever possible. A "need to know" policy should be enforced in module communication. This implies that a module should *have access only to the data it needs to accomplish* its prescribed task. Indiscriminate access should be avoided.

In a block-structured language, the ability to reference variables that are declared globally is detrimental to realizing a "need to know" policy (Wulf, Shaw, 1973). Consider, for example, the use of *internal* procedures in realizing the SORT algorithm. This situation is illustrated in Fig. 8.9. By default, any variable declared in the main program can be referenced in the internal procedures. This fact often leads to the use of global variables as a method of communication between program modules. Such an approach violates the principle that communication lines should be specifically laid out, not hidden by means of a default capability in the language. In addition, whenever internal routines are used, there is always the possibility of indiscriminate access, since there is no way to prohibit references to global variables.

One method of implementing a "need to know" policy with explicit communiation lines is to use *external* as opposed to internal routines. This technique, when applied to SORT, yields the structure layout depicted in Fig. 8.10. PL/M supports the use of external routines by providing for the declaration of

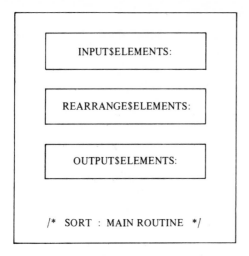

Fig. 8.9 SORT implementation with internal procedures.

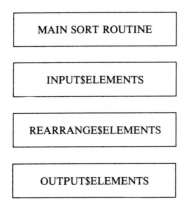

Fig. 8.10 SORT implementation with external procedures.

PUBLIC and EXTERNAL variables. In addition, the language provides for the independent compilation of modules and subsequent linkage to external modules. The following paragraphs illustrate how these concepts could be applied to the SORT example.

Let us assume in the following discussion that REARRANGE$ELEMENTS has the responsibility of actually sorting an array into an ascending sequence. To accomplish this task, REARRANGE$ELEMENTS will have two parameters: the array itself and the value of the last legal subscript for the array. The following format would be used in defining this module as an external routine:

```
REARRANGE$ELEMENTS:PROCEDURE(A$PTR,DIM)PUBLIC:
    DECLARE DIM BYTE,
        A$PTR ADDRESS,
        A BASED A$PTR BYTE;
```

```
⎯⎯⎯⎯⎯⎯ ⎤
⎯⎯⎯⎯⎯⎯ ⎥ Additional declarations
⎯⎯⎯⎯⎯⎯ ⎥ and the procedure body
⎯⎯⎯⎯⎯⎯ ⎦
```

```
END REARRANGE$ELEMENTS;
```

Note that the procedure has been given the public attribute. The effect of this attribute is to make it possible for REARRANGE$ELEMENTS to be invoked from other separately compiled modules. To complete the linkage, a module that needs to use REARRANGE$ELEMENTS must have a *usage definition* of this procedure:

```
REARRANGE$ELEMENTS:PROCEDURE(A$PTR,DIM)EXTERNAL;
    DECLARE DIM BYTE,
        A$PTR ADDRESS;
    END REARRANGE$ELEMENTS;  /*USAGE DEFINITION*/
```

In particular, the main routine SORT should include this usage definition in its declaration section so that it may invoke the external routine. Note that the usage definition specifies both the module name and the types of parameters that will be passed. This explicit form of module communication is much less permissive and therefore less error prone than a global variable default mechanism.

External routines may also share access to simple variables. For example, if module A contains the declaration

```
DECLARE X BYTE PUBLIC;
```

and module B contains the declaration

```
DECLARE X BYTE EXTERNAL;
```

then references to X in both A and B will access the same memory location. Once again the communication link is explicit, not the result of a default.

The restrictive call-by-value parameter mechanism supported by PL/M encourages the realization of a "need to know" policy in intermodule communication. Since the default parameter mechanism gives access only to the value of an argument, it is difficult to inadvertently change the value of an external (global) variable by means of an assignment to a formal parameter. If this capability is desired, the programmer must explicitly set up a call-by-reference mechanism as described in Sec. 8.1.6.

8.2.1 Comments and Readability in General

The maintenance phase of the software life cycle is an aspect of software development that is difficult to simulate in an academic situation. Most projects undertaken by students are quickly developed and then discarded as soon as the grade is received. This situation bears little resemblance to the real world where systems are used and maintained for years. In fact, the cost of maintenance usually contributes more than half of the total software production cost. Since the readability factor of a program is directly related to the ease with which a program can be maintained, there is a great deal of pressure to produce readable programs.

Readability is enhanced by using the techniques mentioned previously—basic control structures, paragraphing, and others. Combining these techniques with meaningful identifier names helps to produce more readable code. Comments are also critical in this respect. For instance, comments should be used to identify the function of each major section of code and to highlight subtle points in the algorithm.

EXERCISES

Rewrite each of the program fragments given below, removing all GOTO's. Include a comment in the revised fragments that indicates the function that the program performs. You may introduce new variables if necessary in rewriting the code.

```
1.  DO I = 0 TO LAST(X);
      IF (X(I) = 'A') THEN
         GO TO FOUND;
      END;

      INDEX = 0FFH;
      GO TO DONE;
    FOUND: INDEX = I;
    DONE:  RETURN INDEX;

2.  AGAIN: I = (START + FINISH)/2;
      IF TABLE(I) = ITEM THEN
         GO TO FOUND;
      IF TABLE(I)<ITEM THEN
         START = I + 1;
      IF TABLE(I)>ITEM THEN
         FINISH = I - 1;
      IF FINISH>START THEN
         GO TO AGAIN;
      IF TABLE(START) = ITEM THEN
         GO TO FOUND;
      IF TABLE(FINISH) = ITEM THEN
         GO TO FOUND;
         FLAG = 0;
         GO TO DONE;
    FOUND: FLAG = 1;
    DONE:  RETURN FLAG;
```

```
3.            I  =  1 ;
    LOOP :    J  =  I ;
              TEST :  I F  TABLE( J )<TABLE( J  +  I )  THEN
                 GO TO I NC ;
              TEMP  =  TABLE( J ) ;
              TABLE( J )  =  TABLE( J  +  1 ) ;
              TABLE( J  +  1 )  =  TEMP ;
    INC:      J  =  J  +  1 ;
              I F  J<N THEN
                 GO TO TEST ;
              I  =  I  +  1 ;
              I F  ( I <( N  +  1 ) )  THEN
                 GO TO LOOP ;
              RETURN ;
```

8.3 HIGH-LEVEL VERSUS ASSEMBLY-LANGUAGE VERSUS CONVENTIONAL MACHINE-LANGUAGE PROGRAMMING

In following this text, the reader has been exposed to programming at different computing-system levels. It seems appropriate at this time to consider the advantages and disadvantages of programming at each of the levels: high-level languages, assembly-language level, and the conventional machine-language level.

Since this text deals with PL/M and microcomputers, the discussion that follows is oriented toward this environment. It should be noted that, for the most part, the analysis is applicable in a more general environment.

In a software production environment, the choice of a language-development tool is dictated largely by economic considerations. There are several factors that contribute to the overall cost of a software system. We will consider some of these in the following paragraphs.

Personnel salaries are related to the amount of programmer time necessary to develop a system. In studying programmer productivity on several large-scale projects, an interesting fact has been discovered: namely, that a programmer will, on the average, produce 100 to 200 lines of debugged code per month. Moreover, these figures are independent of the language the programmer is using (Corbató, 1969). This discovery, combined with the fact that a line of high-level code is equivalent to several lines of assembly-language code, supports the use of a high-level language for software development. For example, it has been found that one line of PL/M code is, on the average, equivalent to five lines of assembly code. Based on the previous figures, one could project that a software system might take five times as long to complete if assembly language was used for the implementation language rather than PL/M (Brooks, 1975).

Aside from the initial software development, personnel salaries are a major consideration in the maintenance phase of the software cycle. Maintenance, in this sense, includes not only the time spent fixing errors that have been discovered, but also system enhancements (adding new features to the system). The increased readability and clarity supported by high-level languages, particularly those that support structured-programming techniques, results in increased programmer productivity during the maintenance phase. It is much easier to successfully modify a high-level routine as opposed to an assembly-language routine.

The previous discussion has argued strongly in favor of high-level language software developments. It should be noted that the investment cost necessary to provide a program-development environment will be highest for high-level languages. After all, a machine-language programmer needs only a pad of paper, pencils, and several erasers. An assembly-language programmer will need an assembler, and a high-level language programmer will need a compiler. In addition, for the last two cases, it will be necessary to provide hardware that can execute the assembler and/or compiler.

Against the added investment cost incurred in providing an assembly language and/or a high-level language programming environment, we must weigh the number of projects that will be developed in the new environment. The investment cost is paid only once, and this cost may be completely offset if a number of projects are scheduled for development in the new environment.

Efficiency considerations are often used as an argument against the use of high-level languages for software development. Since early compilers were notorious for generating code that required more memory space and ran less efficiently than routines written in assembly language, the use of assembly language is often advocated in situations where space and time requirements are critical.

Microprocessor-based computing systems place a higher emphasis on reducing memory-space requirements. This is a result of the manner in which microprocessors are marketed. In a typical microprocessor application system, one could expect to find the microprocessor itself, ROM modules that contain the program necessary to support the system, and various I/O interfaces. These systems are totally dedicated, in the sense that they will continually perform a single function for the lifespan of the system. In addition, they are very inexpensive, and as a result, they have a high-volume market. The competitive nature of this market forces the designer to place a high emphasis on reducing the unit cost of such a system. The cost of developing the software and the hardware cost of the microprocessor and I/O interfaces are somewhat fixed in this respect. The ROM cost per unit can be critical, however. Whether the software developed for a system requires 1K or 2K memory modules may seem unimportant when initially developed. However, when you enter production and intend to manufacture one million of these systems, the cost of the additional memory will become critical. In addition, since manufacturing costs must be passed on to the consumer, the reduction of memory-space requirements can give a product a competitive edge in the marketplace.

Before leaping to the conclusion that high-volume applications mandate assembly-language software development, consider some additional facts. First of all, modern compilers are capable of generating code that represents a 20 percent or less increase in space requirements over assembly-language code. In addition, memory costs are not strictly linear; that is, we do not buy memory by the byte. Memory modules are available in basic unit sizes—for example, 1K modules. If you are dealing with an application that can be encoded in 520 bytes by an assembly-language programmer or 760 bytes by a high-level language programmer, there is no difference in the unit system cost if 1K memory modules are being used. Another fact to remember is that hardware technology is constantly increasing the amount of memory that can be held on a single chip. In general, the argument in favor of assembly-language programming (based on reducing memory-space requirements) is losing its validity as a result of advancing hardware and software technologies.

In considering the run-time, execution efficiency of a system, note that it is common to find that 90 percent of execution time is spent in executing 10 percent of the code in the system (Dardner, and Heller, 1970). This observation has supported the use of a tuning procedure in an attempt to decrease system execution time. Under this procedure, the system is first developed in a high-level language, thereby deriving all the previously mentioned advantages of high-level language system development. After the system is developed, timing experiments are run to determine which sections of the code are executed most frequently. These sections are then rewritten in assembly language to increase the system performance time. The resultant system is usually as efficient as a complete assembly-language version.

As indicated in the previous paragraphs, the arguments in favor of, or in opposition to, a particular method of software development are very much dependent upon state-of-the-art technology. It is generally agreed that the trend is toward the use of high-level languages. The reader who is interested in additional information on this subject is referred to the relevant references listed below.

REFERENCES AND SUPPORTIVE MATERIAL

Section 8.1. The PL/M presentation in this section has emphasized the characteristics of the PL/M STAR compiler. Additional information on this compiler can be found in Marks, Tondo, and Smith (1979).

Intel has released several PL/M compilers. McCracken (1978) describes the most recent 8080 version of their compiler. A new PL/M compiler for the 8086, a 16-bit processor, is discussed in Intel (1978).

Section 8.2. In this section, we have introduced some of the issues involved in software engineering and structured programming. A complete discussion of these concepts is beyond the scope of this text. The reader is encouraged to pursue these issues in Dahl, Dijkstra, and Hoare (1972), Kernighan and Plauger (1978), and Myers (1976).

Section 8.3. The question of high-level language versus assembly-language programming has been debated quite often in the literature. Tanenbaum (1976) argues quite effectively for the use of high-level languages and cites several recent reports that support this position. On the other hand, Halpern (1976) argues that there are indeed situations for which assembly-language programming is the preferred implementation language.

1. Böhm, C., and G. Jacopini [1966], "Flow diagrams, Turing machines, and languages with only two formation rules." *CACM,* 9:5.

2. Brooks, Jr., F. P. [1975], *The Mythical Man-Month.* Reading, Mass.: Addison-Wesley.

3. Corbató, F. J. [1969], "PL/I as a tool for systems programming." *Datamation,* 15:5.

4. Dahl, O. J., E. W. Dijkstra, and C. A. R. Hoare [1972], *Structured Programming.* New York: Academic Press.

5. Dardner, S. C., and S. B. Heller [1970], "Streamline your software development." *Computer Decisions,* 2:10.

6. Dijkstra, E. W. [1968], "GOTO statement considered harmful." *CACM,* 11:3.

7. Halpern, M. [1976], "Machine and assembly-language programming," in *Encyclopedia of Computer Science,* Edited by A. Ralston and C. L. Meek. New York: Petrocelli/Charter.

8. Intel [1978], "PL/M-86 Programming Manual." Intel Corporation, 3065 Bowers Ave., Santa Clara, California.

9. Intermetrics [1975], "PL/M6800 Language Specification." Intermetrics, Incorporated, 701 Concord Ave., Cambridge, Massachusetts.

10. Kernighan, B. W., and P. J. Plauger [1978], *The Elements of Programming Style.* Second Edition. New York: McGraw-Hill.

11. Marks, J., C. L. Tondo, and C. L. Smith [1979], "PL/M STAR User's Manual: Release 2." Computer Science Department, Southern Illinois University at Carbondale, Carbondale, Illinois.

12. McCracken, D. D. [1978], *A Guide to PL/M Programming for Microcomputer Applications.* Reading, Mass.: Addison-Wesley.

13. Myers, G. [1976], *Software Reliability: Principles and Practices.* New York: Wiley-Interscience.

14. Smith, C. L., and C. L. Tondo [1978], "PL/M*: A Retargetable Compiler." Second Annual Rocky Mountain Symposium on Microcomputers.

15. Tanenbaum, A. S. [1976], *Structured Computer Organization.* Englewood Cliffs, N.J.: Prentice-Hall.

16. Wulf, W. A., and M. Shaw [1973], "Global variables considered harmful." *SIGPLAN,* 8:2.

CHAPTER NINE

ASSEMBLY LANGUAGE SUPPORT

9.1 THE ASSEMBLER FUNCTION

As indicated previously, the theme of this text is the study of the process by which a basic stripped-down microcomputer evolves into a functional computing system. The creation of the system interface loader and the text editor were key steps in this process. In this chapter, the final step will be taken—the creation of a resident assembler for the microcomputer system.

Just as the compiler is designed to function as a level transversal mechanism, so the assembler (which is also a translator) performs a similar function. For an assembler, however, the source program exists at level 4 (assembly language) and the output is an equivalent representation of the source program in some lower-level target language. For the subsequent discussion it is assumed that the target language is at level 3 (OS code).

For some instructions, the translation is apparent from the instruction itself. Consider, for example, the I8085 instruction

MVI   A , 3

Since it would not be difficult to record for the assembler, in table form, the association between mnemonic instruction names and hex-code equivalents, the translation of this instruction would not be difficult. In general, the table that provides the assembler with this correspondence between mnemonic instruction names and their hex-code equivalents is called the *opcode table*. The particular form of the opcode table varies considerably depending on the machine under consideration. We shall examine the structure of the assembler in some detail for specific subsets of each of the I8085 and M6800 instruction sets. The case for the I8085 is taken up first.

9.1.1 The I8085S Assembler

The specific subset of the I8085 instruction set for which we want to examine the assembler process is referred to as the I8085S assembly language. Figure

9.1 contains a predefined opcode table for this subset, where the FORMULA codes imply:

$$0 \rightarrow \text{hex opcode} = \text{HEX}$$
$$1 \rightarrow \text{hex opcode} = \text{HEX} + \text{OPND1}$$
$$2 \rightarrow \text{hex opcode} = \text{HEX} + 8 * \text{OPND1}$$
$$3 \rightarrow \text{hex opcode} = \text{HEX} + 8 * \text{OPND1} + \text{OPND2}$$

As we shall see, the structure of this opcode table is very much dependent on certain patterns prevalent between the various instruction groups and their corresponding hex codes.

Opcode	Hex	Nbytes	Formula
ADD	80	1	1
CMP	B8	1	1
DCR	05	1	2
HLT	76	1	0
INX	03	1	2
JM	FA	3	0
JMP	C3	3	0
JP	F2	3	0
JZ	CA	3	0
LDA	3A	3	0
LDAX	0A	1	2
LXI	01	3	2
MOV	40	1	3
MVI	06	2	2
STA	32	3	0
STAX	02	1	2

Fig. 9.1 I8085S predefined opcode table.

For some instructions, the table contains all that is needed for translation: The HLT instruction, for instance, is a one-byte instruction whose opcode is 76. This information may be found directly from the opcode table—as indicated by HLT's FORMULA value (0), its opcode is just the HEX value given in the table. Other instructions require additional information. Consider the "MVI A,3" instruction mentioned above. Through a table lookup it can be determined that this is a two-byte instruction with FORMULA value 2. In this case the opcode is derived using the given formula—that is,

$$\mathtt{opcode \ = \ HEX \ + \ 8 \cdot OPND1.}$$

In this formula, OPND1 is to be set to the preassigned value associated with the register named in the first operand position. Thus, the assembler must have access to a table that lists the values associated with each of the register symbols. A table that gives this correspondence appears in Fig. 9.2. From this Predefined Symbol-Value Table we see that the value associated with the symbol "A" is 7, and, using the specified formula, we have that the opcode for the instruction "MVI A,3" is

$$\mathtt{06H \ + \ 8 \cdot 7 \ = \ 3EH.}$$

The second byte of the instruction is expected to be eight bits of immediate data, so the assembler must convert the character "3" into the hex value 03H, thus completing translation of this instruction.

The formulas included in the opcode table (Fig. 9.1) reflect the instruction mnemonic–hex-code patterns mentioned above. The following examples illustrate how the other formulas are to be used.

```
 i) MOV    C, D
    FORMULA: 3
    hex opcode  = HEX  + 8 · OPND1  + OPND2
                = 40H  + 8 · 1  + 2
                = 4AH
ii) ADD    M
    FORMULA: 1
    hex opcode  = HEX  + OPND1
                = 80H  + 6
                = 86H

iii) LDAX   SP
    FORMULA: 2
    hex opcode  = HEX  + 8 · OPND1
                = OAH  + 8 · 6
                = 3AH
```

Symbol	Value
A	7
B	0
C	1
D	2
E	3
H	4
L	5
M	6
SP	6

Fig. 9.2 I8085S predefined symbol values.

The opcode table and predefined symbol table contain all the information that is necessary to assemble nine of the instructions found in I8085S; namely ADD, CMP, DCR, HLT, INX, LDAX, MOV, MVI, and STAX. The seven remaining instructions (JM, JMP, JP, JZ, LDA, LXI, and STA) have an additional complicating factor—an address or 16-bit immediate value for OPND1. This complication arises because the needed address may be not yet determined when the instruction is scanned. Consider, for example, the following program:

```
           NAME    FREF
           ORG     2000H
           MOV     A, B
           STA     TEMP
           MOV     B, C
           LDA     TEMP
           MOV     C, A
           HLT
   TEMP :  DS      1
           END
```

Here the address associated with TEMP will not be known when the "STA TEMP" instruction is scanned. This is known as the *forward reference* problem; i.e., TEMP is referenced before it is defined.

The simplest way to overcome this problem is to make two scans over the assembly-language source program. An assembler that uses this technique is called a *two-pass assembler*. During the first pass, the assembler constructs a symbol table that associates each user-defined symbol with its appropriate address value. We might view this symbol table as an extension of the predefined symbol table (Fig. 9.2). Thus the symbol table is initialized with the entries of the predefined symbol table and completed during pass 1 with the addition of all "symbol, address" pairs. With respect to the sample program above, pass 1 would complete the symbol table by adding the pair "TEMP, 200A".

To accomplish this, the assembler must maintain the location counter during pass 1. This location counter (LC) represents the address at which the current byte of OS code is to be stored. Maintaining the LC requires (1) initializing it, and (2) updating it appropriately. The LC can be initialized by an ORG statement to a specified value. The LC will need to be updated to a new LC by additional ORG's or to the old LC plus an increment for instructions and data definition statements such as DB, DW, and DS. For the data-definition statements, the increment can be derived from the definition statement itself; e.g., for "DS 3" the increment is 3. For I8085S instructions the increment can be found in the opcode table (NBYTES field).

After building the symbol table during pass 1, the two-pass assembler uses this table in pass 2 to replace symbolic locations by actual address values. The opcode table is also used in pass 2 to replace the instruction mnemonics by their corresponding hex opcodes.

We are assuming that I8085S contains only the instructions listed in the opcode table of Fig. 9.1. We shall restrict immediate data to hexadecimal values and direct addresses to symbols. In addition, I8085S supports the following:

i) *Comments.* If a ";" is found on a line, then everything appearing to the right of the ";" is a comment, i.e., the assembler ignores everything to the right of a ";".

ii) *Assembler directives of the form:*

```
NAME    module name
ORG     hex number
DB      hex number
DW      hex number
DS      hex number
END
```

where "hex number" is a series of hex digits followed by an "H".

To further illustrate the nature of the pass 1 and pass 2 algorithms, we now consider how they might be realized as PL/M procedures. The PL/M procedure PASS1 for I8085S is given in Fig. 9.3. Before considering the actual flow of PASS1, we shall examine the variables it accesses and the routines it invokes.

PASS1 directly accesses structure variable LINE and its members LAB, OPERATION, OPERAND1, and OPERAND2. These members of LINE correspond directly to the syntax label fields, i.e., the label field, the operation field, and the two possible components of the operand field. In addition we shall use the variable LC to represent the location counter, NULL to represent the empty string, and a structure variable OPTABLE with members representing the various components of the predefined opcode table. Declarations for these variables that are consistent with their intended usage are as follows:

```
DECLARE
    LINE STRUCTURE(
       LAB(7) BYTE,
       OPERATION(5) BYTE,
       OPERAND1(7) BYTE,
       OPERAND2(7) BYTE),
    LC ADDRESS,
    NULL LITERALLY '0FFH' ;

DECLARE OPTABLE(16) STRUCTURE(
       OPCODE(5) BYTE,
       HEX BYTE,
       NBYTES BYTE,
       FORMULA BYTE) INITIAL(
    'ADD',NULL,NULL,80H,1,1,
    'CMP',NULL,NULL,0B8H,1,1,
       etc.);
```

```
PASS1 : PROCEDURE ; / *SYMBOL TABLE DEFINITION PHASE FOR I8085S*/
        /*LOCAL DECLARATIONS GO HERE*/
        CALL GET$LINE ( @LINE ) ;
        /*LOOK FOR FIRST LINE OF PROGRAM*/
        DO WHILE( NOT EQUAL( @LINE. OPERATION, @(' NAME' , NULL ) ) ) ;
          CALL GET$LINE( @LINE ) ;
          END ;
        CALL GET$LINE( @LINE ) ;
        /*PASS1 WILL TERMINATE WHEN END STATEMENT ENCOUNTERED*/
        DO WHILE( NOT EQUAL( @LINE. OPERATION, @(' END' , NULL ) ) ) ;
          IF (EQUAL( @LINE. OPERATION, @(' ORG' , NULL ) ) ) THEN
            /*RESET LC FOR NEW ORG*/
            LC=HEX$CONVERT( @LINE. OPERAND1 ) ;
          IF (NOT EQUAL( @LINE. LAB, @( NULL ) ) ) THEN
            /*ADD NEW LABEL TO SYMBOL TABLE*/
            CALL UPDATE$TABLE( @LINE. LAB , LC ) ;
          /*CHECK FOR STORAGE DIRECTIVE OR INSTRUCTION*/
          IF (EQUAL( @LINE. OPERATION, @(' DB' , NULL ) ) ) THEN
            /*DB DIRECTIVE*/
            LC=LC+1 ;
          ELSE IF( EQUAL( @LINE. OPERATION, @(' DW' , NULL ) ) ) THEN
            /*DW DIRECTIVE*/
            LC=LC+2 ;
          ELSE IF( EQUAL( @LINE. OPERATION, @(' DS' , NULL ) ) ) THEN
            /*DS DIRECTIVE*/
            LC=LC+HEX$CONVERT( @LINE. OPERAND1 ) ;
          ELSE IF( NOT EQUAL( @LINE. OPERATION, @( NULL ) ) ) AND
          NOT EQUAL( @LINE. OPERATION, @(' ORG' , NULL ) ) ) THEN
            /*MUST BE AN INSTRUCTION*/
            LC=LC+OPTABLE( OINDEX( @LINE. OPERATION) ). NBYTES ;
          CALL GET$LINE( @LINE ) ;
          END ;
END PASS1 ;
```

Fig. 9.3 PASS1 for I8085S.

The arrays associated with LINE are designed to hold character string values. To simplify the process of comparing character strings, a special end-of-string marker (0FFH) is used. The variable NULL with value 0FFH thereby denotes the empty or null string. The procedure EQUAL (see Sec. 8.1), which is called by PASS1, accepts pointers to two-character strings and tests for equality of these strings.

Dividing a given input line into appropriate fields is the responsibility of the procedure GET$LINE. PASS1 calls this procedure to obtain a new line and thereby set the values of LINE. GET$LINE is assumed to obtain its input lines from the AL code stored in memory by the text editor. If a label is found on the new line, LINE.LAB is set to hold the label. Similarly, if an operation is found on the line, LINE.OPERATION is set to hold the operation. The entries in the operand field are copied into the OPERAND1 and OPERAND2 components of LINE. A single operand is copied into LINE.OPERAND1; if there are two operands, the second is copied into LINE.OPERAND2. The behavior of GET$LINE is further illustrated in the following examples:

i)   Input line: MOV C,A

```
L I NE. LAB ( 0 ) =0 F FH              ( NULL )
L I NE. OPERAT I ON ( 0 ) =' M'
L I NE. OPERAT I ON ( 1 ) =' O '
L I NE. OPERAT I ON ( 2 ) =' V'
L I NE. OPERAT I ON ( 3 ) =0 FFH     ( NULL )
L I NE. OPERAND1 ( 0 ) =' C'
L I NE. OPERAND1 ( 1 ) =0 FFH        ( NULL )
L I NE. OPERAND2 ( 0 ) =' A'
L I NE. OPERAND2 ( 1 ) =0 FFH        ( NULL )
```

ii)   Input line: TEMP: DS 20H

```
L I NE. LAB ( 0 ) =' T '
L I NE. LAB ( 1 ) =' E '
L I NE. LAB ( 2 ) =' M'
L I NE. LAB ( 3 ) =' P'
L I NE. LAB ( 4 ) =0 F FH            ( NULL )
L I NE. OPERAT I ON ( 0 ) =' D'
L I NE. OPERAT I ON ( 1 ) =' S'
L I NE. OPERAT I ON ( 2 ) =0 FFH     ( NULL )
L I NE. OPERAND1 ( 0 ) =' 2 '
L I NE. OPERAND1 ( 1 ) =' 0 '
L I NE. OPERAND1 ( 2 ) =' H'
L I NE. OPERAND1 ( 3 ) =0 FFH        ( NULL )
L I NE. OPERAND2 ( 0 ) =0 FFH        ( NULL )
```

iii)   Input line: ;COMMENT

```
L I NE. LAB ( 0 ) 0 FFH              ( NULL )
L I NE. OPERAT I ON ( 0 ) =0 FFH     ( NULL )
L I NE. OPERAND1 ( 0 ) =0 FFH        ( NULL )
L I NE. OPERAND2 ( 0 ) =0 FFH        ( NULL )
```

PASS1 also invokes the procedure HEX$CONVERT. This procedure converts the character (ASCII) representation of a hexadecimal number to a hexadecimal value, which is returned as an ADDRESS value.

The UPDATE$TABLE routine, which is called by PASS1 whenever a label is present on a line, actually constructs the symbol table. The label (LINE.LAB) and the current value of LC are added as a pair to the symbol table. PASS1 maintains the correct LC value by examining the OPERATION and OPERAND fields. The algorithm for updating LC is straightforward:

```
       ORG  → LC=HEX$ CONVERT  ( @LI NE. OPERAND1 ) ;
        DB  → LC=LC +1 ;
        DW  → LC=LC +2 ;
        DS  → LC=LC+HEX$ CONVERT  ( @LI NE. OPERAND1 ) ;
instruction  → LC=LC+OPTABLE  ( OI NDEX  ( @LI NE. OPERAT I ON ) ). NBYTES ;
```

In the latter case, when LINE.OPERATION is an instruction, PASS1 calls the procedure OINDEX which searches the opcode table (OPTABLE) and returns the subscript (line number) corresponding to the particular instruction. The NBYTES value found on this line of OPTABLE gives the proper increment for LC.

When PASS1 is completed, the symbol table will hold all (symbol, value) pairs needed for code generation. As noted above, the actual code generation is performed in a second pass. A PL/M procedure for PASS2 is given in Fig. 9.4. GET$LINE again fetches and dissects the lines of input code for this pass. Thus the variable LINE and its members are again accessed in this pass, except that LINE.LAB, the label field, is no longer needed. LC and NULL are used again, as well.

```
PASS2 :PROCEDURE ;/ •CODE GENERATION PHASE FOR I8085•/
        / •LOCAL DECLARATIONS GO HERE•/
        CALL GET$LINE( @LINE) ;
        / •LOOK FOR FIRST LINE OF PROGRAM•/
        DO WHILE(NOT EQUAL( @LINE. OPERATION , @('NAME' ,NULL) ) ) ;
           CALL GET$LINE( @LINE) ;
           END ;
        CALL GET$LINE( @LINE) ;
        / •PASS2 WILL TERMINATE WHEN END STATEMENT ENCOUNTERED•/
        DO WHILE(NOT EQUAL( @LINE. OPERATION , @('END' ,NULL) ) ) ;
           IF (EQUAL( @LINE. OPERATION , @('ORG' ,NULL) ) )THEN
           / •RESET LC FOR NEW ORG•/
              LC = HEX$CONVERT( @LINE. OPERAND1 ) ;
           ELSE IF (EQUAL( @LINE. OPERATION , @('DS' ,NULL) ) ) THEN
           / •DS DIRECTIVE•/
              LC=LC+HEX$CONVERT( @LINE. OPERAND1 ) ;
           ELSE IF (EQUAL( @LINE. OPERATION , @('DB' ,NULL) ) ) THEN
           / •DB DIRECTIVE•/
              DO ;
              CODE = HEX$CONVERT( @LINE. OPERAND1 ) ;
              LC = LC + 1 ;
              END ;
           ELSE IF (EQUAL( @LINE. OPERATION , @('DW' ,NULL) ) ) THEN
           / •DW DIRECTIVE•/
              DO ; / •INVERSION NECESSARY BEFORE STORING•/
              WORD$VALUE =HEX$CONVERT( @LINE. OPERAND1 ) ;
              CODE=LOW( WORD$VALUE) ;LC=LC + 1 ;
              CODE=HIGH( WORD$VALUE) ;LC=LC + 1 ;
              END ;
           ELSE IF(NOT EQUAL( @LINE. OPERATION , @( NULL) ) ) THEN
           / •ASSEMBLER INSTRUCTION•/
              CALL INSTRUCTION( @LINE. OPERATION , @LINE. OPERAND1 ,
              @LINE. OPERAND2 ) ;
           CALL GET$LINE( @LINE) ;
           END ;
END PASS2 ;
```

Fig. 9.4 PASS2 for I8085S.

A new variable CODE is used to store the generated object code. The following declaration is assumed:

```
DECLARE CODE BASED LC BYTE;
```

Since CODE is based on LC, an assignment to CODE will store the generated code at the appropriate memory slot. Note that code is actually generated only for operation codes that are instructions or DB and DW directives. The built-in functions HIGH and LOW are used to dissect the DW value and generate the inverted (low, high) form. The object code required for instructions is not generated directly by PASS2. This code is generated by another routine called INSTRUCTION, which is called by PASS2. INSTRUCTION is given @LINE.OPERATION, @LINE.OPERAND1 and @LINE.OPERAND2 as input. The procedure INSTRUCTION also accesses the opcode table (OPTABLE), CODE, LC, and the symbol table. We shall assume this latter table has been declared as follows:

```
DECLARE SYMTABLE(50) STRUCTURE(
    SYMBOL(7) BYTE,
    VALUE ADDRESS)
    INITIAL ( .  . );
```

In this declaration, the first nine lines of SYMTABLE are to be INITIALized with the predefined symbols (A,B,. . . . , SP) and their corresponding values. Note that, since SYMTABLE has been defined to have 50 entries, this will provide space for up to 41 user-defined symbols in an I8085S assembly-language program.

INSTRUCTION has three parameters corresponding to the operation and operands that might appear in an I8085S instruction. In the following discussion we assume that INSTRUCTION has the following heading

```
INSTRUCTION:PROCEDURE(OPERATION$PTR,OPERAND1$PTR,OPERAND2$PTR);
```

and that the parameter/argument linkage is set up by the following declaration:

```
DECLARE (OPERATION$PTR,OPERAND1$PTR,OPERAND2$PTR) ADDRESS;
```

This implies that, within INSTRUCTION, OPERATION$PTR will reference the beginning address of the operation, OPERAND1$PTR the beginning address of the first operand, and the OPERAND2$PTR the beginning address of the second operand. Within this context, INSTRUCTION can be readily implemented using a DO CASE construct based on the FORMULA value of a given instruction: specifically,

```
DO CASE OPTABLE(OINDEX(OPERATION$PTR)).FORMULA;.
```

Thus INSTRUCTION would entail four cases corresponding to the four possible values of FORMULA. The case corresponding to a FORMULA value

```
/ • CASE FOR OPTABLE( OINDEX( OPERATION$ PTR) ) . FORMULA =2 • /
  DO ;
  / • SET I EQUAL TO OPCODE TABLE • /
  / • INDEX FOR THE OPERATION • /
  I = OINDEX( OPERATION$ PTR) ;
  CODE = LOW( OPTABLE( I ) . HEX +8 • SYMTABLE( SINDEX( OPERAND1 $ PTR) ) . VALUE) ;
  LC = LC +1 ;
  IF ( OPTABLE( I ) . NBYTES =2 ) THEN
  / • MVI INSTRUCTION • /
    DO ;
    CODE = LOW( HEX$ CONVERT ( OPERAND2$ PTR) ) ;
    LC = LC +1 ;
    END ;
  IF ( OPTABLE( I ) . NBYTES =3 ) THEN
  / • LXI INSTRUCTION • /
    DO ;
    D16 = HEX$ CONVERT ( OPERAND2$ PTR) ;
    / • INVERSION NECESSARY BEFORE STORING • /
    CODE = LOW( D16 ) ; LC = LC +1 ;
    CODE = HIGH( D16 ) ; LC = LC +1 ;
    END ;
  END ;
```

Fig. 9.5 Instruction's formula = 2 case.

of 2 is given in Fig. 9.5. Note that INSTRUCTION involves a procedure SINDEX which, when given a pointer to a particular symbol, returns the subscript (line number) of SYMTABLE that corresponds to that particular symbol.

Referring to Fig. 9.1, we see that in those cases where the FORMULA value of an instruction is 2, the instruction may be 1, 2, or 3 bytes long. The segment of code in Fig. 9.5 is constructed accordingly. In each case, the first byte (opcode) is determined using the formula given for this case. One additional byte (immediate data for MVI) of CODE is set for the two-byte case and two additional bytes (immediate data for LXI) are set for the three-byte case. Note that for I8085S we are assuming that the second operand of the LXI instruction must be a hexadecimal constant.

The location counter (LC) must be incremented by INSTRUCTION each time an object byte is generated. LC functions as an output pointer for the assembler during PASS2. During PASS1 it is used to determine the address values that must be associated with assembly-language symbols.

When the I8085S assembler is executing, there are two areas in memory that it must access: An input area where an I8085S source program is residing and an output area where the subject program will be stored (see Fig. 9.6).

The input area, which starts at address TEXT as denoted in Fig. 9.6, should contain an I8085S assembly-language program that has been loaded into memory using the text editor. This area will be accessed (read) by the GET$LINE routine during both PASS1 and PASS2.

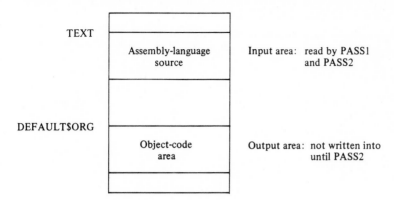

Fig. 9.6 I8085S memory configuration.

The output area, which starts at address DEFAULT$ORG, constitutes the beginning of a range of valid addresses that can be used to store an I8085S object program.

In calling PASS1 and PASS2, the main driver routine must set the input and output pointers:

```
SOURCE$PTR=@TEXT ;
LC=@DEFAULT$ORG ;
CALL  PASS1 ;
SOURCE$PTR=@TEXT ;
LC=@DEFAULT$ORG ;
CALL  PASS2 ;
```

This sets up SOURCE$PTR as the input pointer that can be used by GET$-LINE and LC as the output pointer.

9.1.2 The M6800S Assembler

In this section we will consider writing an assembler for a subset of the M6800 assembler, M6800S. An opcode table for M6800S is depicted in Fig. 9.7. Since M6800 instructions can be used with several addressing modes, the predefined opcode table is more complicated than the I8085S version. In particular, very few patterns (formulas) can be used in determining hex opcodes for a given instruction. Consequently, the hex opcodes are explicitly given in the opcode table.

We will briefly discuss the structure of a two-pass assembler for M6800S, and note in particular those aspects in which it differs from the I8085S assem-

Addressing modes (Mode value)

Opcode	IMMED (0) HEX	IMMED (0) NBYTES	EXT (1) HEX	EXT (1) NBYTES	INDX (2) HEX	INDX (2) NBYTES	REL (3) HEX	REL (3) NBYTES	IMPL (4) HEX	IMPL (4) NBYTES
ADDA	8B	2	BB	3	AB	2	—	—	—	—
ADDB	CB	2	FB	3	EB	2	—	—	—	—
BEQ	—	—	—	—	—	—	27	2	—	—
BGT	—	—	—	—	—	—	2E	2	—	—
BLT	—	—	—	—	—	—	2D	2	—	—
BRA	—	—	—	—	—	—	20	2	—	—
CMPA	81	2	B1	3	A1	2	—	—	—	—
CMPB	C1	2	F1	3	E1	2	—	—	—	—
INX	—	—	—	—	—	—	—	—	08	1
LDAA	86	2	B6	3	A6	2	—	—	—	—
LDAB	C6	2	F6	3	E6	2	—	—	—	—
LDX	CE	3	FE	3	EE	2	—	—	—	—
STAA	—	—	B7	3	A7	2	—	—	—	—
STAB	—	—	F7	3	E7	2	—	—	—	—
STX	—	—	FF	3	EF	2	—	—	—	—
SWI	—	—	—	—	—	—	—	—	3F	1

Fig. 9.7 Opcode table for M6800S.

bler discussed in the preceding section. In addition to the instructions noted in Fig. 9.6, the M6800S assembler supports

i)   *Comments* (signalled by an asterisk in column 1).

ii) The *directives* NAM, END, ORG, RMB, FCB, and FDB. The operand fields of ORG, RMB, FCB, and FDB are assumed to contain hexadecimal data.

More generally, we shall restrict entries in the operand fields according to the addressing mode as follows:

Addressing mode	Operand field entries
Immediaie	# hex number
Extended	symbol
Relative	symbol
Indexed	hex number , X

All hexadecimal data will again be appended with an "H". Note that M6800S does not support direct addressing. The assembler is assumed to access the predefined opcode table. This might be declared as:

```
DECLARE OPTABLE(16) STRUCTURE (
            OPCODE(5) BYTE,
            HEXCODE(5) BYTE,
            NBYTES(5) BYTE) INITIAL (. . . .);
```

Moreover, OPTABLE will be INITIALized as specified in Fig. 9.7. The variables LINE, LC, and NULL will be used as in Sec. 9.1.1. A PL/M version of the M6800S assembler's PASS1 appears in Fig. 9.8.

As can be seen, PASS1 for the M6800S case is quite similar in overall structure to PASS1 for the I8085 case (Fig. 9.3). The procedures EQUAL, UPDATE$TABLE, OINDEX, and GET$LINE function as in the preceding case, although GET$LINE must appropriately reflect the idiosyncrasies of the

```
PASS1:  PROCEDURE;/*SYMBOL TABLE DEFINITION PHASE FOR M6800S*/
        /*LOCAL DECLARATIONS GO HERE*/
        CALL GET$LINE(@LINE);
        /*LOOK FOR FIRST LINE OF PROGRAM*/
        DO WHILE (NOT EQUAL(@LINE.OPERATION,@('NAM',NULL)));
           CALL GET$LINE(@LINE);
           END;
        CALL GET$LINE(@LINE);
        /*PASS1 WILL TERMINATE WHEN END STATEMENT ENCOUNTERED*/
        DO WHILE (NOT EQUAL(@LINE.OPERATION,@('END',NULL)));
           IF (EQUAL(@LINE.OPERATION,@('ORG',NULL))) THEN
           /*RESET LC FOR NEW ORG*/
           LC=HEX$CONVERT(@LINE.OPERAND1);
           IF (NOT EQUAL(@LINE.LAB,@(NULL))) THEN
           /*ADD NEW LABEL TO SYMBOL TABLE*/
              CALL UPDATE$TABLE(@LINE.LAB,LC);
           /*CHECK FOR STORAGE DIRECTIVE OR INSTRUCTION*/
           IF (EQUAL(@LINE.OPERATION,@('FCB',NULL))) THEN
           /*FCB DIRECTIVE*/
              LC=LC+1;
           ELSE IF (EQUAL(@LINE.OPERATION,@('FDB',NULL))) THEN
           /*FDB DIRECTIVE*/
              LC=LC+2;
           ELSE IF (EQUAL(@LINE.OPERATION,@('RMB',NULL))) THEN
           /*RMB DIRECTIVE*/
              LC=LC+HEX$CONVERT(@LINE.OPERAND1);
           ELSE IF (NOT EQUAL(@LINE.OPERATION,@(NULL))) AND
           NOT EQUAL(@LINE.OPERATION,@('ORG',NULL))) THEN
           /*MUST BE AN INSTRUCTION*/
              LC=LC+OPTABLE(OINDEX(@LINE.OPERATION))
                 .NBYTES(MODE(@LINE.OPERATION,@LINE.OPERAND1,
                 @LINE.OPERAND2));
           CALL GET$LINE(@LINE);
           END;
END PASS1;
```

Fig. 9.8 PASS1 for M6800S.

respective assemblers. (For example, labels must start in column 1 in the M6800 case.) The only LINE.OPERAND2 value for M6800S would be 'X',NULL, indicating the indexed addressing mode; LINE.OPERAND1(0) = '#', 23H, would signal the immediate addressing mode.

This version of PASS1 also invokes a procedure MODE that determines an identifying addressing-mode value (0,1,2,3, or 4) as a function of an instruction's operation and operand fields. The correspondence between mode values and addressing modes is indicated in the opcode table (Fig. 9.7). For the case in which the input line is an instruction, OINDEX determines the row and MODE determines the column in OPTABLE.NBYTES to find the number of bytes by which LC should be incremented.

PASS1 again generates a symbol table, which is used during the second pass to replace symbols by their corresponding address values. The PL/M ver-

```
PASS2 :   PROCEDURE ;/ * CODE  GENERATION  PHASE  FOR  M6800S * /
          / * LOCAL  DECLARATIONS  GO  HERE * /
          CALL  GET$LINE( @LINE) ;
          / * LOOK  FOR  FIRST  LINE  OF  PROGRAM * /
          DO  WHILE  (NOT  EQUAL( @LINE. OPERATION, @( ' NAM' ,NULL) ) ) ;
            CALL  GET$LINE( @LINE) ;
            END ;
          CALL  GET$LINE( @LINE) ;
          / * PASS2  WILL  TERMINATE  WHEN  END  STATEMENT  ENCOUNTERED * /
          DO  WHILE  (NOT  EQUAL( @LINE. OPERATION, @( ' END' ,NULL) ) ) ;
            IF  (EQUAL( @LINE. OPERATION, @( ' ORG' ,NULL) ) )  THEN
            / * RESET  LC  FOR  NEW  ORG * /
              LC  =  HEX$CONVERT ( @LINE. OPERAND1 ) ;
            ELSE  IF  (EQUAL( @LINE. OPERATION, @( ' RMB' ,NULL) ) )  THEN
            / * RMB  DIRECTIVE * /
              LC=LC+HEX$CONVERT ( @LINE. OPERAND1 ) ;
            ELSE  IF  (EQUAL( @LINE. OPERATION, @( ' FCB' ,NULL) ) )  THEN
            / * FCB  DIRECTIVE * /
              DO ;
              CODE =HEX$CONVERT ( @LINE. OPERAND1 ) ;
              LC=LC+1 ;
              END ;
            ELSE  IF  (EQUAL( @LINE. OPERATION,. ( ' FDB' ,NULL) ) )  THEN
            / * FDB  DIRECTIVE * /
              DO ;
              DB$VALUE =HEX$CONVERT ( @LINE. OPERAND1 ) ;
              CODE =HIGH( DB$VALUE) ;LC=LC+1 ;
              CODE =LOW( DB$VALUE) ;LC=LC+1 ;
              END ;
            ELSE  IF  (NOT  EQUAL( @LINE. OPERATION, @( NULL) ) )  THEN
            / * ASSEMBLER  INSTRUCTION * /
              CALL  INSTRUCTION( @LINE. OPERATION, @LINE. OPERAND1 ,
              @LINE. OPERAND2);
            CALL  GET$LINE( @LINE) ;
            END ;
END  PASS2 ;
```

Fig. 9.9 PASS2 for M6800S.

sion of PASS2 for the M6800S case appears in Fig. 9.9. Note that the variable CODE is used here as before (and is again based on LC). CODE is actually generated only when a LINE involves one of the directives FCB or FDB or an instruction. In the latter case, the procedure INSTRUCTION is called to generate the actual CODE. INSTRUCTION is the key component of PASS2, and a PL/M version of this procedure appears in Fig. 9.10.

INSTRUCTION first finds the instruction's mode value (MVALUE). This value, together with the index (line number) of the instruction in OPTABLE (found by OINDEX), produces the instruction's hex opcode from OPTABLE. Thereafter, INSTRUCTION consists of a "DO CASE" based on the instruction's mode value (MVALUE). Symbols appearing in the operand field must be replaced by the corresponding addresses found in SYMTABLE. As in the case of the I8085S, a procedure SINDEX is used to find the index of a given symbol in SYMTABLE. In the case of the relative-addressing mode, the procedure REL is used to calculate the relative address as a function of LC

```
INSTRUCTION: PROCEDURE(OPERATION$PTR,OPERAND1$PTR,OPERAND2$PTR);
        DECLARE (OPERATION$PTR,OPERAND1$PTR,OPERAND2$PTR) ADDRESS;
        DECLARE (MVALUE) BYTE;
        DECLARE (D16) ADDRESS;
        MVALUE = MODE(OPERATION$PTR,OPERAND1$PTR,OPERAND2$PTR);
        /·SET OPCODE·/
        CODE=OPTABLE(OINDEX(OPERATION$PTR)).HEXCODE(MVALUE);
        LC=LC+1;
        DO CASE MVALUE;
            /·CASE FOR IMMEDIATE MODE·/
            DO;D16=HEXCONVERT(OPERAND1$PTR);
            IF (OPTABLE(OINDEX(OPERATION$PTR)).NBYTES(MVALUE)=3)THEN
                DO;CODE=HIGH(D16);LC=LC+1;END;
            CODE=LOW(D16);LC=LC+1;
            END;
            /·CASE FOR EXTENDED MODE·/
            DO;
            ADDRESS=SYMTABLE(SINDEX(OPERAND1$PTR)).VALUE;
            CODE=HIGH(ADDRESS);LC=LC+1;
            CODE=LOW(ADDRESS);LC=LC+1;
            END;
            /·CASE FOR INDEXED MODE·/
            DO;
            CODE=HEX$CONVERT(OPERAND1$PTR);LC=LC+1;
            END;
            /·CASE FOR RELATIVE MODE·/
            DO;
            CODE=REL(LC,SYMTABLE(SINDEX(OPERAND1$PTR)).VALUE);
            LC=LC+1;
            END;
            /·CASE FOR IMPLIED MODE·/
            ;
        END;
END INSTRUCTION;
```

Fig. 9.10 PASS2's INSTRUCTION procedure.

and the branch destination. Note that, in case the mode value is 4 (implied-addressing mode), nothing more is to be done.

The main driver routine for the M6800S assembler must invoke PASS1 and PASS2. As noted in Sec. 9.1.1, the input pointer (for GET$LINE) and the output pointer, LC, must be set appropriately before each invocation.

9.1.3 Extending the Subset Assemblers

As noted, the preceding sections have dealt only with small subsets of the corresponding instruction sets of assembler functions. It should be clear, however, that essentially all of the important ideas and constructs are encountered in these restricted cases. Extending the subset assemblers to the corresponding general cases is conceptually straightforward. For example, extending the I8085S to include the "ADI" instruction requires only an addition to OPTABLE. The M6800S INSTRUCTION routine remains essentially unchanged as new instructions are added; a new case would have to be added if one wished to include instructions in the direct mode.

Most assemblers provide some facility for identifying and signaling errors in the syntax of the source code. Such a facility would typically be enabled by including additional information in the opcode table. In the I8085 opcode table, for example, we might include information on the operand types (predefined symbol, immediate data, etc.) allowed for each instruction. The assembler would then check each operand on each input line to see if it is of the proper type. Similarly, an assembler with an error-detecting capability would check to ensure that each user-defined symbol occurs exactly once as a label.

Although most assemblers involve two passes, as outlined in the preceding sections, one-pass assemblers are not uncommon. One-pass assemblers are somewhat more complicated than two-pass assemblers. A one-pass assembler usually maintains a table that indicates those statements not yet assembled because they contain a forward reference. At the end of the single pass, once all symbols have been defined, the statements indicated in the table can be completed. As noted above, however, most assemblers utilize two passes.

EXERCISES

1. Write a two-pass assembler for I8085S in PL/M.

2. Write a two-pass assembler for M6800S in PL/M.

3. Verify the correctness of your resident-system software packages for the I8085S by performing the following test:

    a) Use your system interface loader to load your text editor.

b) Use your text editor to create the following test program:

```
        NAME  TEST
;  TEST CASE:I8085S
        ORG   8700H
        LXI   D,8805H
        LXI   H,8800H
        MVI   B,4H          ;COUNTER
L1:   MOV   A,M
        STAX  D
        INX   H    ;INCREMENT
        INX   D    ;POINTERS
        DCR   B    ;L1DECREMENT  COUNTER
        JP    L1
        HLT
        ORG   8800H
P:    DB    1H
        DB    2H
        DB    3H
        DB    4H
        DB    5H
Q:    DS    5H
        END
```

c) Assemble this program with your assembler, execute the program, and verify that the Q array is assigned the values 1, 2, 3, 4, and 5.

4. Do Exercise 3 above for the M6800S, using the following test program:

```
        NAM   TEST
*  TEST CASE:M6800S
        ORG   0700H
        LDX   #800H      * * *
        STX   PSAVE      *      SET
        LDX   #805H      *POINTERS
        STX   QSAVE      * * *
        LDAB  #0H
TOP   LDX   PSAVE
        LDAA  0H,X
        INX
        STX   PSAVE
        LDX   QSAVE
        STAA  0H,X
        INX
        STX   QSAVE
        ADDB  #1H            INCREMENT  POINTER
        CMPB  #6H
        BLT   TOP
        SWI
        ORG   0800H
P       FCB   1H
        FCB   2H
        FCB   3H
        FCB   4H
        FCB   5H
Q       RMB   5H
PSAVE  RMB   2H
QSAVE  RMB   2H
        END
```

9.2 MACRO ASSEMBLERS

Assemblers will often provide capabilities beyond the straightforward translation of AL level instructions into OS- (or CML)-level instructions. The existence of some of these added features is implicit in our earlier discussion of relocating and linking loaders (cf. Chapter 7, Secs. 7.2 and 7.3). In this and the
next section, other common assembler functions are considered.

Many assemblers provide a mechanism whereby a section of code may be
named once and then subsequent references to this name will be expanded
into the code that it denotes. Such a section of code might be viewed as a kind
of subroutine. In particular, the subroutines considered prior to this point
were written and expanded once and then accessed separately for each invocation. Such subroutines are called *closed* subroutines. The subroutines that will
be discussed in this section are written once and then expanded inline for each
invocation. These *open* subroutines are often called *macros.*

In this section we will consider the macro facility provided by the Intel
I8085 assembler (Intel, 1977), and indicate how such a facility may be implemented. The Intel assembler provides a set of assembler directives that can be
used in defining macros. Two of these directives—MACRO and ENDM—are
used in the macro definition in Fig. 9.11. A definition consists of three parts:
the naming statement, the body, and the end-of-definition marker. The naming statement contains the assembler directive MACRO preceded by a user-
defined name that will be associated with the macro that is being defined. For
the example shown in Fig. 9.11, the macro has been given the name
BDXCHG. The body of the macro consists of all the statements that follow
the naming statement up to but not including the end-of-definition marker,
which is the ENDM directive for the I8085 assembler.

The macro definition itself merely associates the name given in the naming statement with the body of code given in the body. Once this definition has
been made, the macro may be used in the subsequent assembler program. A
macro is invoked by using its name in the operation field, just as an instruction
is used. Consider the following example:

```
                    NAME  FLIPS
      BDXCHG        MACRO
                    PUSH  B
                    PUSH  D
                    POP   B
                    POP   D
                    ENDM
                    ORG   2000H
                    LXI   H,ADD1
                    LXI   D,ADD2
                    LXI   B,ADD3
                    XCHG
                    BDXCHG
                    HLT
                      .
                      .
                      .
```

```
BDXCHG    MACRO              Naming statement
          PUSH    B  ⎫
          PUSH    D  ⎬
          POP     B  ⎬  Body
          POP     D  ⎭
          ENDM               End of definition
```

Fig. 9.11 Macro definition of BDXCHG.

Whenever a macro is invoked, the code corresponding to the macro name is expanded inline at the point of invocation. This expansion can take place during a prepass that precedes PASS1 of the assembler. During the prepass, the macro definitions are first recorded and then the invocations are expanded. The output from the prepass for the example listed above would be:

```
              NAME    FLIPS
              ORG     2000H
              LXI     H,ADD1
              LXI     D,ADD2
              LXI     B,ADD3
              XCHG
              PUSH    B
              PUSH    D
              POP     B
              POP     D
              HLT
               .
               .
               .
```

At the conclusion of the prepass, macro definitions are removed and invocations are replaced by the designated macro body. Each invocation that appears in the program is expanded; for example, if the macro BDXCHG were used at two points in the program, the inline expansion would appear twice.

```
         .                    .
         .                    .
         .                   PUSH    B
    BDXCHG                   PUSH    D
         .                   POP     B
         .                   POP     D
         .                    .
         .                    .
         .                    .
         .                   PUSH    B
    BDXCHG                   PUSH    D
         .                   POP     B
         .                   POP     D
         .                    .
         .                    .
```

(Before prepass)   (After prepass)

Once again, this should be contrasted with the behavior of closed subroutines, in which a single body of code is used in conjunction with one or more calls to the subroutine.

The macro facility provided by the MACRO and ENDM directives provides the capability for replacing identical patterns of code with macro definitions and subsequent invocations. For example, we can define macros for saving and restoring the registers as follows:

```
SAVE     MACRO
         PUSH     PSW
         PUSH     B
         PUSH     D
         PUSH     H
         ENDM

RESTOR   MACRO
         POP      H
         POP      D
         POP      B
         POP      PSW
         ENDM
```

Given these definitions, we can invoke SAVE to store the register values on the stack and RESTOR to retrieve these values.

The fact that macro calls are replaced by an inline expansion of the code during the prepass can cause problems if the code contains label definitions. Consider the macro MAX shown below. MAX's function is to place the larger of the values found in the B and C registers into the D register.

```
MAX      MACRO
         MOV      A , B
         CMP      C
         JP       OK
         MOV      A , C
OK :     MOV      D , A
         ENDM
```

If this macro is invoked more than once, the label OK will appear more than once in the AL code that is input to PASS1; for example,

```
         .
         .
         .               MOV      A , B
MAX                      CMP      C
         .               JP       OK
         .               MOV      A , C
         .      OK :     MOV      D , A
         .               .
         .               .
         .               .
```

```
MAX              MOV   A , B
 .               CMP   C
 .               JP    OK
 .               MOV   A , C
          OK :   MOV   D , A
                        .
                        .
                        .
```

(Before prepass)　(After prepass)

The multiple definition of OK is clearly illegal and would be flagged as an error during PASS1. To overcome this difficulty, macro assemblers must provide some mechanism for generating distinct labels (and references to these labels) for each macro call. In the I8085 macro assembler, this is supported by the LOCAL directive. Labels that are declared to be LOCAL are effectively defined to have meaning only within a current expansion of the macro. To implement this feature, LOCAL labels are assigned a unique symbol of the form '??nnnn'. Note that for the I8085 assembler '?' is a legal character that can be used in label names. The 'nnnn' in the label name refers to a string of digits that will be generated during the prepass, 0001, 0002, ... The prepass never duplicates a generated symbol. The most recent symbol name will indicate the total number of symbols that have been created for *all* macro expansions. The problem noted with MAX can therefore be avoided as follows:

```
                                       .                   MOV   A , B
                                       .                   CMP   C
                               MAX      .                  JP    ??0001
                                       .                   MOV   A , C
                            ??0001 :    .                  MOV   D , A
MAX    MACRO                 .                               .
       LOCAL   OK            .                               .
       MOV     A , B         .                               .
       CMP     C             .
       JP      OK            .                              MOV   A , B
       MOV     A , C         .                              CMP   C
OK :   MOV     D , A      MAX                               JP    ??0002
       ENDM                  .                              MOV   A , C
                         ??0002 :                           MOV   D , A
```

(Definition)　　　　　(Before prepass)　　　(After prepass)

Since macros are really a particular kind of subroutine, it is natural to expect some capability whereby different expansions can apply to different argument values. This suggests the need for some kind of parameter/argument mechanism.

As an example of this, consider the following segment of code:

```
LDA  J
STA  I
LDA  J + 1
STA  I + 1
```

The intent of this code is simply to assign J's value to I, where I and J are word or double-byte quantities. It is very possible that one might require several instances of this word-assignment segment in a program, with different locations (symbols) involved in the different instances. We can write a word assignment macro as follows:

```
WASSIG    MACRO  X,Y
          LDA    Y
          STA    X
          LDA    Y+1
          STA    X+1
          ENDM
```

The X and Y listed in the macro heading are dummy parameters. Actual arguments are associated with the dummy parameters via the macro call; for example,

```
WASSIG  I,J
```

associates X with I, Y with J, and generates

```
LDA  J
STA  I
LDA  J+1
STA  I+1
```

The reader should note that, for macros, the association between parameters and arguments is done on a textual basis; e.g., the character X is replaced by the character I. Since we are dealing with an assembly-time function, the values of arguments have no meaning within this context. Several additional examples of macros that involve parameters appear in the following sections.

The existence of a macro facility can be a great benefit to a programmer. In particular, it can be used to overcome some of the readability problems common in AL programs. Consider the following example: Assume that we have two word quantities whose values we wish to interchange. At the HL level we could write

```
TEMP = I
I = J
J = TEMP
```

Without using macros we might use the following AL code:

```
LDA   I
STA   TEMP
LDA   I +1
STA   TEMP +1
LDA   J
STA   I
LDA   J +1
STA   I +1
LDA   TEMP
STA   J
LDA   TEMP +1
STA   J +1
```

If we use the WASSIG macro defined previously, this becomes

```
WASSIG  TEMP , I
WASSIG  I , J
WASSIG  J , TEMP
```

which closely resembles the HL code and is much more readable than the AL version.

    In one sense the use of macros constitutes the definition of new instructions. Thus, given the definition of WASSIG, programs can be written that assume the existence of a word-assignment instruction. The extension, of course, is defined in terms of the base instruction set. This process can be generalized, in that additional macros may be defined in terms of previously defined macros. Consider the definition of a WSWAP macro that interchanges the values of two word values. Using the WASSIG macro, WSWAP could be defined as:

```
WSWAP   MACRO   X , Y , T
        WASSIG  T , X
        WASSIG  X , Y
        WASSIG  Y , T
        ENDM
```

Note that, in the case of WSWAP, two levels of expansion will be required during the prepass. Thus we have:

```
                                                    LDA   I
                          WASSIG  T , I             STA   T
WSWAP       I , J , T  →   WASSIG  I , J   →        LDA   I +1
            .             WASSIG  J , T             STA   T +1
            .                   .                   LDA   J
            .                   .                   STA   I
            .                   .                   LDA   J +1
            .                   .                   STA   I +1
            .                   .                   LDA   T
```

(continued)

```
      .                        .              STA    J
      .                        .              LDA    T +1
      .                        .              STA    J +1
      .                        .
      .                        .
      .                        .
      .                        .              LDA    P
      .                        .              STA    T
      .                        .              LDA    P +1
                       WASSIG   T , P         STA    T +1
WS WA P      P , N , T  →  WASSIG   P , N  →  LDA    N
                       WASSIG   N , T         STA    P
      .                        .              LDA    N+1
      .                        .              STA    P +1
      .                        .              LDA    T
      .                        .              STA    N
      .                        .              LDA    T +1
      .                        .              STA    N+1
      .                        .
      .                        .
      .                        .
      .                        .
```

(Before prepass)   (After prepass)

The implementation of the prepass within the framework of the macro facility described in this section is fairly straightforward. Keep in mind that AL programs, including macro definitions and calls, will be the input to the prepass. During the prepass macros are expanded and the output is in turn submitted to PASS1. We shall now examine this prepass in somewhat greater detail. In so doing, we assume that macro definitions precede the AL code, so that input to the prepass is as follows:

```
┌─────────────────┐
│     Macro       │
│   definitions   │
├─────────────────┤
│    AL code      │
│   including     │
│  macro calls    │
└─────────────────┘
```

With this assumption, the prepass can be discussed in terms of two phases: a definition phase and an expansion phase. The macro definitions themselves are processed during the definition phase, while the remainder of the code is processed during the expansion phase.

In discussing the prepass, we will use the program listed in Fig. 9.12 as an example. The definition phase is concerned with recording the macro definitions in a tabular form so that these definitions can be retrieved during the expansion phase. To support this phase, a macro table is used. The macro table has an entry for each macro found in the program, and each entry contains the following information: macro name, number of parameters, and the text body. The macro table that would be built during the definition phase for the program listed in Fig. 9.12 is shown in Fig. 9.13. Within the text section the parameters are replaced by numerical indicators, i.e., $<1>$ for the first parameter, $<2>$ for the second parameter, etc. During the expansion phase these indicators will be replaced by the appropriate arguments as supplied in the macro call.

After all macro definitions have been recorded in the macro table, the expansion phase of the prepass begins. During this phase, input lines are checked to see if they contain a macro call. If none is found, the line is submitted to PASS1 unaltered. When a macro call is found, the appropriate text,

0		NAME	MEXP
1	WASSIG	MACRO	X , Y
2		LDA	Y
3		STA	X
4		LDA	Y + 1
5		STA	X + 1
6		ENDM	
7	WSWAP	MACRO	P , Q , T
8		WASSIG	T , P
9		WASSIG	P , Q
10		WASSIG	Q , T
11		ENDM	
12		ORG	2000H
13		MVI	A , 12H
14		STA	I
15		MVI	A , 0FAH
16		STA	I +1
17		MVI	A , 03H
18		STA	J
19		MVI	A , 1FH
20		STA	J +1
21		WASSIG	N , I
22		WSWAP	I , J , T
23		WASSIG	P , I
24		HLT	
25	I :	DS	2
26	J :	DS	2
27	P :	DS	2
28	N :	DS	2
29	T :	DS	2
		END	

Fig. 9.12 Input to prepass.

Name	WASSIG	
# Parameters	2	
Text	LDS	<2>
	STA	<1>
	LDA	<2>+1
	STA	<1>+1

Name	WSWAP	
# Parameters	3	
Text	WASSIG	<3>, <1>
	WASSIG	<1>, <2>
	WASSIG	<2>, <3>

Fig. 9.13 Macro table.

updated with the actual arguments, is submitted to PASS1. For the program in Fig. 9.12, lines 12–20 would be left unaltered. In line 21 the WASSIG macro would be found, together with arguments N and I. N would be associated with < 1 > and I with < 2 >. The prepass would then yield the text of WASSIG as follows:

```
LDA   N
STA   I
LDA   N+1
STA   I +1
```

When the text is exhausted, the prepass would continue with the original input text at line 22.

In expanding WSWAP in line 22, the prepass would have to go two levels deep. This nested expansion can be viewed as follows:

i) WSWAP found

I ~< 1 >
J ~< 2 >
T~< 3 >

ii) WASSIG found in WSWAP

a) T ~ <1>
P ~ <2>

b) WASSIG expands to

```
LDA  P
STA  T
LDA  P +1
STA  T +1
```

iii) WASSIG found in WSWAP

a) $I \sim <1>$
$J \sim <2>$

b) WASSIG expands to

```
LDA   J
STA   I
LDA   J +1
STA   I +1
```

iv) WASSIG found in WSWAP

a) $J \sim <1>$
$T \sim <2>$

b) WASSIG expands to

```
LDA   T
STA   J
LDA   T + 1
STA   J + 1
```

v) WSWAP exhausted.

Note that, even with the multiple levels of expansion, the prepass still consists of a single pass.

As with most macro facilities, the I8085 macro assembler provides mechanisms that allow for a given section of a macro definition to be repeated a specified number of times. For example, the REPT directive functions in this manner. The following segment and its corresponding expansion illustrate this:

```
MACRO

   .                    .
   .                    .
   .                    .
REPT   3             RLC
RLC                  RLC
ENDM                 RLC
                        .
                        .
                        .
```

(Definition)   (Expansion)

As indicated in this example, "REPT expression" causes the subsequent segment of code, up to ENDM, to be repeated "expression" times. Other "repeat" directives, IRP (indefinite repeat) and IRPC (indefinite repeat character), also cause a section of code to be repeated, but substitute different (specified) parameters in each of the successive expansions of the code.

In summary, a macro facility can be a most useful programming aid. Moreover, macros are conceptually quite straightforward, in that calls are handled by a simple inline expansion and the parameter/argument association is made on a textual basis. We shall consider a further possible extension of the assembler capability in the next section.

EXERCISES

1. Explain how LOCAL symbols could be implemented during the prepass.

2. What values would the variables I,J,P,N, and T have after executing the program listed in Fig. 9.12?

3. How would you implement the prepass if it were permissible to use a macro before it had been defined? For example,

```
                    WASSIG   X , Z
                      .
                      .
                      .
         WASSIG   MACRO    X , Y
                      .
                      .
                      .
              ENDM
```

4. Write an I8085 macro named MBLK X,Y,N, which will move N consecutive bytes beginning at location X, to N consecutive bytes beginning at location Y.

9.3 CONDITIONAL ASSEMBLY

A capability for conditional assembly is an additional feature that may be supported by an assembler. Conditional assembly provides a mechanism for determining, at assembly time, whether or not a given section of code should be processed by the assembler. In order to motivate conditional assembly, we consider a situation in which several different types of assignment are needed, e.g., byte assignment, double byte assignment, and triple byte assignment. To support this, we might develop three macros: ASSIG1, ASSIG2 and ASSIG3, as shown below.

```
         ASSIG1   MACRO    X , Y
                  LDA      Y
                  STA      X
                  ENDM
         ASSIG2   MACRO    X , Y
                  LDA      Y
                  STA      X
                  LDA      Y +1
                  STA      X +1
                  ENDM
```

(continued)

```
ASSIG3    MACRO   X , Y
          LDA     Y
          STA     X
          LDA     Y + 1
          STA     X + 1
          LDA     Y + 2
          STA     X + 2
          ENDM
```

As we shall see, conditional assembly provides another approach to this problem.

In the I8085 macro assembler, conditional assembly is supported by the IF, ELSE, and ENDIF assembler directives. An IF directive is always used in conjunction with an ENDIF direcitve. The ELSE directive may optionally be used in conjunction with IF and ENDIF. The two forms are shown in Fig. 9.14. In this figure, sections A, B, and C denote sections of AL code. The two forms are similar to the IF-THEN and IF-THEN-ELSE constructs found in many programming languages. For Form 1, the expression is evaluated* and if it is true, the code represented by A is assembled. If the expression is false, the assembler ignores the section of code represented by A and continues processing at the input line following the ENDIF. In the case of Form 2, the code represented by B is assembled if the expression is true and processing continues following the ENDIF. If the expression is false, the code represented by B is ignored and that represented by C is assembled. Form 2 therefore provides a mechanism for selecting one of two sections of code to be assembled.

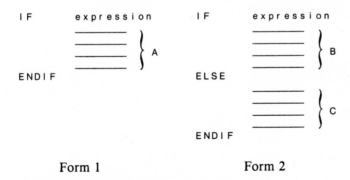

Form 1   Form 2

Fig. 9.14 Conditional assembly format.

---

*This is an assembly-time evaluation, so only values known at assembly time are used. If a symbolic name is used in the expression, the value used is the location value associated with this symbol.

The logical expression following an IF directive may be formed using any one of the following seven compare operators:

EQ   equal
GE   greater than or equal
GT   greater than
LE   less than or equal
LT   less than
NE   not equal
NUL tests for null (missing) macro argument

We now return to the problem of optionally handling a one-, two-, or three-byte assignment. A single macro called ASSIGN, which solves this problem using the conditional-assembly directives, appears in Fig. 9.15. For this example it is assumed that TWOB and THREEB have been previously defined by EQUates as follows:

```
TWOB      EQU  2
THREEB    EQU  3
```

Under these assumptions, we have the following sample invocations and corresponding expansions of ASSIGN:

```
ASSIGN   I ,J ,1  →  { LDA   J
                     { STA   I

                     ( LDA   Q
ASSIGN   P ,Q ,2  →  { STA   P
                     { LDA   Q+1
                     ( STA   P+1

                     ( LDA   N
                     | STA   K
ASSIGN   K ,N ,3  →  { LDA   N+1
                     | STA   K+1
                     | LDA   N+2
                     ( STA   K+2
```

Note that the first two lines of ASSIGN will be assembled for each macro call. The remaining code sections may or may not be assembled, depending on the value of the third parameter.

As is generally true with conditional assembly, the directives IF, ELSE, and ENDIF can be used anywhere in the assembly-language program and not just within a macro definition.

Although not specifically available in the I8085 assembler, many assemblers provide additional features that further enhance the macro and conditional-assembly capabilities. Examples of such features include unconditional branch directives and special variables that may be initialized and modfied

```
ASSIGN    MACRO  X,Y,TYPE
          LDA    Y
          STA    X
          IF     TYPE EQ    TWOB
                 LDA   Y+1
                 STA   X+1
          ELSE
                 IF TYPE EQ THREEB
                       LDA  Y+1
                       STA  X+1
                       LDA  Y+2
                       STA  X+2
                 ENDIF
          ENDIF
          ENDM
```

Fig. 9.15 ASSIGN macro.

during the assembly process. Although these and similar features tend to be quite useful, they also tend to move assembler language (level 4) in the direction of a high-level language (level 5).

EXERCISES

1. Given the definitions of the prepass, PASS1, and PASS2, is it possible to implement the conditional-assembly facility during the prepass?

2. Outline a scheme for implementing conditional assembly.

9.4 CROSS, RESIDENT, AND SELF-ASSEMBLERS

The function of any assembler is the translation of assembly-language code to a lower-level object code. As noted in the preceding sections, many assemblers provide facilities that go beyond the straightforward translation of instructions. In addition, assemblers can be characterized with regard to the machine upon which they are intended to be executed and the language in which they are written.

We have used the term *cross assembler* in reference to an assembler that executes on one computer, but produces code for another. As noted in Chapter 6, the assemblers that reside in microcomputer development systems are cross assemblers. Such assemblers are very important in developing microprocessor-application software.

A *resident assembler* executes on the computer for which it is generating code. In the present context, the subset assemblers discussed in Secs. 9.1.1 and 9.1.2 are examples of resident assemblers. Thus the I8085S assembler is designed to execute on the I8085 computer and produce I8085 object code. In the process of developing these resident assemblers, a special-purpose assembler called a self-assembler has also been utilized.

A *self-assembler* is an assembler that is written in the same language that it accepts as input. For example, a M6800 assembler written in M6800 assembly code would be a self-assembler. It should be noted that the creation of self-assemblers is a byproduct of the implementation of our subset assemblers. When the I8085 assembler (which is written in PL/M) is compiled, the result of the compilation is a I8085S assembler written in I8085 assembly language. Even if the compiler should produce I8085 object code (at the CML level), the corresponding AL code (at level 4) is at least conceptually present. In Chapter 10 we shall explore, in somewhat greater detail, the role of the self-assembler in the development of resident software for a microcomputer system.

REFERENCES AND SUPPORTIVE MATERIAL

Sections 9.1, 9.2 and 9.3. I8085S and M6800S are based on the assembler descriptions provided by Intel (Intel, 1977) and Motorola (Motorola, 1976). The reader should consult these manuals for details on the full assemblers.

For more detail concerning the techniques of assembler implementation, including macro and conditional-assembly capabilities the reader is referred to Barron (1969), Donovan (1972), Gear (1974), Graham (1975) and Tanenbaum (1976).

References

1. Barron, D. W. [1969], *Assemblers and Loaders.* New York: American Elsevier.
2. Donovan, J. J. [1972], *Systems Programming.* New York: McGraw-Hill.
3. Gear, C. W. [1974], *Computer Organization and Programming* (Second Edition). New York: McGraw-Hill.
4. Graham, R. M. [1975], *Principles of Systems Programming.* New York: John Wiley & Sons.
5. Intel [1977], "8080/8085 Assembly-Language Programming Manual." Intel Corporation, 3065 Bowers Avenue, Santa Clara, California.
6. Motorola [1976], "M6800 Cross-Assembler Reference Manual." Motorola Semiconductor Products, Incorporated, Box 20912, Phoenix, Arizona.
7. Tanenbaum, A. S. [1976], *Structured Computer Organization.* Englewood Cliffs, N.J.: Prentice-Hall.

CHAPTER TEN

ADVANCED SYSTEM SOFTWARE SUPPORT

The resident microcomputer software system that has been developed in the Laboratory Assignment sections of the previous chapters consists of the following software packages: System Interface Loader (Sec. 7.1), Text Editor (Sec. 7.4), and a two-pass assembler (Sec. 9.1). These software systems are typically found in any computing system. In this chapter we will discuss additional software packages that are often present in modern computing systems.

10.1 COMPILERS

The use of a high-level language, such as PL/M, in the program-development process implies the existence of some method of converting the high-level code into a language that can be "understood" by the computer upon which the software will eventually be executed. As noted in Sec. 1.1.2, high-level languages usually exist at level 5 in a typical computing system. The conversion of a high-level language program into an equivalent lower-level program is the function of a *compiler*.

The compiler, which is normally a translator, accepts as input a level 5 source program and generates as output an equivalent object program encoded in a lower-level target language. If the target language is assembly language, then the compiler will perform a single-level transversal, i.e., from level 5 to level 4. In some cases the compiler performs multilevel transversals. For example, if the target language is OS code, then the compiler will transform a level 5 source program into a level 3 target program.

The subject of compilation (i.e., the techniques used in high-level language translation) is quite complex; a thorough discussion of this process is beyond the scope of this text. In the following paragraphs we will illustrate the nature of the compilation process by considering some sample program translations compiled by the PL/M STAR compiler. As noted in Sec. 8.1, the STAR compiler is capable of generating both I8085 and M6800 assembly code. We will consider both target languages.

```
PL/ M STAR

OPTIONS  IN EFFECT :     ORG = 768    SSIZE = 100
          LINE  NO       STATEMENT
            1              E1 :DO;  / •   CONVERSIONS•/
            2               DECLARE A1  ADDRESS  INITIAL(1024),
            3                       A2  ADDRESS,
            4                       B1  BYTE  INITIAL(27),
            5                       B2  BYTE;
            6              A2  = B1;       / •  BYTE ASSIGNED TO ADDRESS•/
            7              B2  = B1  + A1  + A2:   / •ADDRESS ASSIGNED TO BYTE•/
            8              END E1;
            9              EOF
```

Fig. 10.1 Conversions: PL/M representation.

Our first example is shown in Fig. 10.1. This is a very simple PL/M program that contains only two assignment statements. Note, however, that both
of these assignment statements involve conversions. In

$$A2 = B1 ;$$

the BYTE value B1 must be converted to an ADDRESS value before the
assignment to A2. In

$$B2 = B1 + A1 + A2 ;$$

the addition of B1 and A1 yields an ADDRESS value, which is then added to
A2. The resulting ADDRESS value must be truncated to a BYTE value for the
assignment. The realization of these conversions in the translated assembly-
language code is illustrated in Fig. 10.2. Figure 10.2(a) lists the I8085 code produced by the STAR compiler, while Fig. 10.2(b) depicts the M6800 assembly
code that is generated. The numbers in parentheses to the right of the
assembly-language code represent the line numbers of the PL/M source line
that corresponds to the generated code.

In translating a PL/M program into an assembly-language program, the
STAR compiler associates generated symbolic names with the variable names
used in the PL/M program. For the conversion program the following associations hold:

PL/M variable name	Symbolic assembly name
A1	Z10550
A2	Z10560
B1	Z10570
B2	Z10580

Note that assembler definitions for the symbolic names mirror the semantics
of the PL/M program; that is, Z10550 and Z10560 are associated with 16-bit

```
          NAME   E1                        ( 1 )                    NAM    E1                     ( 1 )
          ORG    00300H                    ( 1 )                    ORG    00300H                 ( 1 )
          LXI    H,00064H  +  EOP          ( 1 )                    LDS    #00064H+EOP            ( 1 )
          SPHL                             ( 1 )                    JMP    •+9                    ( 2 )
          JMP    $+9                       ( 2 )        Z10550      FDB    00400H                 ( 2 )
Z10550 :  DW     00400H                    ( 2 )        Z10560      RMB    2                      ( 3 )
Z10560 :  DS     2                         ( 3 )        Z10570      FCB    01BH                   ( 4 )
Z10570 :  DB     01BH                      ( 4 )        Z10580      RMB    1                      ( 5 )
Z10580 :  DS     1                         ( 5 )                    LDAA   Z10570                 ( 6 )
          LHLD   Z10570                    ( 6 )                    STAA   Z10560+1               ( 6 )
          MVI    H,0                       ( 6 )                    CLR    Z10560                 ( 6 )
          SHLD   Z10560                    ( 6 )                    LDAA   Z10570                 ( 7 )
          LHLD   Z10570                    ( 7 )                    CLRB                          ( 7 )
          MOV    E,L                       ( 7 )                    ADDA   Z10550+1               ( 7 )
          MVI    D,0                       ( 7 )                    ADCB   Z10550                 ( 7 )
          LHLD   Z10550                    ( 7 )                    ADDA   Z10560+1               ( 7 )
          DAD    D                         ( 7 )                    ADCB   Z10560                 ( 7 )
          XCHG                             ( 7 )                    STAA   Z10580                 ( 7 )
          LHLD   Z10560                    ( 7 )                    SWI                           ( 8 )
          DAD    D                         ( 7 )        EOP         END                           ( 8 )
          XCHG                             ( 7 )
          MOV    A,E                       ( 7 )
          STA    Z10580                    ( 7 )
          HLT                              ( 8 )
EOP :     END                              ( 8 )
```

(a) I8085 assembly code   (b) M6800 assembly code

Fig. 10.2 Conversions: assembly-language representations.

storage cells, and Z10570 and Z10580 are associated with eight-bit storage cells. Furthermore, Z10550 and Z10570 are given initial values.

Note that, in both listings, the symbols are defined before the executable code for the assignment statements is generated. This implies the need for an instruction that will "jump over" these definitions during execution. The instruction "JMP $+9" accomplishes this for the I8085, while "JMP * +9" is used for the M6800. The symbols "$" and " * " are used in these respective assembly languages to denote the PC value of the instruction in which they are used—for this case, the address of the location where the JMP opcode resides.

It is possible to relate each PL/M statement with the code generated by the STAR compiler for that statement. For example, the PL/M statement

$$A2 \ = \ B1 \ ;$$

generates the following M6800 assembly code:

```
          LDAA     Z10570
          STAA     Z10560 + 1
          CLR      Z10560
```

Note that the CLR instruction is necessary in performing the BYTE-to-ADDRESS assignment.

The M6800 assembly code generated for the second assignment, that is,

```
LDAA  Z10570
CLRB
ADDA  Z10550 + 1
ADCB  Z10550
ADDA  Z10560 + 1
ADCB  Z10560
STAA  Z10580
```

illustrates a basic design strategy used in the code-generation scheme for the M6800. In particular, in generating code for expressions, the STAR compiler will, if possible, hold temporary values in the A (low-byte) and B (high-byte) registers. Note that only the low byte is assigned to Z10580 as a result of the ADDRESS-to-BYTE assignment.

The second compilation example we will consider is listed in Fig. 10.3. This problem illustrates a fundamental name-accessing problem that must be resolved in translating block-structured languages. Note that, in the nested-block example, nine variables are declared: three in each block. During the code-generation phase of the translation process, care must be taken in asso-

```
PL/M STAR


OPTIONS IN EFFECT:  ORG = 768      SSIZE = 100
         LINE NO     STATEMENT
            1         E2:DO;/•  NESTED DO--END BLOCKS•/
            2             DECLARE(A,B,C)  BYTE;
            3             A = 1;
            4             B = 2;
            5             C = 3;
            6                 DO; DECLARE (A,B,D) BYTE;
            7                     A = 4;
            8                     B = 5;
            9                     D = 6
           10                     C = A + B + D;    /•   GLOBAL USE OF C•/
           11                 END;
           12                 DO;DECLARE (B,C,D) BYTE;
           13                     B = 7;
           14                     C = 8;
           15                     D = A + B + C;/•       GLOBAL USE OF A•/
           16                 END;
           17             A = B + C;
           18             END E2;
           19             EOF
```

Fig. 10.3 Nested DO—END blocks: PL/M representation.

ciating a variable reference with the appropriate variable definition. Consider, for example, line 10 of the nested-block example, that is,

$$C \; = \; A \; + \; B \; + \; D \, ;$$

The variables A, B, and D used in this line refer to local variables, whereas the C reference is to the global variable declared in the outer block.

The STAR compiler uses a straightforward method for distinguishing between similarly named variables. At the assembly-language level, each variable used in the PL/M source program is given a unique symbolic name.* Consider, for example, the M6800 assembly code generated for the nested-block example (see Fig. 10.4). The variable name/symbolic assembly name associations for this example are listed below.

PL/M variable name		Symbolic assembly name
OUTER BLOCK	A B C	Z10550 Z10560 Z10570
FIRST INNER BLOCK	A B D	Z10580 Z10590 Z10600
SECOND INNER BLOCK	B C D	Z10610 Z10620 Z10630

The use of distinct symbolic names at the assembly-code level does not solve the problem of associating a particular variable reference with the appropriate symbolic name. The solution of this problem requires that the compiler maintain a symbol table, which pairs variable names to symbolic names. The symbol table must be updated upon block entry and block exit. For example, when the compiler is translating code in the outer block, the symbol table would have the following format:

Static chain pointer:	Ω
A	Z10550
B	Z10560
C	Z10570

---

*This technique can be criticized for its inefficient use of memory. However, the resulting generated code highlights the issue we wish to consider, i.e., resolution of name accessing for block structured languages. In addition, PL/M as defined by Intel does not support the runtime storage administration that is typically found in block-structured languages.

```
            NAM     E2                          ( 1 )
            ORG     00300H                      ( 1 )
            LDS     #00064H+EOP                 ( 1 )
            JMP     * +6                        ( 2 )
Z10550      RMB     1                           ( 2 )
Z10560      RMB     1                           ( 2 )
Z10570      RMB     1                           ( 2 )
            LDAA    #001H                       ( 3 )
            STAA    Z10550                      ( 3 )
            LDAA    #002H                       ( 4 )
            STAA    Z10560                      ( 4 )
            LDAA    #003H                       ( 5 )
            STAA    Z10570                      ( 5 )
            JMP     * +6                        ( 6 )
Z10580      RMB     1                           ( 6 )
Z10590      RMB     1                           ( 6 )
Z10600      RMB     1                           ( 6 )
            LDAA    #004H                       ( 7 )
            STAA    Z10580                      ( 7 )
            LDAA    #005H                       ( 8 )
            STAA    Z10590                      ( 8 )
            LDAA    #006H                       ( 9 )
            STAA    Z10600                      ( 9 )
            LDAA    Z10580                      ( 10 )
            ADDA    Z10590                      ( 10 )
            ADDA    Z10600                      ( 10 )
            STAA    Z10570                      ( 10 )
            JMP     * +6                        ( 12 )
Z10610      RMB     1                           ( 12 )
Z10620      RMB     1                           ( 12 )
Z10630      RMB     1                           ( 12 )
            LDAA    #007H                       ( 13 )
            STAA    Z10610                      ( 13 )
            LDAA    #008H                       ( 14 )
            STAA    Z10620                      ( 14 )
            LDAA    Z10550                      ( 15 )
            ADDA    Z10610                      ( 15 )
            ADDA    Z10620                      ( 15 )
            STAA    Z10630                      ( 15 )
            LDAA    Z10560                      ( 17 )
            ADDA    Z10570                      ( 17 )
            STAA    Z10550                      ( 17 )
            SWI                                 ( 18 )
EOP         END                                 ( 18 )
```

Fig. 10.4 Nested DO—END blocks: M6800 assembly-language representation.

A static chain pointer must be included for each block. This pointer will reference the statically enclosing program block. Since the outer block is not enclosed by another block, a null pointer (Ω) is used as the static chain value for this block.

In entering the first inner block, the symbol table must be updated to include the local declarations for A, B, and D, thus:

Static chain pointer:	Ω
A	Z10550
B	Z10560
C	Z10570
Static chain pointer:	
A	Z10580
B	Z10590
D	Z10600

The static chain pointer for the inner block will of course reference the outer block. This pointer is used in solving the variable-reference problem. The algorithm used in solving this problem may be stated as:

Given a reference use of a PL/M variable 'i', the symbolic name associated with 'i' can be determined as follows:

Step 1. Let B denote the current local block. This will always be the last block entry in the symbol table.

Step 2.
```
if 'i' is in B then
     return the associated symbolic name
else
     if the static chain pointer of B = Ω
     then report variable not declared
     else
          Set B = the block referenced by
          the static chain pointer of B
          and reapply Step 2.
```

Consider the application of this algorithm in generating code for line 10 of the nested-block example shown in Fig. 10.3. This line references four variables C, A, B, and D. Using the symbol table given above that will exist while the compiler is scanning the inner block, variables A, B, and D will be found in the current local block and will be associated with Z10580, Z10590, and Z10600, respectively. On the other hand, C will not be found in the local block, and this will imply a search along the static chain; C will then be found in the outer block, and the symbolic name Z10570 will be returned. Assuming M6800 as the target machine, this will result in the following generated code (see Fig. 10.4).

$$\begin{array}{ll} \text{LDAA} & \text{Z10580} \\ \text{ADDA} & \text{Z10590} \\ \text{ADDA} & \text{Z10600} \\ \text{STAA} & \text{Z10570} \end{array}$$

In exiting the first inner block (that is, when the compiler detects the END statement in line 11 of the nested-block example), the symbol-table entries for the inner block will be deleted. The same technique will be used for the second inner block. For example, while scanning the second block, the symbol table would have the following organization:

Static chain pointer:	Ω
A	Z10550
B	Z10560
C	Z10570
Static chain pointer:	
B	Z10610
C	Z10620
D	Z10630

For the nested-block example, the static chain pointer always referenced the block that both statically enclosed and dynamically preceded (was executed prior to) the current local block. An exception to this is noted for procedures. Consider, for example, the PL/M procedure shown in Fig. 10.5. The I8085 generated code for this example is listed in Fig. 10.6. When the compiler is scanning line 6 of this program, the symbol table will be configured as

Static chain pointer:	Ω
A	Z10550
BUMP	Z10560

The generated I8085 code for this line (see Fig. 10.5) would then be

$$\text{MVI A,001H}$$
$$\text{STA Z10550}$$

```
PL/ M  STAR

OPTIONS  IN  EFFECT :    ORG = 256    SSIZE = 100
            LINE  NO      STATEMENT
              1           E3 : DO ; / •  NESTED  PROCEDURE   • /
              2             DECLARE  A  BYTE ;
              3             BUMP :  PROCEDURE ;
              4                 A  =  A + 1 ;
              5                 END  BUMP ;
              6             A  =  1 ;
              7                 DO ;  DECLARE  A  BYTE ;
              8                     A  =  2 ;
              9                     CALL  BUMP ;
             10                 END ;
             11           END  E3 ;
             12           EOF
```

Fig. 10.5 Nested procedure PL/M representation.

```
                    NAME   E3                              ( 1 )
                    ORG    00100H                          ( 1 )
                    LXI    H,00064H+EOP                    ( 1 )
                    SPHL                                   ( 1 )
                    JMP    $+4                             ( 2 )
     Z10550 :       DS     1                               ( 2 )
                    JMP    L10010                          ( 3 )
     Z10560 :       LDA    Z10550                          ( 4 )
                    ADI    001H                            ( 4 )
                    MOV    E,A                             ( 4 )
                    MOV    A,E                             ( 4 )
                    STA    Z10550                          ( 4 )
                    RET                                    ( 5 )
     L10010 :       MVI    A,001H                          ( 6 )
                    STA    Z10550                          ( 6 )
                    JMP    $+4                             ( 7 )
     Z10570 :       DS     1                               ( 7 )
                    MVI    A,002H                          ( 8 )
                    STA    Z10570                          ( 8 )
                    CALL   Z10560                          ( 9 )
                    HLT                                    ( 11 )
     EOP :          END                                    ( 11 )
```

Fig. 10.6 Nested procedure: I8085 assembly-language representation.

In scanning line 8, the symbol table would be

Static chain pointer:	Ω
A	Z10550
BUMP	Z10560
Static chain pointer:	
A	Z10570

The generated code for line 8 is

$$\text{MVI A ,002H}$$
$$\text{STA Z10570}$$

In this last case, the static chain pointer of the bottom symbol-table entry references the outer block, which both statically encloses and dynamically precedes the inner block. Consider, however, what the symbol-table configuration should be when the compiler is scanning line 4 of the nested-procedure example. The procedure BUMP is itself a block, and the symbol table must be augmented to include the static chain pointer for this block. Since BUMP has no parameters or local variables, no additional entries are necessary. The question is which block will be referenced by BUMP's static chain pointer. The answer is found in the PL/M language specification; the chain pointer must reference the statically enclosing block. Given this configuration,

Static chain pointer:	Ω
A	Z10550
BUMP	Z10560
Static chain pointer:	•

the code generated for line 4 would be

> LDA Z10550
> ADI   001H
> MOV E,A

Note that the dynamically preceding block, the nested DO—END block, is not accessible when the compiler is scanning the procedure.

The last example we will consider is the BASED-variable example shown in Fig. 10.7. The I8085 assembly code generated for this program by the STAR compiler is listed in Fig. 10.8. Note that indirect addressing through the H and L register pair has been used to implement the indirection implied by BASED variables. For example, the code generated for line 6 of the PL/M representation, 'C = 1;' is

> LHLD   Z10570
> MVI   M,001H

where Z10570 is the symbolic name associated with C.

```
PL/M STAR

OPTIONS IN EFFECT:   ORG = 256      SSIZE = 100
            LINE NO      STATEMENT
               1         E4:DO;/* BASED VARIABLES */
               2           DECLARE (A,B)  BYTE,
               3             PTR          ADDRESS,
               4             C            BASED PTR BYTE;
               5           PTR = .A:
               6           C = 1;
               7           PTR = .B;
               8           C = 2;
               9           END E4;
              10         EOF
```

Fig. 10.7 BASED variables: PL/M representation.

```
            NAME    E4                      ( 1 )
            ORG     00100H                  ( 1 )
            LXI     H,00064H+EOP            ( 1 )
            SPHL                            ( 1 )
            JMP     $+7                     ( 2 )
Z10550 :    DS      1                       ( 2 )
Z10560 :    DS      1                       ( 2 )
Z10570 :    DS      2                       ( 3 )
            LXI     D,Z10550                ( 5 )
            XCHG                            ( 5 )
            SHLD    Z10570                  ( 5 )
            LHLD    Z10570                  ( 6 )
            MVI     M,001H                  ( 6 )
            LXI     D,Z10560                ( 7 )
            XCHG                            ( 7 )
            SHLD    Z10570                  ( 7 )
            LHLD    Z10570                  ( 8 )
            MVI     M,002H                  ( 8 )
            HLT                             ( 9 )
EOP :       END                             ( 9 )
```

Fig. 10.8 BASED variables: I8085 assembly-language representation.

10.1.1 System Bootstrapping Procedures

System bootstrapping is a term that is used to define the process of creating a software system for a machine that initially has no software support. As noted in the previous chapters, the bootstrapping procedure used in creating the resident microcomputer software support system consisted of the following:

a) Implementing the system interface loader in assembly language,

b) Implementing the text editor in assembly language, and

c) Implementing a two-pass assembler in PL/M.

In this section we will consider the procedures that might be used in creating a resident compiler system.

In Sec. 9.4, the concept of a self-assembler was introduced. A self-assembler is really a special case of a self-translator, where a *self-translator* is defined to be a translator that is implemented in the same language that it accepts as input. In addition to a self-assembler, another example of a self-translator would be a self-compiler, for example, a PL/M compiler written in PL/M. Self-compilers can be used in the same way that self-assemblers are used in generating software systems for an initially unsupported machine.

To illustrate some of the methods that might be used to generate resident software for a machine, we consider some specific examples. In these examples, the notation $C_Z^{X \rightarrow Y}$ is used to denote a compiler for some language X that is written in language Z and produces object code for language Y. We will assume that the generated object code can be executed by machine Y without further modification.

Example 1 Assume that we wish to create a resident PL/M compiler system for the M6800. For this example we will also assume that we have some large machine that has a PL/I compiler, but no PL/M cross-compiler. Our solution involves three phases, as follows:

i) Write a PL/M compiler in PL/I that generates M6800 object code. In terms of our special notation, this is

$$C_{PL/I}^{PL/M \rightarrow M6800}$$

ii) Write a PL/M compiler in PL/M that generates M6800 object code; i.e., create the self-compiler denoted by

$$C_{PL/M}^{PL/M \rightarrow M6800}$$

iii) Run $C_{PL/I}^{PL/M \rightarrow M6800}$ on the large machine using $C_{PL/M}^{PL/M \rightarrow M6800}$ as input. The output will be a M6800 hex representation of

$$C_{M6800}^{PL/M \rightarrow M6800},$$

which is the desired result. A loader can then be used to load the hex object code and thereby install a resident PL/M compiler on the M6800.

Example 2 For this example, we will assume that we wish to create a resident PL/M compiler for the I8085. We will also assume that, on some larger development machine, we have a PL/M cross-compiler that produces I8085 hex object code. The cross-compiler will be denoted by

$$C_{LARGE}^{PL/M \rightarrow I8085}.$$

LARGE is used to denote the object code of the development machine. If, for example, the development machine is an IBM 370, then LARGE denotes 370 object code. Our solution in this example involves only two steps:

i) Write a self-compiler for PL/M; call it

$$C_{PL/M}^{PL/M \rightarrow I8085}.$$

ii) Run $C_{PL/M}^{PL/M \rightarrow I8085}$ on the development machine, using this program itself $(C_{PL/M}^{PL/M \rightarrow I8085})$ as input. The output from this run is

$$C_{I8085}^{PL/M \rightarrow I8085},$$

the desired resident compiler.

It should be noted that in both this section and the previous chapters we have relied on high-level languages to implement the major components of a resident software support system. This is consistent with the arguments in favor of the use of high-level languages that were presented in Sec. 8.5. For both application programs and system programs, the use of high-level language development is the rule rather than the exception.

EXERCISES

1. With respect to the conversion example depicted in Figs. 10.1 and 10.2, indicate
    the I8085 code generated by STAR for each of the following assignment state-
    ments.

    a) A2 = B1 ;
    b) B2 = B1 + A1 + A2 ;

    As indicated in the text, in generating M6800 code, STAR uses registers A (low-
    byte) and B (high-byte) to hold the temporary results of an expression evalua-
    tion. Where does the STAR compiler hold these temporary results in I8085
    code generation?

2. Indicate the symbol-table contents that would exist when the compiler is scan-
    ning line 17 of the nested-block example (Fig. 10.3).

3. In the text we considered the I8085 code that would be generated for a BASED-
    variable access. Devise a scheme for representing a BASED-variable reference in
    the M6800. Indicate what code would be generated for the statement

    $$C = 1 ;$$

    using your scheme (assuming C is a BASED variable with symbolic assembly
    name Z10570).

4. This problem concerns the function example listed in Fig. 10.9. The M6800 gen-
    erated code is listed in Fig. 10.10. Note that the function MAX is expected to
    return the larger of the values of A and B. What mechanism is used to pass this
    value back to the calling routine from MAX?

```
PL/ M STAR

OPTIONS  IN EFFECT :    ORG = 768      SSIZE = 100
          LINE  NO      STATEMENT
             1           E5 : DO ; / * FUNCTION CALL * /
             2             DECLARE ( A , B , C )  BYTE ;
             3             MAX : PROCEDURE ( X , Y )  BYTE ;
             4               DECLARE ( X , Y )  BYTE ,
             5                 RESULT BYTE ;
             6               IF  X > Y  THEN
             7                 RESULT  = X ;
             8               ELSE
             9                 RESULT  = Y ;
            10               RETURN RESULT ;
            11             END MAX ;
            12           A  = 5 ;
            13           B  = 7 ;
            14           C  = MAX ( A , B );
            15           END E5 ;
            16           EOF
```

Fig. 10.9 Function call: PL/M representation.

```
                NAM     E5                      ( 1 )
                ORG     00300H                  ( 1 )
                LDS     #00064H+EOP             ( 1 )
                JMP     *+6                     ( 2 )
    Z10550      RMB     1                       ( 2 )
    Z10560      RMB     1                       ( 2 )
    Z10570      RMB     1                       ( 2 )
                JMP     L10010                  ( 3 )
    Z10580      RMB     0                       ( 3 )
                JMP     *+6                     ( 4 )
    Z10590      RMB     1                       ( 4 )
    Z10600      RMB     1                       ( 4 )
    Z10610      RMB     1                       ( 5 )
                LDAA    Z10590                  ( 6 )
                CMPA    Z10600                  ( 6 )
                BHI     *+5                     ( 6 )
                CLRA                            ( 6 )
                BRA     *+4                     ( 6 )
                LDAA    #0FFH                   ( 6 )
                CLRB                            ( 6 )
                ANDA    #1                      ( 6 )
                BNE     *+5                     ( 6 )
                JMP     L10020                  ( 6 )
                LDAA    Z10590                  ( 7 )
                STAA    Z10610                  ( 7 )
                JMP     L10030                  ( 7 )
    L10020      RMB     0                       ( 8 )
                LDAA    Z10600                  ( 9 )
                STAA    Z10610                  ( 9 )
    L10030      RMB     0                       ( 10 )
                LDAA    Z10610                  ( 10 )
                RTS                             ( 10 )
    L10010      RMB     0                       ( 12 )
                LDAA    #005H                   ( 12 )
                STAA    Z10550                  ( 12 )
                LDAA    #007H                   ( 13 )
                STAA    Z10560                  ( 13 )
                LDAA    Z10550                  ( 14 )
                PSHA                            ( 14 )
                LDAA    Z10560                  ( 14 )
                PSHA                            ( 14 )
                PULA                            ( 14 )
                STAA    Z10600                  ( 14 )
                PULA                            ( 14 )
                STAA    Z10590                  ( 14 )
                JSR     Z10580                  ( 14 )
                STAA    Z10570                  ( 14 )
                SWI                             ( 15 )
    EOP         END                             ( 15 )
```

Fig. 10.10 Function call: M6800 assembly-language representation.

5. Let $C_Z^{X \to Y}$ be defined as in the preceding section. Given $C_Z^{X \to Y}$, $C_X^{M \to N}$, and $C_M^{Y \to N}$, show how to obtain $C_N^{M \to N}$.

6. Assume that you have an I8085 microcomputer system that has no resident software. Further assume that you have a large development machine that sup-

ports a PL/M cross-compiler that generates I8085 hex object code and an I8085 cross-assembler. Given this environment, outline a scheme for implementing the following resident software packages:

a) bootstrap loader   b) absolute loader

c) assembler   d) text editor

e) PL/M compiler

Your scheme should use high-level language development whenever possible.

10.2 SIMULATORS AND DEBUGGERS

Simulators and debuggers are two software packages that are often used in testing situations. A *simulator* is a program that mimics the behavior of a given machine. It is, in effect, an *interpreter,* which accepts as input the object code for some machine. It responds to this input by simulating, in the software, the effects of the various microinstructions that would be expected by the hardware when executing the object code. Simulators can be very useful in performing preliminary testing before the actual hardware is built.

A *debugger* is an interactive software package that can be used to monitor execution of a program and thereby isolate errors in the program that is being monitored. A debugger will typically include capabilities for examining memory, changing memory, displaying registers, starting execution at a particular point in a program, and terminating execution at some specified point in a program. Note that these functions are similar to the microcomputer monitor commands discussed in Sec. 6.2.1. This implies that the monitor software code is really a form of debugger that can be used to monitor user programs that are executing in the RAM. Debuggers can also be used in conjunction with simulators and thereby monitor the simulated execution of a user program.

The best way to appreciate the types of activities performed by a simulator or a debugger is to examine some of the typical components. In the following paragraphs we will outline the types of functions that might be found in a PL/M simulator/debugger package for the M6800.

The declaration section of the simulator must include declarations for variables that will be used to simulate the actual hardware components. For the M6800, we might expect to see the following:

```
DECLARE
    XR        ADDRESS ,    / •   I NDEX  REGI STER•/
    PC        ADDRESS ,    / •   PROGRAM  COUNTER•/
    SP        ADDRESS ,    / •   STACK  POI NTER  •/
    A         BYTE ,       / •   ACCA            •/
    B         BYTE ,       / •   ACCB            •/
    I R       ADDRESS ,    / •   I NSTRUCTI ON  REGI STER•/
    ADDR      ADDRESS ,    / •   ADDRESS  LI NES•/
    (H , I ,N ,Z ,V ,C)    BYTE ;    / •CONDI TI ON  CODES•/
```

The reader should compare these declarations with the M6800 block diagram depicted in Fig. 5.4 and note that variables are being used to represent the major hardware components found in the M6800 microprocessor. At the software level, the condition code register has been configured as a collection of bytes rather than bits. This is due to the fact that it is easier to manipulate the individual condition code flags as bytes in PL/M.

The simulator must also include a declaration for memory, for example,

```
DECLARE  MEMORY  (MSIZE)  BYTE ;
```

where MSIZE is used to denote the size of the simulated memory.

Assuming that we have a loader routine that is used to load MEMORY and set the initial PC value, the fetch cycle of the simulator could be written as

```
DO  WHILE  (TRUE) ;
   IR  =  MEMORY  (PC) ;        / *  FETCH  INSTRUCTION  */
   PC  =  PC + 1 ;              / *  UPDATE  PC  */
   CALL  DECODE ;
   END ;
```

where TRUE is assumed to have the value '0FFH'. Note that the fetch cycle is an infinite loop. Each time through the loop the next opcode is fetched from memory and placed in the instruction register (IR). The PC is then updated and a routine called DECODE is invoked.

The DECODE routine has the responsibility of decoding the contents of IR, the opcode, and transferring to the appropriate simulation routine. In the following we will assume that DECODE has the following format:

```
DECODE :  PROCEDURE ;
   / *  CODE  FOR  EXAMINING  IR  AND         */
   / *  TRANSFERRING  TO  THE  APPROPRIATE    */
   / *  SIMULATION  ROUTINE
```

```
┌────────────────────────────┐
│   SIMULATION ROUTINE 1      │
└────────────────────────────┘
```

```
┌────────────────────────────┐
│   SIMULATION ROUTINE 2      │
└────────────────────────────┘
```

```
┌────────────────────────────┐
│   SIMULATION ROUTINE 3      │
└────────────────────────────┘
```

$$\vdots$$

```
┌────────────────────────────┐
│   SIMULATION ROUTINE n      │
└────────────────────────────┘
```

```
END  DECODE ;                                          */
```

Within this environment we will now consider what some of the simulation routines might look like.

Example 1 LDAA immediate routine:

```
H86 :DO;
    A = MEMORY (PC); / * FETCH IMMEDIATE DATA */
    PC = PC + 1;        / * UPDATE PC;
    IF (A = 0)          / * DETERMINE ZERO FLAG */
       THEN Z = 1;
       ELSE Z = 0;
    IF (A<0)            / * DETERMINE NEGATIVE FLAG */
       THEN N = 1;
       ELSE N = 0;
    V = 0;             / *RESET OVERFLOW FLAG */
    END H86 ;
```

Example 2 LDAA direct routine:

```
H96 :DO;
    ADDR = MEMORY (PC); / * FETCH DIRECT ADDRESS   */
    PC = PC + 1;        / * UPDATE PC              */
    A = MEMORY (ADDR);  / * LOAD ACCA DIRECT       */
    IF (A = 0)          / *DETERMINE ZERO FLAG     */
       THEN Z = 1;
       ELSE Z = 0;
    IF (A<0)            / *DETERMINE NEGATIVE FLAG */
       THEN N = 1;
       ELSE N = 0;
    V = 0;             / *RESET OVERFLOW FLAG      */
    END H96 ;
```

Example 3 BEQ routine:

```
H27 : DO;
    IF (Z = 1) THEN
       PC = PC + MEMORY(PC) + 1; / * TAKE THE BRANCH */
    ELSE
       PC = PC + 1; / * IGNORE BRANCH; UPDATE PC */
    END H27 ;
```

Note that, for the BEQ routine, the branch is taken only if the zero flag is 1. The reader should verify that the correct PC for the branch is given by

$$' PC + MEMORY(PC) + 1'.$$

Example 4 JSR extended:

```
HBD : DO;
    / * STACK RETURN PC VALUE */
    MEMORY(SP) = LOW(PC + 2);
    SP = SP - 1;
    MEMORY(SP) = HIGH(PC + 2);
    SP = SP - 1;
    / * SET NEW PC VALUE FOR JSR */
    PC = SHL(DOUBLE(MEMORY(PC)),8) + MEMORY(PC + 1);
    END HBD ;
```

Note that, for the JSR instruction, the updated PC must be stored on the stack. Upon entry to HBD, the PC has been incremented only once, so the updated PC would be PC + 2.

The new PC value is formed by using bytes 2 and 3 of the instruction. These bytes must be merged to form a 16-bit address. The SHL is used to form the high byte of this address value.

Example 5 LDX indexed:

```
HEE: DO;
    / * FETCH OFFSET */
    ADDR=MEMORY(PC);
    PC=PC+1;
    / * LOAD THE INDEX REGISTER INDIRECT */
    XR=SHR(DOUBLE(MEMORY(XR+ADDR)),8)+MEMORY(XR+ADDR+1);
    IF (XR = 0) / * DETERMINE ZERO FLAG */
        THEN Z = 1;
        ELSE Z = 0;
    IF (XR<0)/ * DETERMINE NEGATIVE FLAG */
        THEN N = 1;
        ELSE N = 0;
    V = 0;        / * RESET OVERFLOW FLAG */
    END HEE;
```

For this example, the index register, XR, must be loaded with the contents of the two memory locations found at $\overline{XR}$ + offset and $\overline{XR}$ + offset + 1, where $\overline{XR}$ denotes the value of the index register prior to execution of this instruction. The SHL built-in is used to form the high byte of the new XR value.

When a debugging package is used with a simulator, the simulator is actually a subroutine of the debugger. The debugger then functions as the main driver, which will invoke the simulator as necessary. The debugger may also have a subroutine that functions as a loader.

To clarify the concept of a debugger we will consider what would be necessary to set one up. We will assume that the debugger supports the following commands:

Command	Action
LOAD MEM	The loader subroutine is invoked to read the object code and store it in the MEMORY array.
SET REG (reg name, value)	The specified register is given the specified value, e.g., SET REG (PC,0020H) would set PC ≡ 0020H.

(continued)

Command	Action
SET MEM (location, value)	The specified location is given the specified value; that is, MEMORY (location) ≡ value.
DISPLAY REG (reg name)	The contents of the specified register are displayed.
DISPLAY MEM (location)	The contents of the specified location are displayed.
RUN	The simulator is invoked. The current PC value determines where execution begins.
SET BREAKPOINT (location)	The debugger marks the specified location so that when the simulator attempts to 'execute' the instruction found at this location, control is returned to the debugger.
CLEAR BREAKPOINTS	All locations 'marked' by previous SET BREAKPOINT commands are cleared.
END SIM	This is the termination command for the debugger.

For the most part, implementing a debugger with this command structure would be a straightforward task. The SET REG and SEG MEM commands, for example, would involve simple assignments either to the register variables or to the MEMORY array. The DISPLAY commands would involve a simple output routine to display the appropriate values.

The implementation of the SET BREAKPOINT command involves establishing a mechanism for returning from the simulator to the debugger whenever an instruction in a "marked" location is fetched. One method for accomplishing this would be to set up an array of marked locations. Each SET BREAKPOINT command would add an entry, the specified location, into this array. The CLEAR BREAKPOINTS command would clear this array.

Given this array, we could modify the fetch cycle of the simulator so that, prior to each instruction fetch, the PC value would be checked against the values held in the marked location array. If the PC matches a marked location, then we must return to the debugger.

While the scheme outlined above would be quite easy to implement, it is very inefficient. Note that a search of the marked location array would be required for each instruction that is fetched. An alternative solution that is much more efficient is outlined below.

Assume, in the following discussion, that the object code that is being simulated has the following format:

Location	Hex code
0100	B6 01 14
0103	F6 01 13
0106	BB 01 16
0109	F9 01 15
010C	B7 01 18
010F	F7 01 17
0112	3F
0113	04 00
0115	02 F1
0117	00 00

Further assume that we wish to set breakpoints at locations 0106H and 010CH. We will do this by changing the contents of MEMORY(0106H) and MEMORY(010CH) to a special illegal opcode, 00H. Furthermore, we will use an array to hold the values of the opcodes that have been changed in MEMORY, which are BBH and B7H. These values are saved, so we can clear the breakpoints by restoring the proper opcodes in the correct locations.

In using a special opcode pattern to denote a breakpoint location, we have eliminated the need for testing for a marked location on every instruction fetch. What we must do is include a new simulation routine in the DECODE routine that will process the 00H opcode. This routine (H00) will effect a return to the debugger.

As noted earlier, and as can be seen from the examples above, a simulator for a machine M actually mimics, in software, the effects of M's various microinstructions. Thus a machine M′, when running the simulator, behaves like M (at least at the level at which the simulator is written). The most basic form of simulation is called *emulation*. For emulation, the simulator itself is written at the microinstruction level. If the machine M′ is microprogrammable, so that one can write programs using (and create CML instructions from) the set of microinstructions of M′, then in particular one can write an interpreter that will execute programs written in M's machine language. This interpreter is an emulator for M.

Emulation is a very useful notion, since it often allows users to replace older machines with newer versions without forcing the rewriting of large quantities of software. If the new machine emulates the old machine, no software changes have to be made.

LABORATORY ASSIGNMENTS

1. Write a simulator for I8085S.

2. Write a simulator for M6800S.

EXERCISES

1. Write simulation routines (PROCEDURES) for the M6800 instructions LDAA IND (HA6) and RTS (H39).

2. The FETCH cycle of the preceding section is described as an infinite loop. How does the program escape from this cycle?

10.3 TRAVERSING THE LEVELS

In the preceding sections of this text we have discussed, at varying levels of detail, each of the five levels found in modern computing systems. Our coverage of the operating-system level (OS) has been quite sketchy, for the reason that there is usually very little difference between the conventional machine-language level (CML) and the OS level on microcomputer systems. Rather extensive operating system support can be found in larger machines but, since microcomputers are normally single-user, dedicated systems, they usually have no need for large operating systems.

In this section we will enumerate some of the functions typically provided by an operating system. Our discussion of this subject is intended to provide only a brief introduction to the topic. We will also examine the process of traversing from the OS level to the CML level. Finally we will conclude this chapter by traversing all five of the levels for a specific example.

10.3.1 Operating System Support

An operating system provides a runtime support environment for all executing programs that are in the system. The operating system is responsible for monitoring all of the resources of the system, both hardware and software. For example, the operating system must allocate memory for users and ensure that each user is protected from all other users in the system. The software resources managed by the operating system would include loaders, text editors, assemblers, and compilers. The interface between a user's program and the operating system consists of the OS-level instructions that are found in the user's program. We will consider an example of such an interface. In the following we will use the SDK-85 microcomputer system (Intel, 1977c) as the host machine. The SDK-85 has an I8085 microprocessor, RAM, ROM, peripheral interface devices, etc. The monitor, which is stored in ROM on the SDK-85, serves as a simple operating system for users of the SDK system. Not only does the monitor provide a general context within which programs can be loaded, debugged, and executed; it also provides routines that can be employed in user programs. These routines, or *utility functions,* include a time delay, hex converter, read-keyboard function and various routines associated with monitor teletype (console) functions. Each of these functions has an associated address in ROM, so a program CALL to such a routine might be viewed as an OS-level instruction. Each routine is terminated with a return instruction, which will return control to the user's program. As an example, consider the following AL program, which invokes the time-delay routine that is stored starting at 05F1H in the SDK-85 monitor.

Al code for user's program

```
DELAY  EQU   05F1H
       ORG   2000H
       LXI   D,0FFFFH
       CALL  DELAY
       HLT
       END
```

The time-delay routine, as it appears in the monitor, is shown below.

CML Code				AL Code		
Location	Hex code					
05F1	1B			DELAY:	DCX	D
05F2	7A				MOV	A,D
05F3	B3				ORA	E
05F4	C2	F1	05		JNZ	DELAY
05F7	C9				RET	

Note that the DELAY routine assumes that the D–E register pair holds a 16-bit integer that indicates the number of times the loop will be repeated and thereby determines the extent of the time delay.

If we assemble the user's AL program, that is, take it from the AL-level to the OS-level, we'll obtain the OS-level code shown below.

OS code for user's program

```
2000  11  FF FF
2003  CD  F1 05
2006  76
```

As noted in Chapter 1, the OS level contains a mixture of OS- and CML-level instructions and is therefore supported by partial interpretation. The OS instructions are interpreted to the CML level, while the CML instructions pass on directly to the microprogramming level. For this example the LXI instruction (11 FF FF) and the HLT (76) are at the CML level, while the CALL (CD F1 05) is at the OS level. This can be more fully appreciated by considering the sequence of instructions that are executed when the program is started at location 2000H. A trace for the LXI and CALL on DELAY would look like

2000	11	FF	FF	Executed in RAM
2003	CD	F1	05	
05F1	1B			
05F2	7A			
05F3	B3			
05F4	C2	F1	05	
05F1	1B			Executed in ROM
.				
.				
.				
05F4	C2	F1	05	
05F7	C9			

In a sense, the ROM instructions constitute the interpretation of the OS-level DELAY call into CML-level instructions. To demonstrate that OS- to CML-level transversals are not fundamentally different on larger machines, we will consider such a transversal on the IBM 370 system.

The assembly language for the 370 (Struble, 1975) provides a large number of predefined macro definitions that can be used for I/O. One of these, the OPEN macro, provided for the initialization of input or output files, for example,

OPEN   INDATA

will open a file called INDATA for input. When the OPEN macro is expanded, the following AL code is generated:

```
CNOP  0,4
BAL   1,*+8
DC    AL1(128)
DC    AL3(INDATA)
SVC   19
```

The DC statements provide parameters to the OS; that is, they provide the name of the file and a flag indicating that input is the desired operation. The SVC 19, when assembled, becomes an OS-level instruction; a supervisor call. When executed, this instruction causes an interrupt and a new PC is obtained from location 60H. This effects a transfer into the CML-level code that will interpret this OS-level instruction. This situation is not dissimilar from the DELAY call for the SDK-85 system.

10.3.2 An Example of Level Transversals

To complete our discussion of computing-system levels, we will consider a particular example that will take us through all five of the levels. We will start at level five, the high-level language, with the PL/M segment shown below.

```
DO I =1  TO  500 ;
    CALL  TIME  ( 1 0 0 )
END ;
```

This segment uses the PL/M built-in function TIME. TIME has one argument, n, and it produces a time delay of $n*100$ microseconds. Since n must be a BYTE value, the largest time delay that can be obtained by a single call on TIME is 25,500 microseconds or 0.0255 seconds. Longer time delays can be obtained by a loop. The loop shown above would produce a delay of five seconds.

The reason for introducing the TIME function at this point is to use it as an example in level transversals. The PL/M statement "CALL TIME(100);" exists at level five, the HL level. When this HL code is compiled, the compiler will translate this statement into level four or AL statements. This might be accomplished as follows:

In this example, it is assumed that the compiler is generating I8085 AL code that will use the monitor DELAY routine introduced in the previous section. Since the loop in the DELAY routine requires 7.68 μseconds for each execution, the D–E pair is loaded with 1303, so that the call on DELAY will cause a delay of approximately 0.01 seconds.

The level 4 AL instructions are then submitted to an assembler for another level transversal; to level 3, the OS level. For the CALL DELAY statement, this would be represented as follows:

CALL DELAY ⟶ [INTEL I8085 ASSEMBLER] ⟶ CD F1 05

As noted in the previous section, the CD F1 05 is a OS-level instruction that is supported by interpretation. The transversal to level 2, the CML level, can be depicted as

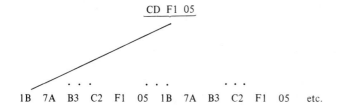

In other words, the execution of CD F1 05 effectively becomes the sequence of CML instructions found in the DELAY loop.

Each of the instructions in the DELAY loop exists at level 2, the CML level. The final level transversal, to level 1 (the microprogramming level), is again supported by interpretation. Consider the 1B (DCX D) instruction (see Sec. 5.2.2). This instruction is interpreted in one machine cycle, which consists of six clock cycles. During clock cycle 1 (T1), the address of the opcode is placed on the address bus. The opcode (1B) is loaded into the instruction register (IR) during clock cycles 2 and 3 (T2 and T3), and the opcode is decoded during cycle 4 (T4). The decrement of the register pair takes place during clock cycles 5 and 6 (T5 and T6). This interpretation can be diagrammed as follows:

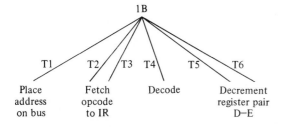

The last sequence of instructions is directly executed in the hardware; i.e., this is the lowest level of the system.

REFERENCES AND SUPPORTIVE MATERIAL

Section 10.1. The operating environment for the PL/M STAR compiler is described in Marks, Tondo, and Smith (1979). The reader interested in an excellent treatment of compilation techniques should consult Aho and Ullman (1977).

Section 10.2. Both Intel and Motorola have developed simulator/debugger packages that can be used for their microprocessors (Intel, 1975, and Motorola, 1977). These manuals should be consulted for further details on the capabilities of these systems.

1. Aho, A. V., and J. D. Ullman, [1977], *Principles of Compiler Design*. Reading, Mass.: Addison-Wesley.

2. Intel [1975], "Interp/80 User's Manual." Intel Corporation, 3065 Bowers Ave., Santa Clara, California.

3. Intel [1977c], "SDK-85 User's Manual." Intel Corporation, Santa Clara, California.

4. Marks, J., C. L. Tondo, and C. L. Smith, [1979], "PL/M STAR Operations Manual: Release 2." Computer Science Department, Southern Illinois University at Carbondale, Carbondale, Illinois.

5. Motorola [1977], "M6800 Simulator Reference Manual." Motorola Integrated Circuit Division, 3102 North 56th Street, Phoenix, Arizona.

6. Struble, G. W. [1975], *Assembler Language Programming: The IBM System/360 and 370,* Second Edition. Reading, Mass.: Addison-Wesley.

CHAPTER ELEVEN

MICROPROCESSOR INTERRUPT SYSTEMS

11.1 INTERRUPT-DRIVEN I/O

We have seen several examples of busy-wait I/O in connection with the loaders and text-editors of Chapters 6 and 7. All of this I/O involved serial interface devices. We wish to consider interrupt systems in somewhat greater detail here and shall do so largely in the context of parallel I/O. Recall that the subject of interrupts has been treated briefly from a hardware point of view in Sec. 5.3.3. Busy-wait I/O techniques can be very wasteful of CPU time, particularly when transmission rates are slow. Interrupts provide an alternative to busy-wait I/O by allowing the CPU to carry on other activities and having it service peripheral I/O requests only upon signal from the peripheral device.

In addition to handling I/O, interrupts can also be useful as debugging aids (for insertion of breakpoints) and for control by the operating system. Interrupts can also be used to allow a system to save its data or switch to a backup power supply in the case of a power or hardware failure. An important factor in determining the usefulness of interrupts is the required response time between interrupting events.

It should be noted, however, that interrupts are asynchronous from the perspective of the CPU and its processing activity, since they are determined by external events and thus may occur at any point in the CPU's primary activity. Consequently, interrupt-driven programs can be difficult to debug and test. Interrupt routines themselves must be written with great care since they must execute properly independent of their location in the main routine. The use of interrupt routines in programs tends to run counter to the principles of structured programming and software engineering.

If a system has several possible sources of interrupts, there must be some means of identifying the actual source of the interrupt. Two common methods for doing this are *vectoring* and *polling*. When vectoring is used, each possible interrupt source provides data that the CPU can use for identification. With polling, the CPU must examine each possible interrupt source in turn until it finds the one that is active. Thus polling requires less hardware and more software, but is generally slower than vectoring.

11.1.1 Interrupts on the M6800

Recall from Sec. 5.3.3 that the M6800 has two low-active interrupt inputs $\overline{IRQ}$ (interrupt request) and $\overline{NMI}$ (nonmaskable interrupt), in addition to the two special interrupt instructions SWI (software interrupt) and WAI (wait for interrupt). When a signal occurs on $\overline{IRQ}$, the processor completes execution of the current instruction. Then, if the interrupt mask bit of the condition code register is clear, the processor stacks the contents of its registers, sets the interrupt mask so that no further interrupts can occur, and fetches the address of an interrupt service routine from locations FFF8H and FFF9H. The RTI (return from interrupt) instruction essentially reverses this process: Restoring the old PC allows the CPU to continue what it was doing prior to the interrupt; restoring the condition code register clears the interrupt mask once again. Note that, in general, the instruction CLI (clear interrupt) enables interrupts on $\overline{IRQ}$ while SEI (set interrupt) disables them.

$\overline{NMI}$ represents a nonmaskable interrupt line. Apart from the fact that the interrupt mask is ignored in this case, the effect is similar to that described above. The address of the interrupt service routine is fetched from locations FFFCH and FFFDH in the case of $\overline{NMI}$.

Each hardware interrupt line and each interrupt instruction is associated with a unique memory location (vector), from which the address of the interrupt routine is fetched. However, if several external devices were present, each would normally interrupt the CPU through $\overline{IRQ}$, and thus polling would be required to determine the particular source of the interrupt.

A typical M6800 interrupt system would utilize the Peripheral Interface Adaptor (specifically the 40-pin MC6820). We shall refer to this device as the MPIA. As can be seen from the block diagram of Fig. 11.1, the MPIA is a parallel interface device containing two essentially symmetric sections (A and B).

Each of A and B sections contains three CPU-accessible registers, a control register, a data-direction register, and a peripheral register. Each section also contains an interrupt output, $\overline{IRQA}$ and $\overline{IRQB}$, which would typically be ORed together to form the $\overline{IRQ}$ input to the processor. As we shall see, lines CA1, CA2, CB1, CB2 are important when utilizing the MPIA as part of an interrupt system. The specific role played by these lines is determined by the control-register settings.

Access to the various registers within the MPIA is determined by the two low-order address bits (RSO and RS1) and bit 2 of the respective control regis-

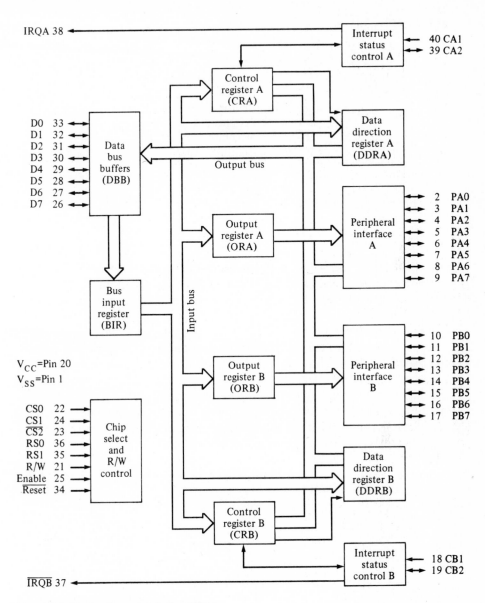

Fig. 11.1 Block diagram of the MPIA.

ter (CRA-2 or CRB-2), as indicated in Fig. 11.2. Thus, to access peripheral register A, the CPU would first write a 1 in bit 2 of control register A (the latter accessed with RS0 = 1, RS1 = 0, and the remaining address bits determined by the location of the MPIA in the particular system configuration),

RS1	RS0	Control register bit		Corresponding location
		CRA-2	CRB-2	
0	0	1	×	Peripheral register A
0	0	0	×	Data direction register A
0	1	×	×	Control register A
1	0	×	1	Peripheral register B
1	0	×	0	Data direction register B
1	1	×	×	Control register B

× = don't care

Fig. 11.2 Internal addressing in the MPIA. Small crosses indicate "don't care."

and then access the immediately preceding memory location (RS0 = RS1 = 0). (Recall once again that the M6800 systems utilize memory-mapped I/O and, consequently, the MPIA's registers are manipulated using ordinary instructions.)

Each data-direction register (DDR) consists of eight bits, which correspond, one-to-one, to the eight bits (eight I/O lines) of the associated peripheral register. A DDR bit set to 0 configures the corresponding peripheral data line as an input, and a 1 configures it as an output.

The specific format of control register A is described in Fig. 11.3. The format of control register B is similar.

The interrupt flags (bits 6 and 7) of control register A are "read only" and are typically set by a signal on the corresponding line CA1 or CA2, as indicated in Fig. 11.3. The settings of CA1 and CA2 Control determine the role to be played by lines CA1 and CA2. Figure 11.4 indicates the effects of the

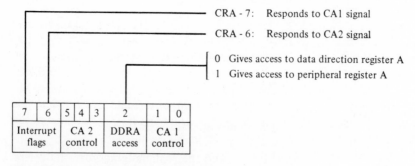

Fig. 11.3 Format of control register A.

CRA-1 (CRB-1)	CRA-0 (CRB-0)	Interrupt input CA1(CB1)	Interrupt flag CRA-7 (CRB-7)	MPU interrupt REQUEST $\overline{IRQA}$ ($\overline{IRQB}$)
0	0	↓ Active	Set high on ↓ of CA1(CB1)	Disabled
0	1	↓ Active	Set high on ↓ of CA1(CB1)	Goes low when CRA-7(CRB-7) goes high
1	0	↑ Active	Set high on ↑ of CA1(CB1)	Disabled
1	1	↑ Active	Set high on ↑ of CA1(CB1)	Goes low when CRA-7(CRB-7) goes high

↑ (↓) indicates low to high (high to low) transitions.

Fig. 11.4 CA1 (and CB1) control settings.

various CA1 control settings. Note, in particular, that the programmer can choose whether CA1 is to be regarded as high- or low-active and whether or not a signal on CA1 merely sets the interrupt flag (CRA-7) or comes on through and interrupts the processor.

Lines CA2 and CB2 are bidirectional and thus can be used for either receiving or transmitting signals. When bit 5 of the control register (CRA-5) is set to 0, line CA2 operates in a receive mode. In this case, the options for CA2 are completely similar to those for CA1, as can be seen from Fig. 11.5.

Setting bit 5 of control register A or B to 1 configures the corresponding line CA2 or CB2 to be an output line. Again Fig. 11.5 surveys the various options possible. We wish to note, in particular, that line CA2 can be used to output a signal (READ strobe) following a CPU READ of output register A, and CB2 can be used to output a signal (WRITE strobe) following a CPU WRITE to output register B.

In summary, we see that lines CA1, CA2, CB1, and CB2 combine to provide great flexibility for intercommunication between the CPU and interrupting peripheral devices. All lines can be used to receive interrupt signals; or one can use CA1 and CB1 to receive interrupt signals and then use CA2 and CB2 to signal back to the peripheral device. Such a return signal might serve to acknowledge acceptance of the interrupt, or it might indicate that the data has been read. In subsequent sections we shall consider specific applications of the MPIA and thereby utilize these control lines in their different roles.

As noted above, in an M6800 system utilizing several MPIA's with all interrupt lines ORed to $\overline{IRQ}$, the source of a given interrupt line would have to

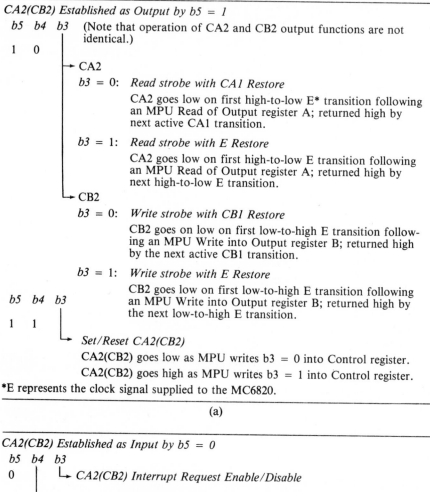

CA2(CB2) Established as Output by b5 = 1

b5 b4 b3   (Note that operation of CA2 and CB2 output functions are not
              identical.)
1   0

→ CA2

b3 = 0:   *Read strobe with CA1 Restore*

CA2 goes low on first high-to-low E* transition following
an MPU Read of Output register A; returned high by
next active CA1 transition.

b3 = 1:   *Read strobe with E Restore*

CA2 goes low on first high-to-low E transition following
an MPU Read of Output register A; returned high by
next high-to-low E transition.

→ CB2

b3 = 0:   *Write strobe with CB1 Restore*

CB2 goes on low on first low-to-high E transition following an MPU Write into Output register B; returned high
by the next active CB1 transition.

b3 = 1:   *Write strobe with E Restore*

CB2 goes low on first low-to-high E transition following
an MPU Write into Output register B; returned high by
the next low-to-high E transition.

b5 b4 b3

1   1

→ *Set/Reset CA2(CB2)*

CA2(CB2) goes low as MPU writes b3 = 0 into Control register.

CA2(CB2) goes high as MPU writes b3 = 1 into Control register.

*E represents the clock signal supplied to the MC6820.

(a)

CA2(CB2) Established as Input by b5 = 0

b5 b4 b3

0   → *CA2(CB2) Interrupt Request Enable/Disable*

b3 = 0:   Disables IRQA(B) MPU Interrupt by CA2(CB2) active
          transition.

b3 = 1:   Enables IRQA(B) MPU Interrupt by CA2(CB2) active
          transition.*

*IRQA(B) will occur on next (MPU generated) positive transi-
tion of b3 if CA2(CB2) active transition occurred while interrupt was disabled.

→ *Determine active CA2(CB2) transition for setting interrupt flag
IRQA(B)2 - (bit b6)*

b4 = 0:   IRQA(B)2 set by high-to-low transition on CA2(CB2).

b4 = 1:   IRQA(B)2 set by low-to-high transition on CA2(CB2)

(b)

Fig. 11.5 Control of CA2 and CB2 lines.

be determined by polling. Typically, the processor would examine the control register of each MPIA in turn checking to see which interrupt flag bit has been set.

It should be noted that any such polling by the software must entail examining the interrupt flag bits in some particular sequence. Hence if two devices were to interrupt the CPU simultaneously, that device whose corresponding interrupt flag bit occurs earlier in the polling sequence would be serviced first. Thus we see that any such polling procedure necessarily induces a prioritizing of the peripheral devices.

11.1.2 Interrupts on the I8085

As noted in Sec. 5.3.3, the I8085 provides a more extensive interrupt capability than the M6800. The four hardware interrupt lines TRAP, RST 7.5, RST 6.5, and RST 5.5 were discussed. Although TRAP is nonmaskable, the other three RST (RESTART) interrupts can be either individually or globally enabled or disabled. The EI and DI instructions enable and disable the entire interrupt system; the SIM instruction can be used to individually set or reset interrupt masks for each of the three RST lines on the basis of the contents of the accumulator (see Fig. 5.15). Thus, when an interrupt occurs on a given line, a check is made to see if the interrupt system is enabled and if interrupts are enabled for the particular line. Finally a check is made to ensure that no interrupts with higher priorities are pending. Recall that TRAP has the highest priority followed in turn by RST 7.5, RST 6.5, and RST 5.5. These priorities are used in determining which interrupt is serviced when more than one is pending.

If all of the above conditions are satisfied, the interrupt sequence proceeds with the current PC value being placed on the stack. (Recall that, in the M6800 case, all register values were stacked.) The interrupt system is then disabled and remains so until enabled once again by an EI instruction. Finally, the PC is loaded with an address assigned to the particular interrupt line. The correspondences between the interrupt lines and their assigned addresses are

0024	for	TRAP
002C	for	RST 5.5
0034	for	RST 6.5
003C	for	RST 7.5

The instructions found at the corresponding location must effect the transfer to the interrupt service routine. The return from the interrupt routine is accommodated by one of the I8085 return instructions, which restores the original PC value and thus allows the CPU to continue with its original activity.

An I8085 interrupt system might incorporate a parallel interface adaptor similar to the MPIA or one of the other I/O interface capabilities available in the I8085 family. In order to look more closely at a specific example of such a

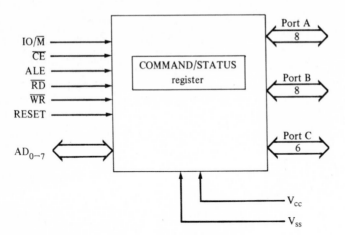

Fig. 11.6 Block diagram of 8155 I/O section.

system, we shall consider the I/O section available on Intel's 8155 RAM DIP (see Sec. 5.3.2). A block diagram for the I/O portion of the 8155 appears in Fig. 11.6.

Note that the I/O section of the 8155 consists of a command status register (C/S), two eight-bit I/O ports (A and B) and a six-bit port (C). This portion of the 8155 is separate or *isolated* from the memory section of the I8085 system and is accessible from the CPU only through the IN and OUT instructions.

In any particular instance, Port C can be utilized in any one of the following four roles:

Alternative	Port C role
ALT 1	input port
ALT 2	output port
ALT 3	bits 0,1,2 are interrupt, buffer full and strobe bits for Port A. bits 3,4,5 are output bits.
ALT 4	bits 0,1,2 as in ALT 3 bits 3,4,5 are interrupt, buffer full and strobe bits for Port B.

Thus in some cases, Port C can serve as a control port for Ports A and B. When, for example, bits 0, 1, and 2 are used for control purposes relative to Port A, bit 0 is an interrupt that the 8155 sends out, bit 1 is an output signal indicating whether the buffer is full or empty, and bit 2 is an input pin that can accept a "strobe" or signal from an external device.

The Command/Status register corresponds to a single location; a command is written into the register during a CPU WRITE operation, and the status of the I/O ports is available to the CPU upon a READ operation. The

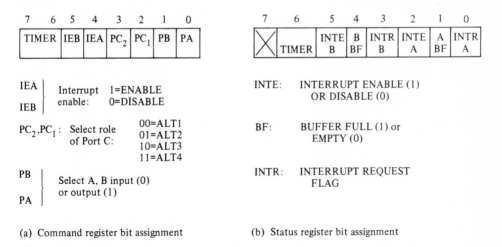

(a) Command register bit assignment   (b) Status register bit assignment

Fig. 11.7 Command/status register formats.

formats of these two components of the Command/Status register are given in Fig. 11.7.

The roles of the various bits in the Command/Status register will be brought out in our ensuing discussion. The I/O portion of the 8155 can function in either a basic mode or, when performing as part of an interrupt system, in a strobed mode. The programmer chooses the strobed mode for Port A when ALT 3 is selected, or for both Ports A and B when ALT 4 is selected. Basically, the strobed mode provides additional signal capability for facilitating the transfer of data between the CPU and a peripheral device.

When the strobed mode is used for input, a signal from the peripheral device to the appropriate strobe bit (bit 2 or bit 5 of Port C) is followed by a transfer of the data from the corresponding Port A or B to a buffer within the 8155. This in turn causes the buffer full bit (bit 1 or bit 4 of Port C) to go high. At the end of the strobe signal, the interrupt bit (bit 0 or bit 3 of Port C) will go high if the respective port interrupt (bit 4 or 5) of the Command register (see Fig. 11.7) has been enabled. The interrupt pin in Port C might typically be connected to one of the interrupt pins on the I8085; and thus at this point the CPU would be interrupted and presumably would read the data from the corresponding port. This reading of the data (accompanied by a signal on $\overline{RD}$) effects the resetting of the interrupt and buffer full bits in Port C. Figure 11.8 contains a timing diagram that further illustrates the sequence of actions just described.

In the strobed output mode, a WRITE to Port A or C (accompanied by a signal on $\overline{WR}$) results in a signal on the corresponding interrupt bit (bit 0 or 3) of Port C. The end of the WRITE initiates an output signal on the buffer full bit, and the responding strobe signal indicating acknowledgment by the pe-

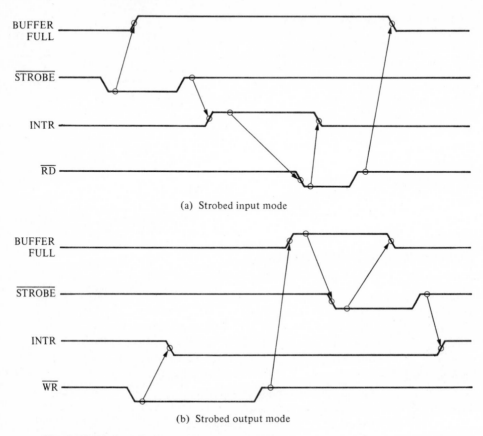

(a) Strobed input mode

(b) Strobed output mode

Fig. 11.8 Timing diagrams for strobed mode.

ripheral device effects the resetting of the interrupt and buffer full bits. Again these events are illustrated in Fig. 11.8.

The status of the various components of the I/O system when in the strobed mode is reflected in the bits of the status register (Fig. 11.7). In particular, the Interrupt Request flag (INTR) can be read by the CPU to determine the status of the corresponding interrupt bit (0 or 3) in Port C. Note again that one can choose to enable or disable interrupt signals to the 8155 from reaching the I8085 itself by appropriately setting the command register (bits 4,5). The status register (bits 2 and 5) reflects the condition of this aspect of the interrupt system.

From the above, it can be seen that the 8155 provides a very versatile I/O section as far as interrupt-system capabilities are concerned. We shall consider a particular application of a system utilizing the 8155 in the next chapter.

11.2 AN EXAMPLE USING INTERRUPT I/O

In order to illustrate some of the concepts of the preceding sections, we now consider a specific application of an interrupt system. The general version of the problem involves the control of a traffic light, in which the regular sequence pattern of the lights can be altered by a signal from sensors in the roadbeds. A special case of the problem is analyzed, and then the general version is left as an exercise.

The special case is as follows: The problem involves one input and output. In general, the output is to turn a light on and off at regular intervals; however a pulse on the input line will always reset the light back to the beginning of its "on" cycle.

The program solution to the problem simply entails repeated cycling through a delay loop with the light alternatively on and off. An input pulse will cause an interrupt to the microprocessor, forcing it to respond immediately. We shall discuss the details of the solution for the M6800 system and its MPIA (the special case will be expanded to a parallel I/O situation).

Referring to Sec. 11.1.1 and the details of the MPIA, we shall use line CA1 for the input pulses and peripheral I/O line PA0 for the output signals to the light (see Fig. 11.1).

Relative to setting the MPIA, our program must first configure I/O line PA0 to be an output line. This is accomplished by initially setting CRA-2 (bit 2 of the control register A) to 0 (which, according to Fig. 11.2, allows subsequent access to data-direction register A) and then storing 01H in the data-direction register.

Control register A (see Fig. 11.3) is then set to 00000111B in order to achieve the following effects: Setting CA1 control to 11B allows signals on CA1 to pass through the MPIA to the M6800's interrupt request line $\overline{\text{IRQ}}$ (see Fig. 11.4); setting CRA-2 to 1B ensures subsequent access of peripheral register A (see Fig. 11.2); and, since line CA2 is not used, CA2 control is set to 000B. Recall that the interrupt flag bits CRA-6 and CRA-7 are read-only bits.

A PL/M program to implement this special case of the traffic-light controller appears in Fig. 11.9. This program incorporates the features mentioned above, and we wish to note in particular the main elements of the interrupt routine. The declaration PROCEDURE INTERRUPT 1 tells the PL/M STAR compiler that SIGNAL is an interrupt-service routine, the digit 1 indicating that the routine is to be associated with the M6800's $\overline{\text{IQR}}$ interrupt line. The compiler thus automatically places the address of this routine at locations FFF8, FFF9. The interrupt routine itself is quite simple. An interrupt must cause the light to be reset to the beginning of its "on" cycle. To achieve this, the interrupt routine first tests to see whether the light is off. If so, the index of the "OFF" loop is reset to the limit so that the program will drop out of the

```
LIGHT : DO ;
   DECLARE
     LIGHT BYTE AT (xxxxH) ,
     DDRA BYTE AT (xxxxH) ,
     CREGA BYTE AT (yyyyH) ,
     FOREVER LITERALLY 'WHILE 0FFH' ,
     I BYTE ;
   SIGNAL : PROCEDURE INTERRUPT 1 ;
     IF LIGHT=00H THEN                    / • IF LIGHT IS OFF•/
       I =200 ;                           / •FORCE OUT OF OFF LOOP•/
       ELSE IF (0<I) AND (I<200)  THEN       / •IF LIGHT IS ON•/
         I =0 ;                           / •RESET TO START OF ON LOOP•/
         ELSE LIGHT=00H ;                 / •OR FORCE THROUGH OFF LOOP•/
   END SIGNAL ;
   / •MAIN PROGRAM•/
     CREGA=00H ;                          / •INITIALIZE MPIA•/
     DDRA=0FFH ;
     CREGA=07H ;
     ENABLE ;
     DO FOREVER ;
       LIGHT=0FFH ;                       / •TURN LIGHT ON•/
       I =0 ;
       DO WHILE (I<200) AND (LIGHT=0FFH) ; / •5 SECOND DELAY•/
         CALL TIME(250) ;
         I =I +1 ;
       END ;
       I =0 ;
       LIGHT=COMP(LIGHT) ;                / •TURN LIGHT OFF•/
       DO WHILE (I<200 AND LIGHT=00H) ;       / •5 SECOND DELAY•/
         CALL TIME(250) ;
         I =I +1 ;
       END ;
     END ;
     END LIGHT ;
   EOF
```

Fig. 11.9 Solution to special case of the traffic light controller.

"OFF" loop upon return from the interrupt. If the light is on when the interrupt occurs, the index of the "ON" loop is reinitialized unless the program has
just left the "ON" loop but has not yet turned the light off. In this latter case,
the interrupt routine turns the light off so that, on return from the interrupt,
the light is turned back on. This will again result in a fall through the "OFF"
loop.

The built-in procedure TIME is used to effect the appropriate delays.
TIME (expr) will produce a delay of $100n$ microseconds, where n is the value
of the argument expr. The actual addresses of the MPIA registers are left
undefined in the program; they may be determined by the layout of the particular system in which the program is to be executed.

EXERCISE

Write a PL/M program to control a traffic light at an intersection.

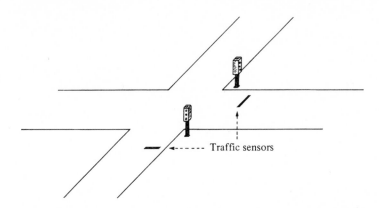

Traffic sensors

　　　Each traffic light contains the usual green, yellow, and red lights. A light should be green for 20 seconds, yellow for four seconds, and then red for 24 seconds. During this time the other light will be red for 24 seconds, green for 20 seconds and then yellow for four seconds, etc. A pulse on the traffic sensor for a street while the light for the other street is on green should cause the remaining "green time" for the other street to be cut in half. Pulses at other times should be ignored.

　　　Signals to the six lights should be output through the MPIA's peripheral register. Pulses from the sensors should be input through lines CA1 and CA2 on the MPIA and should interrupt the processor.

REFERENCES AND SUPPORTIVE MATERIAL

Leventhal (1978) is recommended for additional reference material on microprocessor interrupt systems. Osborne (1976) also contains sections covering interrupt I/O in microcomputer systems. Osborne, Jacobson, and Kane (1977) include chapters that discuss interrupt systems based on the particular parallel interface devices covered in this chapter.

　　　Detailed coverage of the MPIA (Motorola's MC6820) can be found in Motorola (1976a). Additional application material on the MC6820 and its use in interrupt I/O systems can be found in Motorola (1975). Intel (1977a) provides technical data on the 8155 device and its related system components.

1.　Intel [1977a], "MCS-85 User's Manual." Intel Corporation, 8065 Bowers Ave., Santa Clara, California.

2.　Leventhal, L. A. [1978], *Introduction to Microprocessors: Software, Hardware, Programming.* Englewood Cliffs, N.J.: Prentice-Hall.

3.　Motorola [1976a], "M6800 Microcomputer: System Design Data." Motorola Semiconductor Products Inc., Box 20912, Phoenix, Arizona.

4. Motorola [1975], "M6800 Microprocessor Applications Manual." Motorola Semiconductor Products Inc., Box 20912, Phoenix, Arizona.

5. Osborne, A. [1976], *An Introduction to Microcomputers; Volume 1: Basic Concepts*. Adam Osborne and Associates, Inc., Berkeley, California.

6. Osborne, Jacobson, and Kane [1977], *An Introduction to Microcomputers; Volume II: Some Real Products*. Adam Osborne and Associates, Inc., Berkeley, California.

CHAPTER TWELVE

APPLICATIONS AND FUTURE DIRECTIONS

12.1 UTILIZING MICROPROCESSORS IN DEDICATED SYSTEMS

For the most part, this book has tended to regard microprocessors in the role of the CPU for a general-purpose computing system. In this final chapter, we consider microprocessors in a somewhat more restricted, but also more typical setting. In particular, we wish to discuss various application areas of microprocessors in which they are commonly programmed to perform some specific function, e.g., to simulate a particular sequential circuit (cf. Sec. 5.1 and especially Exercises 5 and 6). The use of microprocessors for such purposes is extensive and increasing dramatically. In fact, it is the large number of sales in the different application areas that accounts for the surprisingly low cost of microprocessors.

A rather common characteristic of these various applications is that they involve *real-time* processing. The phrase "real-time" implies that, whatever the role of the CPU, the response must be in *real time as the physical events take place.* This is in contrast, for example, to a batch-processing environment or a data-processing situation, where the processing takes place at prescribed intervals. Real-time data acquisition often involves measurements of physical variables such as speed, temperature, voltage, or size. Measured values of such variables are called *analog data,* since they have continuous (as opposed to discrete) distributions. Where analog data is involved, a conversion of the analog data to digital format is required prior to input to the computer.

In this section we shall survey some of the application areas. We note that the traffic-light controller of the last chapter is one example of a broad application area—the general area of monitoring and control. The typical pattern here is that various measurements are made by sensing devices, this data is input to the processor, and various control signals are output in response.

Figure 12.1 depicts an instance of such an application. Here an automobile ignition system utilizes a microprocessor to continually monitor the indicated variables (inputs). In response to this input data, the processor con-

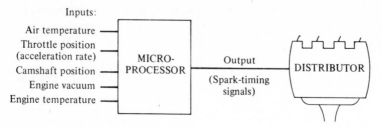

Fig. 12.1 Ignition timing application.

stantly issues signals that control the engine's ignition timing so that engine efficiency is optimal and pollutant emission is minimal at all times.

As noted, one can find numerous similar situations in which a processor is used to control machine processes, household appliances, or heating systems. The small size and weight of microprocessors has changed the nature of many kinds of applications where large computers were previously involved. As one example of this, Fig. 12.2 indicates a "distributed computation" possibility in a jet aircraft.

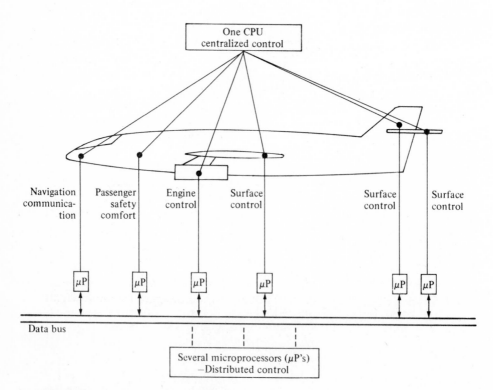

Fig. 12.2 Aircraft control application.

In Fig. 12.2, the monitor and control of the various systems with a central processor (top) involve large quantities of control and information cables running between the CPU and the various systems sites. The alternative (bottom) utilizes "on-site" microprocessors which carry out the different functions locally. The various processors can communicate through a common data bus.

The fields of medicine and health are also making increased use of microprocessors in monitor/control applications. A single machine can monitor a variety of patient functions, analyze the data, and provide a continuous readout of patient condition.

Microelectronics in general and microprocessors in particular are revolutionizing the communications field. Switching machines that control the routing of telephone calls are built around a central processor unit. Satellites now handle a heavy volume of telecommunication traffic, and again this is enabled primarily by the small size and weight of microelectronic components. Telephones that can "remember" frequently called numbers are available. Microprocessors are also common in electronic games such as pinball machines and TV video games.

"Point-of-sale" merchandising systems utilize electronic processor-controlled cash registers, which read an item's binary price code with a light-beam scanner. Such a machine can carry out calculations involving price, tax, and daily sales records on a local basis and subsequently transfer all such data to a central processing unit for more general inventory management. This use of microprocessors to perform many local and preliminary calculations has given rise to the terms "smart" and "intelligent" terminals.

Back in the area of general-purpose computing systems, the availability of intelligent terminals and small low-cost computers is forcing a restructuring of the very idea of a computing system. As an alternative to the idea of a "central processing system," we are encountering the concept of "distributed intelligence" or networks of processors. A variety of possible such multiprocessor configurations have been suggested. Figure 12.3 depicts a "peer-structure" form, in which all elements are on the same level and can communicate with all other elements. A variation on the peer-structure arrangement is the hierarchical configuration, in which each processor can subdivide its task and allocate the subtasks to one or more "slave" processors. This arrangement is also shown in Fig. 12.3.

This evolution of the architecture of computing systems has motivated the search for, and development of, new fast algorithms designed for implementation in multiprocessing systems. The structure of a particular algorithm is often dependent upon the processor configuration that will be utilized to implement the algorithm. More generally, the architectural changes are inducing changes in the software of computing systems so that the software is becoming more modularized and hence more compatible with the distributed character of the hardware.

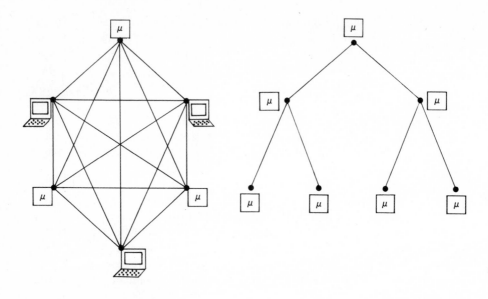

(a) Structure arrangement   (b) Hierarchical arrangement

Fig. 12.3 Distributed processing configurations.

12.2 INTERPROCESSOR COMMUNICATION

In the preceding section it was noted that multiprocessing systems are becoming increasingly popular. A problem that must be dealt with in any such system is the means by which processors will communicate with each other. In this section we briefly consider a relatively straightforward method by which one processor can pass data to another. This will provide us with another example of parallel I/O and also allow us to take a closer look at the I/O capabilities of the I8085 system.

Specifically, we wish to pass data from the M6800 to the I8085. The M6800 will output data through an MPIA device (see Sec. 11.1.1) and the I8085 will receive data through the I/O section of its 8155 RAM device (see Sec. 11.1.2). In passing data between the two different processors, we must allow for the fact that they are synchronized by different clocks. We will deal with this matter by having the processors communicate through what is known as *handshaking*. Specifically, when one processor outputs data, it sends a signal to the other processor. Upon receiving the signal, the second processor fetches and stores the data and then signals back so that the cycle may be repeated. By this method the processors are locked in step with each other.

For our present situation, we will use the MPIA's lines CB1 and CB2 (Fig. 11.1) for receiving and transmitting, respectively, the M6800's handshake signals. The B side of the MPIA is used since it provides an option which allows CB2 to serve as a WRITE strobe (see Fig. 11.5). Specifically we shall want to set the CB2 control section (bits 3, 4, 5) of control register B to 101B, so that CB2 goes low on the first low-to-high E transition (E represents the clock signal supplied to the MC6820) following a WRITE to output register B. This will serve as the signal to the I8085 that data is ready. The M6800 will then wait for the return signal from the I8085, which will arrive on line CB1. In this particular example, we shall simply have the signal on CB1 set the interrupt flag bit (bit 7) in the control register (and not interrupt the processor). As we shall see later, the signal from the I8085 will be a high-to-low transition. Consequently, according to Fig. 11.4, we want to set CB1 control (bits 0, 1) in control register B to 00B. The M6800 will thus wait for the return signal by continuously polling bit 7 of control register B.

On the I8085 side, port A of the 8155 will be used to receive the data from the M6800 (see Fig. 11.6). We shall utilize port C as a control port for port A by selecting the third alternative (ALT 3) for port C. Thus bits 0, 1, 2 become interrupt, buffer full, and strobe bits, respectively for port A. Line CB2 from the MPIA will be connected to the strobe pin ($\overline{\text{STROBE}}$) and line CB1 will be connected to the buffer full pin of port C. The interrupt pin will be connected to the I8085's RST 6.5 interrupt line. This linkage is depicted in Fig. 12.4.

Looking back at the timing diagram in Fig. 11.8, we can now see how the interchange will take place: Following an M6800 WRITE to its output register B, a signal on CB2 will strobe the 8155. This leads to an interrupt signal to the I8085 tself. The I8085, which will simply be "busy-waiting" (see Sec. 5.3), will jump to its interrupt service routine, which will fetch and store the byte of data. The READ of port A by the I8085 will send the buffer full bit low, thus providing the return signal to the M6800 on line CB1. The M6800 will then fetch and output another byte of data. This interaction is shown in Fig. 12.5.

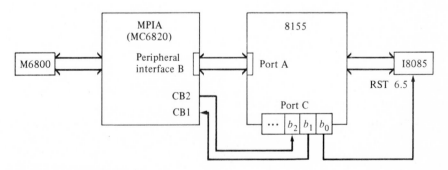

Fig. 12.4 M6800–I8085 interface.

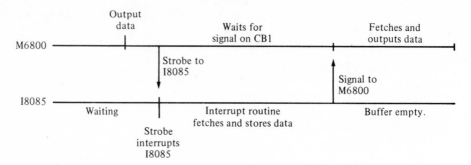

Fig. 12.5 Handshaking interaction between processors.

Referring to Fig. 11.7, we see that, to enable interrupts, select ALT 3, and configure port A as an input port, we should set the 8155's command register to 00011000B. Figure 12.6 contains two PL/M programs that reflect the fore-

```
M6800: DO;
       DECLARE
          OUTREGB BYTE AT (xxxxH),
          DDRB    BYTE AT (xxxxH),
          CREGB   BYTE AT (yyyyH),
          MORE$DATA$1 BYTE INITIAL (OFFH);
          .
          .
          .
          /* OTHER DECLARATIONS */
          .
          .
          .
       OUTBYTE:    PROCEDURE;
          .
          .
          .
          /*OUTBYTE MUST OUTPUT DATA, UPDATE*/
          /*MEMORY POINTER AND MORE$DATA$1*/
          .
          .
          .
       END OUTBYTE;
          /*MAIN PROGRAM*/
       CREGB=00H;
       DDRB=0FFH;
       CREGB=2CH;
       DO WHILE (MORE$DATA$1);
          DO WHILE ((CREGB AND 10000000B) =0);
          END;
          CALL OUTBYTE;
       END;
END M6800;
```
                    a) Routine for M6800.

Fig. 12.6 PL/M routines for passing data between processors.

```
I 8085: DO ;
       DECLARE
          CSREG BYTE AT ( z z H ) ,
          PORTA BYTE AT ( u u H ) ,
          MORE$DATA$2 BYTE INITIAL ( 0 FFH ) ;
          .
          .
          .
          / * OTHER DECLARATIONS * /
          .
          .
          .
          INBYTE:    PROCEDURE INTERRUPT 6 . 5 ;
          .
          .
          .
          / * INBYTE MUST INPUT DATA, UPDATE * /
          / * MEMORY POINTER AND MORE$DATA$2 * /
          .
          .
          .
          ENABLE ;
       END INBYTE ;
          / * MAIN PROGRAM * /
          OUTPUT ( CSREG) = 1 8 H ;
          ENABLE ;
          CALL SIM( 0 0 H) ;
          DO WHILE ( MORE$DATA$2 ) ;
       END ;
    END I 8085 ;
```

b) Routine for I8085.

Figure 12.6 (continued)

going discussion and effect the passage of data from the M6800 to the I8085.

The routine for the M6800 consists of a simple busy-wait loop, which checks to see if the I8085 is ready for more data. When the M6800 receives the signal from the I8085, the procedure OUTBYTE is called, to transfer a byte of data from memory to the output register. OUTBYTE is expected to maintain a pointer into memory and keep track of how much data remains to be sent (OUTBYTE sets MORE$DATA$1 to 0 when the data is exhausted). The I8085 uses the routine INBYTE in a similar fashion to fetch and store data; however, INBYTE is an interrupt routine (associated with interrupt line RST 6.5), as indicated by its declaration. Note the special statement ENABLE, which is compiled as Enable Interrupts (EI) and the two built-in procedures OUTPUT and SIM. The effect of OUTPUT is to assign the value given on the right of the statement to the indicated I/O location (recall that the I8085 system uses isolated I/O).

The special PL/M STAR function SIM is compiled as the I8085 SIM instruction. Consequently, it causes the indicated interrupt masks to be set as specified in the argument (see Fig. 5.15).

12.3 FUTURE DIRECTIONS

We have noted that the development of microprocessors and their supporting hardware has proceeded rapidly. This development continues, of course; and consequently the processors discussed in this book are rapidly being superseded by even more advanced processors. This does not mean that any particular current processor will become obsolete in the immediate future. However, as many processor users have a considerable software investment with one particular processor and are reluctant to change, manufacturers will often design a new processor in such a way that its instruction set includes the instruction set of its predecessor as a subset. A user will then be able to move upward to the new processor without having to abandon the entire existing software support system. This policy of "upward compatibility" is common among manufacturers of computers of all sizes.

12.3.1 Technologies

In this text we have generally been concerned with functional aspects of microprocessors as opposed to their composition and/or manufacturing process. Technological advances in these latter aspects, however, have made microprocessors possible, and promise continuing developments. In discussing future trends, we should note that most of today's microprocessors are single-chip integrated circuits produced by the *MOS* (metal-oxide semiconductor) process. Alternatively, *bipolar* processors are somewhat faster, but usually involve several chips since the bipolar process cannot be used to produce chips that are as compact as with the MOS approach. The MOS technology is further refined into PMOS (P-channel MOS), NMOS (N-channel MOS) and CMOS (Complementary MOS). NMOS is currently a common technology for medium-speed microprocessors such as the M6800 and I8085. CMOS technology yields rugged components with low-power requirements and consequently CMOS devices are often used in "noisy" environments such as automobiles, or low-power applications such as digital watches.

Bipolar microprocessors are characterized by greater speed and power requirements than MOS devices. However, the bipolar technique generally means fewer components per chip.

Bit-slice processors, which consist of identical sections (slices) of a CPU that may be combined in parallel with other such sections to form complete CPU's of various word lengths, are typically bipolar devices. Bit-slice processors are common in specialized applications requiring great speed.

A new higher-speed variation on MOS is H-MOS, which is being used by Intel in its 16-bit 8086 processor. In the bipolar area, ECL (emitter-coupled logic) technology provides a very high execution rate and will probably see increased use in the future. A second bipolar technology, I^2L (integrated injection logic) is in the early stages of development and shows great promise, since it combines many of the best features of other technologies.

These technological advances are influencing the production-level use of other microcomputer system devices as well. For example, 64K-bit RAM chips are available, and we can expect future RAM chips with even greater capacity. Moreover, memory access times and costs are decreasing: Bipolar ECL memories with access times of less than a nanosecond seem possible; bipolar I^2L technology promises both larger and cheaper single-chip memories. Other developments such as charged-couple devices (CCD's) and magnetic-bubble-domain memories are low-cost devices that can store very large amounts of data cheaply and provide short access times. These could eventually replace mass storage devices such as tapes and disks.

12.3.2 Microprocessor Advances

Trends toward putting more functions on a single chip not only imply complete computer systems on a chip, but more powerful microprocessors. The movement is presently toward 16-bit processors and eventually 32-bit processors. Sixteen-bit processors presently available include the Texas Instruments 9900, the National IMP, and the Intel 8086. Motorola's M68000 will appear soon. When compared with current eight-bit microprocessors, these new processors are seen to have more speed and computing power, more elaborate architectures, and larger instruction sets. To illustrate this, we shall briefly consider the Intel 8086 (I8086) 16-bit processor.

The I8086 is functionally divided into an execution/control unit and a bus-interface unit that can operate independently. Taking advantage of this, the bus-interface unit prefetches instructions before they are needed and can thus buffer up to six bytes of "instruction stream" in an instruction queue. This feature tends to increase CPU speed by shortening the time the execution/control unit must wait during instruction fetches.

The I8086 contains three sets of four 16-bit registers. Although these generally operate as 16-bit registers, in some cases upper and lower bytes are separately accessible. In particular, the I8086 can execute the full I8085 instruction set. Among the 16-bit registers are a base pointer, and source and destination indices, which are used for addressing purposes. Utilizing various combinations of these registers, the I8086 provides 24 addressing modes and supplies a 20-bit operand address to memory. Thus the I8086 can access up to one megabyte of memory.

The I8086's instruction set includes several string-processing operations that provide for automatic updating of source/destination pointers. Multiplication and division instructions as well as decimal arithmetic capability are available. Various iteration-control transfer instructions are included, as well as instructions specifically designed for controlling a multiprocessor configuration.

With faster clock rates in addition to the features noted above, the I8086 is considerably more powerful than the I8085. Indeed, it provides a good example of current trends in microprocessor design. More and more features of large maxicomputers are appearing at the micro level. As noted previously, however, this does not necessarily mean that the current generation of eight-bit processors are becoming obsolete. With their development costs having been paid off, they are very inexpensive and completely adequate for many applications. Moreover, we assert that, because of their relatively straightforward designs and manageable instruction sets (when compared with the newer 16-bit processors), they will continue to be of pedagogical value. Specifically, the developmental process carried out in this text demonstrates that the eight-bit processors provide a completely adequate framework for studying all the major elements of computing systems.

REFERENCES AND SUPPORTIVE MATERIAL

Various application areas of microprocessors are discussed in Leventhal (1978), Toong (1977), and Oliver (1977).

Motorola (1975) provides technical data and application information on the MC6820 parallel interface adaptor. Technical data on Intel's 8155 can be found in Intel (1977a).

Weber (1973) is suggested as a reference on semiconductor technologies, while an appendix in Leventhal (1978) also provides more up-to-date information on this subject. Intel (1978) covers the Intel 8086 microprocessor and other supporting components in the 8086 system.

1. Intel [1978], "MCS-86 User's Manual." Intel Corporation, 3065 Bowers Ave., Santa Clara, California.

2. Intel [1977a], "MSC-85 User's Manual." Intel Corporation, 3065 Bowers Ave., Santa Clara, California.

3. Leventhal, L. A. [1978], *Introduction to Microprocessors: Software, Hardware, Programming*. Englewood Cliffs, N.J.: Prentice-Hall.

4. Motorola [1975], "M6800 Microprocessor Applications Manual." Motorola Semiconductor Products Inc., Box 20912, Phoenix, Arizona.

5. Oliver, B. M. [1977], "The role of microelectronics in instrumentation and control." *Scientific American*, 237.

6. Toong, H-M. D. [1977], "Microprocessors." *Scientific American*, 237.

7. Weber, S. [1973], *Large- and Medium-Scale Integration*. New York: McGraw-Hill.

ASCII CODE

Character	Hex code	Octal code	Decimal code
NUL	00	000	0
SOH	01	001	1
STX	02	002	2
ETX	03	003	3
EOT	04	004	4
ENQ	05	005	5
ACK	06	006	6
BEL	07	007	7
BS	08	010	8
HT	09	011	9
LF	0A	012	10
VT	0B	013	11
FF	0C	014	12
CR	0D	015	13
SO	0E	016	14
SI	0F	017	15
DLE	10	020	16
DC1	11	021	17
DC2	12	022	18
DC3	13	023	19
DC4	14	024	20
NAK	15	025	21
SYN	16	026	22

Character	Hex code	Octal code	Decimal code
ETB	17	027	23
CAN	18	030	24
EM	19	031	25
SUB	1A	032	26
ESC	1B	033	27
FS	1C	034	28
GS	1D	035	29
RS	1E	036	30
US	1F	037	31
SP	20	040	32
!	21	041	33
"	22	042	34
#	23	043	35
$	24	044	36
%	25	045	37
&	26	046	38
/	27	047	39
(	28	050	40
)	29	051	41
*	2A	052	42
+	2B	053	43
,	2C	054	44
-	2D	055	45
.	2E	056	46
/	2F	057	47
0	30	060	48
1	31	061	49
2	32	062	50
3	33	063	51
4	34	064	52
5	35	065	53
6	36	066	54
7	37	067	55
8	38	070	56
9	39	071	57
:	3A	072	58

Character	Hex code	Octal code	Decimal code
;	3B	073	59
<	3C	074	60
=	3D	075	61
>	3E	076	62
?	3F	077	63
@	40	100	64
A	41	101	65
B	42	102	66
C	43	103	67
D	44	104	68
E	45	105	69
F	46	106	70
G	47	107	71
H	48	110	72
I	49	111	73
J	4A	112	74
K	4B	113	75
L	4C	114	76
M	4D	115	77
N	4E	116	78
O	4F	117	79
P	50	120	80
Q	51	121	81
R	52	122	82
S	53	123	83
T	54	124	84
U	55	125	85
V	56	126	86
W	57	127	87
X	58	130	88
Y	59	131	89
Z	5A	132	90
[	5B	133	91
\	5C	134	92
]	5D	135	93
∧	5E	136	94

Character	Hex code	Octal code	Decimal code
—	5F	137	95
`	60	140	96
a	61	141	97
b	62	142	98
c	63	143	99
d	64	144	100
e	65	145	101
f	66	146	102
g	67	147	103
h	68	150	104
i	69	151	105
j	6A	152	106
k	6B	153	107
l	6C	154	108
m	6D	155	109
n	6E	156	110
o	6F	157	111
p	70	160	112
q	71	161	113
r	72	162	114
s	73	163	115
t	74	164	116
u	75	165	117
v	76	166	118
w	77	167	119
x	78	170	120
y	79	171	121
z	7A	172	122
{	7B	173	123
|	7C	174	124
}	7D	175	125
~	7E	176	126
DEL	7F	177	127

M6800 INSTRUCTIONS LISTED NUMERICALLY BY OPCODE

In the table, the following notation has been utilized:

DIR:	direct addressing
EXT:	extended addressing
IND:	indexed addressing
IMM:	immediate addressing
REL:	relative address
*:	unused opcode

Opcode (hex)	Instruction	Opcode (hex)	Instruction
00	*	11	CBA
01	NOP	12	*
02	*	13	*
03	*	14	*
04	*	15	*
05	*	16	TAB
06	TAP	17	TBA
07	TPA	18	*
08	INX	19	DAA
09	DEX	1A	*
0A	CLV	1B	ABA
0B	SEV	1C	*
0C	CLC	1D	*
0D	SEC	1E	*
0E	CLI	1F	*
0F	SEI	20	BRA REL
10	SBA	21	*

Opcode (hex)	Instruction		Opcode (hex)	Instruction	
22	BHI	REL	47	ASR	A
23	BLS	REL	48	ASL	A
24	BCC	REL	49	ROL	A
25	BCS	REL	4A	DEC	A
26	BNE	REL	4B	*	
27	BEQ	REL	4C	INC	A
28	BVC	REL	4D	TST	A
29	BVS	REL	4E	*	
2A	BPL	REL	4F	CLR	A
2B	BMI	REL	50	NEG	B
2C	BGE	REL	51	*	
2D	BLT	REL	52	*	
2E	BGT	REL	53	COM	B
2F	BLE	REL	54	LSR	B
30	TSX		55	*	
31	INS		56	ROR	B
32	PUL	A	57	ASR	B
33	PUL	B	58	ASL	B
34	DES		59	ROL	B
35	TXS		5A	DEC	B
36	PSH	A	5B	*	
37	PSH	B	5C	INC	B
38	*		5D	TST	B
39	RTS		5E	*	
3A	*		5F	CLR	B
3B	RTI		60	NEG	IND
3C	*		61	*	
3D	*		62	*	
3E	WAI		63	COM	IND
3F	SWI		64	LSR	IND
40	NEG	A	65	*	
41	*		66	ROR	IND
42	*		67	ASR	IND
43	COM	A	68	ASL	IND
44	LSR	A	69	ROL	IND
45	*		6A	DEC	IND
46	ROR	A	6B	*	

Opcode (hex)	Instruction			Opcode (hex)	Instruction		
6C	INC		IND	91	CMP	A	DIR
6D	TST		IND	92	SBC	A	DIR
6E	JMP		IND	93		*	
6F	CLR		IND	94	AND	A	DIR
70	NEG		EXT	95	BIT	A	DIR
71		*		96	LDA	A	DIR
72		*		97	STA	A	DIR
73	COM		EXT	98	EOR	A	DIR
74	LSR		EXT	99	ADC	A	DIR
75		*		9A	ORA	A	DIR
76	ROR		EXT	9B	ADD	A	DIR
77	ASR		EXT	9C	CPX		DIR
78	ASL		EXT	9D		*	
79	ROL		EXT	9E	LDS		DIR
7A	DEC		EXT	9F	STS		DIR
7B		*		A0	SUB	A	IND
7C	INC		EXT	A1	CMP	A	IND
7D	TST		EXT	A2	SBC	A	IND
7E	JMP		EXT	A3		*	
7F	CLR		EXT	A4	AND	A	IND
80	SUB	A	IMM	A5	BIT	A	IND
81	CMP	A	IMM	A6	LDA	A	IND
82	SBC	A	IMM	A7	STA	A	IND
83		*		A8	EOR	A	IND
84	AND	A	IMM	A9	ADC	A	IND
85	BIT	A	IMM	AA	ORA	A	IND
86	LDA	A	IMM	AB	ADD	A	IND
87		*		AC	CPX		IND
88	EOR	A	IMM	AD	JSR		IND
89	ADC	A	IMM	AE	LDS		IND
8A	ORA	A	IMM	AF	STS		IND
8B	ADD	A	IMM	B0	SUB	A	EXT
8C	CPX		IMM	B1	CMP	A	EXT
8D	BSR		REL	B2	SBC	A	EXT
8E	LDS		IMM	B3		*	
8F		*		B4	AND	A	EXT
90	SUB	A	DIR	B5	BIT	A	EXT

Opcode (hex)	Instruction			Opcode (hex)	Instruction		
B6	LDA	A	EXT	DB	ADD	B	DIR
B7	STA	A	EXT	DC	*		
B8	EOR	A	EXT	DD	*		
B9	ADC	A	EXT	DE	LDX		DIR
BA	ORA	A	EXT	DF	STX		DIR
BB	ADD	A	EXT	E0	SUB	B	IND
BC	CPX		EXT	E1	CMP	B	IND
BD	JSR		EXT	E2	SBC	B	IND
BE	LDS		EXT	E3	*		
BF	STS		EXT	E4	AND	B	IND
C0	SUB	B	IMM	E5	BIT	B	IND
C1	CMP	B	IMM	E6	LDA	B	IND
C2	SBC	B	IMM	E7	STA	B	IND
C3	*			E8	EOR	B	IND
C4	AND	B	IMM	E9	ADC	B	IND
C5	BIT	B	IMM	EA	ORA	B	IND
C6	LDA	B	IMM	EB	ADD	B	IND
C7	*			EC	*		
C8	EOR	B	IMM	ED	*		
C9	ADC	B	IMM	EE	LDX		IND
CA	ORA	B	IMM	EF	STX		IND
CB	ADD	B	IMM	F0	SUB	B	EXT
CC	*			F1	CMP	B	EXT
CD	*			F2	SBC	B	EXT
CE	LDX		IMM	F3	*		
CF	*			F4	AND	B	EXT
D0	SUB	B	DIR	F5	BIT	B	EXT
D1	CMP	B	DIR	F6	LDA	B	EXT
D2	SBC	B	DIR	F7	STA	B	EXT
D3	*			F8	EOR	B	EXT
D4	AND	B	DIR	F9	ADC	B	EXT
D5	BIT	B	DIR	FA	ORA	B	EXT
D6	LDA	B	DIR	FB	ADD	B	EXT
D7	STA	B	DIR	FC	*		
D8	EOR	B	DIR	FD	*		
D9	ADC	B	DIR	FE	LDX		EXT
DA	ORA	B	DIR	FF	STX		EXT

I8085 INSTRUCTIONS LISTED NUMERICALLY BY OPCODE

In the table, the following notation has been used:

D16: 16-bit immediate data
D8:   8-bit immediate data
ADR: 16-bit address
*:   unused opcode

Opcode (hex)	Instruction		Opcode (hex)	Instruction	
00	NOP		13	INX	D
01	LXI	B,D16	14	INR	D
02	STAX	B	15	DCR	D
03	INX	B	16	MVI	D,D8
04	INR	B	17	RAL	
05	DCR	B	18	*	
06	MVI	B,D8	19	DAD	D
07	RLC		1A	LDAX	D
08	*		1B	DCX	D
09	DAD	B	1C	INR	E
0A	LDAX	B	1D	DCR	E
0B	DCX	B	1E	MVI	E,D8
0C	INR	C	1F	RAR	
0D	DCR	C	20	RIM	
0E	MVI	C,D8	21	LXI	H,D16
0F	RRC		22	SHLD	ADR
10	*		23	INX	H
11	LXI	D,D16	24	INR	H
12	STAX	D	25	DCR	H

Opcode (hex)	Instruction		Opcode (hex)	Instruction	
26	MVI	H,D8	4B	MOV	C,E
27	DAA		4C	MOV	C,H
28	*		4D	MOV	C,L
29	DAD	H	4E	MOV	C,M
2A	LHLD	ADR	4F	MOV	C,A
2B	DCX	H	50	MOV	D,B
2C	INR	L	51	MOV	D,C
2D	DCR	L	52	MOV	D,D
2E	MVI	L,D8	53	MOV	D,E
2F	CMA		54	MOV	D,H
30	SIM		55	MOV	D,L
31	LXI	SP,D16	56	MOV	D,M
32	STA	ADR	57	MOV	D,A
33	INX	SP	58	MOV	E,B
34	INR	M	59	MOV	E,C
35	DCR	M	5A	MOV	E,D
36	MVI	M,D8	5B	MOV	E,E
37	STC		5C	MOV	E,H
38	*		5D	MOV	E,L
39	DAD	SP	5E	MOV	E,M
3A	LDA	ADR	5F	MOV	E,A
3B	DCX	SP	60	MOV	H,B
3C	INR	A	61	MOV	H,C
3D	DCR	A	62	MOV	H,D
3E	MVI	A,D8	63	MOV	H,E
3F	CMC		64	MOV	H,H
40	MOV	B,B	65	MOV	H,L
41	MOV	B,C	66	MOV	H,M
42	MOV	B,D	67	MOV	H,A
43	MOV	B,E	68	MOV	L,B
44	MOV	B,H	69	MOV	L,C
45	MOV	B,L	6A	MOV	L,D
46	MOV	B,M	6B	MOV	L,E
47	MOV	B,A	6C	MOV	L,H
48	MOV	C,B	6D	MOV	L,L
49	MOV	C,C	6E	MOV	L,M
4A	MOV	C,D	6F	MOV	L,A

Opcode (hex)	Instruction		Opcode (hex)	Instruction	
70	MOV	M,B	95	SUB	L
71	MOV	M,C	96	SUB	M
72	MOV	M,D	97	SUB	A
73	MOV	M,E	98	SBB	B
74	MOV	M,H	99	SBB	C
75	MOV	M,L	9A	SBB	D
76	HLT		9B	SBB	E
77	MOV	M,A	9C	SBB	H
78	MOV	A,B	9D	SBB	L
79	MOV	A,C	9E	SBB	M
7A	MOV	A,D	9F	SBB	A
7B	MOV	A,E	A0	ANA	B
7C	MOV	A,H	A1	ANA	C
7D	MOV	A,L	A2	ANA	D
7E	MOV	A,M	A3	ANA	E
7F	MOV	A,A	A4	ANA	H
80	ADD	B	A5	ANA	L
81	ADD	C	A6	ANA	M
82	ADD	D	A7	ANA	A
83	ADD	E	A8	XRA	B
84	ADD	H	A9	XRA	C
85	ADD	L	AA	XRA	D
86	ADD	M	AB	XRA	E
87	ADD	A	AC	XRA	H
88	ADC	B	AD	XRA	L
89	ADC	C	AE	XRA	M
8A	ADC	D	AF	XRA	A
8B	ADC	E	B0	ORA	B
8C	ADC	H	B1	ORA	C
8D	ADC	L	B2	ORA	D
8E	ADC	M	B3	ORA	E
8F	ADC	A	B4	ORA	H
90	SUB	B	B5	ORA	L
91	SUB	C	B6	ORA	M
92	SUB	D	B7	ORA	A
93	SUB	E	B8	CMP	B
94	SUB	H	B9	CMP	C

Opcode (hex)	Instruction		Opcode (hex)	Instruction	
BA	CMP	D	DD	*	
BB	CMP	E	DE	SBI	D8
BC	CMP	H	DF	RST	3
BD	CMP	L	E0	RPO	
BE	CMP	M	E1	POP	H
BF	CMP	A	E2	JPO	ADR
C0	RNZ		E3	XTHL	
C1	POP	B	E4	CPO	ADR
C2	JNZ	ADR	E5	PUSH	H
C3	JMP	ADR	E6	ANI	D8
C4	CNZ	ADR	E7	RST	4
C5	PUSH	B	E8	RPE	
C6	ADI	D8	E9	PCHL	
C7	RST	0	EA	JPE	ADR
C8	RZ		EB	XCHG	
C9	RET		EC	CPE	ADR
CA	JZ	ADR	ED	*	
CB	*		EE	XRI	D8
CC	CZ	ADR	EF	RST	5
CD	CALL	ADR	F0	RP	
CE	ACI	D8	F1	POP	PSW
CF	RST	1	F2	JP	ADR
D0	RNC		F3	DI	
D1	POP	D	F4	CP	ADR
D2	JNC	ADR	F5	PUSH	PSW
D3	OUT	D8	F6	ORI	D8
D4	CNC	ADR	F7	RST	6
D5	PUSH	D	F8	RM	
D6	SUI	D8	F9	SPHL	
D7	RST	2	FA	JM	ADR
D8	RC		FB	EI	
D9	*		FC	CM	ADR
DA	JC	ADR	FD	*	
DB	IN	D8	FE	CPI	D8
DC	CC	ADR	FF	RST	7

MOTOROLA M6800 ASSEMBLER CONVENTIONS

The assembler described here was developed at Southern Illinois University for use in conjunction with the PL/M STAR compiler. In most respects, this assembler is quite similar to the M68SAM cross-assembler developed by Motorola (see Motorola, 1976).

ASSEMBLER OUTPUT

1. *Listing.* The assembler listing includes the source program as well as additional information generated by the assembler.

2. *Object file.* The assembler produces an object file in either a standard or a modified format as follows:

a) Standard Format:

S0 xxxxxx	Header
S1 nnaaaa b1b2b3b4b5b7 . . . bncc	
.	Data
:	
S9 020000FC	Trailer

Relocation dictionary records (1 record per relocation address)
External symbol dictionary records (1 record per symbol)

Where

    nn   = Number of bytes following,
    aaaa = Address,
    bx   = Data bytes,
    cc   = Checksum.

b) Modified Format

This format is appropriate for downloading directly to a microcomputer and assumes that no RSEG or EXTERN directives occur in the source program.

gnnaaaab1b2b3 . . . bn
nnaaaab1b2b3 . . . bn
nnaaaab1b2b3 . . . bn
nnaaaab1b2b3 . . . bn

.
.
.

nnaaaab1b2b3 . . . bn

00

Where

nn	= Number of data bytes following,
aaaa	= Address,
bx	= Data byte,
00	= Contents of very last record,
g	= A "garbage" byte that is inserted so that each record will have exactly 4 bytes in front of it when downloading.

ASSEMBLER STATEMENT FIELDS

An M6800 assembler statement has at most four fields, that is,

label   operation   operand   comment

The fields are free-format with the following exceptions:

1. If a label is used, it must start in column one.

2. If the entire line is a comment, an asterisk must be placed in column one.

3. At least one space must be used to separate the fields.

LABEL FIELD

At most six characters may be used in a label, the first of which must be a letter. The remaining characters must be letters or numbers. The symbols "A", "B", and "X" are used to denote the accumulators and the index register and therefore are not permitted for use as user-defined labels.

Unless otherwise specified, the label field is optional on statements.

OPERATION FIELD

The M6800 mnemonics are placed in the operation field of an instruction. For those instructions that specify an accumulator, the accumulator reference may appear in the operation field or it may be separated from the operation by at most one space, for example,

INC A   and   INCA

are equivalent.

OPERAND FIELD

The information that appears in the operand field is dependent on the type of operation that is specified in the operation field and the addressing mode that is being used. Some instructions do not require that an address be specified, for example, SWI, RTS, and TSX. For instructions in this category, the operand field is empty.

The indexed addressing mode is indicated by using an "X" in the operand field preceded by the indexing offset. The offset and the "X" are separated by a comma. If the offset is zero, it may be omitted, together with the comma.

Examples

a) ADDA   4,X   b) LDAA   X

A "#" sign at the beginning of the operand field is used to denote the immediate addressing mode. In this case the operand is treated as immediate data for the instruction.

Examples

a) LDAA   #0   b) LDAA   #0   c) ADDB   #1

No special notation is needed for relative, direct, or extended addressing since these addressing modes can be determined from context alone. For example, the branch instructions, BRA, BGT, etc., use only relative addressing, so an address found in the operand field of one of these instructions is interpreted relative to the updated value of the PC. For instructions that use either direct, extended, indexed, or immediate addressing, the absence of a "#" or an "X" in the operand field implies the use of either direct or extended addressing. Direct addressing is used if the address is in the range 00 to FF hex, while extended addressing is used if the address is in the range 100 to FFFF hex. If a symbolic name is used in the operand field, the address associated with the same name determines whether direct or extended addressing is used.

Note that this implies that the address associated with a symbolic name is known at the point the symbolic name is referenced. This is quite often not the case, since it is very common, in assembly-language programs, to use a symbolic name prior to the point in the program where it is declared, i.e., where it appears in the label field. This situation is resolved by the M6800 assembler by assuming that extended addressing will be used when the address of a symbolic name is not known at the point of reference. If the user wishes to use direct addressing for certain symbolic names, it is necessary to declare these names prior to any reference usage in the program.

COMMENT FIELD

The M6800 assembler does not require any special symbol to begin the comment field. A blank must follow the operation field, and everything to the right of this blank is treated as a comment. If the assembler statement does not have an operand field, then everything to the right of the blank following the operation field is treated as a comment.

ADDRESS (OPERAND) SPECIFICATION

There are various ways of specifying addresses or operands in the M6800 assembler. The options are illustrated in the following examples:

i) Symbolic Names.

   a) LDAA   TEMP
   b) LDX   #SUM
   c) BRA   LOOP

ii) Hex Constants

These are denoted by a trailing H. If the latter notation is used, the number must start with one of the digits 0–9.

   a) LDAB   #0FAH   b) DEC   5AH

iii) Binary Constants

These are denoted by a trailing B.

   a) ADDB   #10111010B   b) BIT A   #00001111B

iv) Decimal Constants

This is the default case; that is, no special notation is needed.

   a) ADDA   15   b) BRA   17

v) Single ASCII Character Constants

These are denoted by a single leading quote (').

a) LDAA   'B   b) CMPB   'Z

**vi) Expressions Involving Any of the Above
in Combination with +, − and ∗ (multiplication).**

Expressions relative to the current updated value of the PC can be calculated by using ∗ to denote the updated PC value. Used in this sense, ∗ is distinguished from multiplication by context. Expressions are evaluated on a left-to-right basis with multiplication taking a higher precedence than addition and subtraction.

a) LDAB   TEMP + 1   b) BLT   ∗ + 14   c) LDX   T1∗2 + 3

ABSOLUTE AND RELOCATABLE EXPRESSIONS

A symbol is said to be relocatable if:

a) It is a label while the directive RSEG (see below) is in effect.

b) It has been set equal to a relocatable value with the EQU directive (see below).

c) It has been delcared as EXTERNAL using the EXTRN directive (see below).

In all other cases a symbol is absolute, i.e.,

a) It is a label while the directive ASEG (see below) is in effect.

b) It has been set equal to an absolute value with the EQU directive (see below).

Relocatable symbols may appear in expressions under certain circumstances. The table below indicates the type of an expression in terms of the types of its components. In this table, R denotes a relocatable expression, A an absolute expression, and I an illegal combination.

	X:A Y:A	X:A Y:R	X:R Y:A	X:R Y:R
X+Y	A	R	R	I
X−Y	A	I	I	A
X∗Y	A	I	I	I

ASSEMBLER DIRECTIVE STATEMENTS

The M6800 assembler supports several assembler directive statements, including the NAM, END, ORG, EQU, FCC, FCB, FDB, RMB, ASEG, RSEG, EXTRN, PUBLIC, PAGE, and SKIP directives. The label field is required for the EQU directive; it should not be used on the NAM, ORG, ASEG, RSEG, PAGE, and SKIP directives and it is optional on the END, EXTRN, PUBLIC, FCC, FCB, FDB, and RMB directives. In all cases, the directive itself must be placed in the operation field. These directives are grouped into four categories (Assembly Control, Symbol Definition, Data Definition, Storage Control, and Listing Control) and discussed individually below.

1. Assembly Control

    i) NAM

        Format: NAM   program name

        Description: The program name used in this statement must be a symbolic name that conforms with the normal rules for M6800 labels. This directive must be the first statement in a M6800 assembly-language program. Its purpose is to name the program module.

    ii) END

        Format: label   END

        Description: This directive must be the last statement in an M6800 program. Its purpose is to mark the end of the source program. The label, when used, would normally be the program name.

    iii) ORG

        Format: ORG   expression

        Description: This directive changes the location counter of the M6800 assembler by setting it to the value of expression. This value must lie in the range of 0000–FFFF hex. The next memory location used by the assembler will be the location whose address is the value of expression. More than one ORG statement is permitted in an assembler program. If an initial ORG is not present, the location counter is set to 0 by default.

    iv) ASEG

        Format: ASEG

        Description: The ASEG directive indicates that all source statements from then on are to be assembled with absolute addresses. This is the default setting and remains in effect until an RSEG is encountered.

v) RSEG

Format: RSEG

Description: The RSEG directive indicates to the assembler that source statements following are to be relocatable. This directive remains in effect until an ASEG directive is encountered. All labels defined while the RSEG is in effect will be relocatable symbols.

2. Symbol Definition

vi) EQU

Format: label   EQU   expression

Description: The EQU directive must have a label. Its function is to assign the value of the expression to the symbolic name that appears in the label field. The expression may reference symbols, but only symbols whose values are known at the point the EQU is processed. The symbolic name may not be redefined at a later point in the program.

vii) EXTRN

Format: EXTRN   symbol1, symbol2, . . .

Description: The EXTRN directive in this format indicates to the assembler that the symbol names in the operand field are not defined in this program segment, but elsewhere in another program segment.

Format: label   EXTRN   symbol

Description: The EXTRN directive in this format behaves similar to the EQU directive. It is used to inform the assembler that symbol was a variable declared in a PL/M STAR program, and label was the internal name used for that variable. This information is passed on to the loader. This symbol is not declared in this program segment but in another program segment.

viii) PUBLIC

Format: PUBLIC   symbol1, symbol2, . . .

Description: The PUBLIC directive in this format informs the assembler that the symbols appearing in the list may be referenced by other program segments. The symbols must be defined in this program segment.

Format: label   PUBLIC   symbol

The PUBLIC directive in this format is used to indicate to the assembler that symbol is a variable declared in a PL/M STAR program, and label is its name internal to the compiler. Symbol is declared in this program segment but may be accessed in another program segment.

3. Data Definition and Storage Control

ix) FCB

Format: optlabel   FCB   expression list

Description: The label is optional for this directive. The function of the FCB (Form Constant Byte) is to store in successive memory locations the byte values of the operands found in the expression list. If a label is used with this directive, the value of the label will be the address of the location where the first byte value, the value of the first operand, is stored.

The expression list is simply a list of expressions separated by commas. A null expression is also permitted and is indicated by two adjacent commas. The value of the null expression is zero. If the value of any of the expressions is larger than 255 decimal, i.e., it cannot be held in one byte, the value is truncated on the left before the store.

Example

a) L1   FCB   5H,FFH,,32,FFFEH,17H   stores

05	FF	00	20	FE	17

and the value of L1 is the address of the location where "05" is stored.

x) FCC

Format: optlabel   FCC   character form

Description: The FCC (Form Constant Character) directive stores in successive memory locations the ASCII representations of the characters found in the character form. The character form may be expressed in two different ways, i.e.,

1. count, character string, or
2. dcharacter stringd.

In both forms the character string may contain any of the ASCII characters whose values range from 20H(SP) to 5FH($\_$). For form 1, count is a number that denotes the number of characters in the character string. In form 2, a delimiter d is used to mark the beginning and end of the string. The delimiter may be any single ASCII character.

The label field is optional for this directive. If a symbolic name is used in the label field, its value is the address of the location where the first character is stored.

Examples

a) FCC 4,ABCD stores

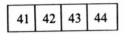

b) FCC 5,AB12 stores

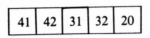

c) FCC /ABC/ stores

d) FCC ABCA stores

42	43

   xi) **FDB**

   Format: optlabel FDB expression list

   Description: The FDB (Form Double Byte) directive stores in successive memory locations the 16-bit values of the operands found in the expression list. Each 16-bit value is stored in most significant byte, least significant byte order. If a label is used with this directive, the value of the label will be the address of the location where the most significant byte of the value of the first operand is stored.

   The expression list is a list of expressions separated by commas. A null expression, indicated by two adjacent commas, is also permitted. The value of the null expression is zero.

Example

a) L1 FDB 01F2H,,0FH stores

01	F2	00	00	00	0F

   xii) **RMB**

   Format: optlabel RMB expression

   Description: The RMB (Reserve Memory Byte) directive sets the location counter of the assembler to the current value of the location counter plus the value of the expression. The effect is that N bytes of successive memory bytes are reserved, where N is the value of the expression. The label is optional, but if used, its value is the address of the first reserved byte. Note that no values are stored in the reserved bytes.

4. Listing Control

xiii) PAGE

Format: PAGE

Description: This directive will cause printer to go to top of next page. There can be no label and no operands. The directive is not printed in the listing.

xiv) SKIP

Format: SKIP   n

Description: This will cause the printer to skip "n" lines in the listing. The directive is not printed. If the skip is past the bottom margin, the directive will go to a new page.

INTEL 8085 ASSEMBLER CONVENTIONS

The assembler described here was developed at Southern Illinois University for use in conjunction with the PL/M STAR compiler. In most respects, this assembler is quite similar to the 8080/8085 assembler developed by Intel (see Intel 1977).

ASSEMBLER OUPUT

1. *Listing.* The assembler listing includes the source program as well as additional information generated by the assembler.

2. *Object file.* The assembler produces an object file in either a standard or a modified format as follows:

a) Standard Format:

S0	xxxxxx	Header
S1	nnaaaa b1b2b3b4b5b6 . . . bncc	Data
	.	
	.	
	.	
S9 030000FC		Trailer

Relocation Dictionary Records (1 record per relocation address)
External Symbol Dictionary Records (1 record per symbol)

where

nn   = Number of bytes following,
aaaa = Address,
bx   = Data bytes,
cc   = checksum.

b) Modified Format:

This format is appropriate for downloading directly to a microcomputer and assumes that no RSEG or EXTERN directives occur in the source program.

gnnaaaab1b2b3 . . . bn
nnaaaab1b2b3 . . . bn
nnaaaab1b2b3 . . . bn
nnaaaab1b2b3 . . . bn

.

.

.

nnaaaab1b2b3 . . . bn
00

where

nn	=	Number of data bytes following,
aaaa	=	Address,
bx	=	Data byte,
00	=	Contents of very last record,
g	=	A "garbage" byte that is inserted so that each record will have exactly 4 bytes in front of it when downloading.

ASSEMBLER STATEMENT FIELDS

An I8085 assembler statement has at most four fields, i.e.,

> label: operation   operand   ;comment

The fields are free-format, but at least one blank must be used to separate the operation field from the operand field.

LABEL FIELD

At most six characters may be used in a label, the first of which must be a letter. The remaining characters must be letters or numbers. The label field must be terminated with a colon. The symbols "A", "B", "C", "D", "E", "H", "L", "M", "SP", and "PSW" are used to denote the registers and therefore are not permitted for use as user-defined labels.

Unless otherwise specified, the label field is optional on statements.

OPERATION FIELD

The I8085 mnemonics are placed in the operation field of an instruction.

OPERAND FIELD

The information that appears in the operand field is dependent on the type of operation that is specified in the operation field. Some instructions do not require that an address be specified, e.g., XCHG, HLT, RAL, etc. For instructions in this category, the operand field is empty.

Most of the I8085 instructions require one or two operands. When two operands are required they are separated by a comma. In this case, the first operand specifies the destination of the instruction, while the second operand specifies the source.

COMMENT FIELD

The beginning of the comment field is signalled by the appearance of a semicolon on the source line. Everything to the right of the semicolon is treated as a comment. If the semicolon appears in column one of the source line, then the whole line is a comment.

ADDRESS (OPERAND) SPECIFICATION

There are various ways of specifying addresses or operands in the I8085 assembler depending on the type of information that is required. There are eight different ways of specifying this information. These options are illustrated in the following examples:

i) User-defined Symbolic Names.

  a) LDA   TEMP   b) JMP   LOOP

ii) Preassigned Symbolic Names.

The reserved symbols that are used to denote the registers have preassigned values as indicated below.

Symbol	Preassigned value (decimal)
A	7
B	0
C	1
D	2
E	3
H	4
L	5
M	6
SP	6
PSW	6

  a) ADD   B   b) MOV   C,A   c) POP   PSW

iii) Hex Constants, Denoted by a Trailing H.

The number must start with one of the digits 0–9.

a) MVI   D,0F9H   b) LXI   B,1F2AH   c) LDA   2000H

iv) Binary Constants, Denoted by a Trailing B.

a) ORI   01101111B   b) MVI   A,00001011B

v) Decimal Constants, the default case; i.e., no special notation is needed. A trailing D may be optionally specified.

a) MVI   D,12   b) LXI   D,1957D

vi) ASCII character constants denoted by a single leading quote ('),

a) MVI   H, 'Z   B) LXI   B, 'AB

vii) Expressions.

Expressions are formed using any of the constants in (i) through (vi) above in combination with the arithmetic operations + , − , * (multiplication) and parentheses. In addition, the special symbol $ may be used in expressions to denote the current value of the location counter. Expressions are evaluated on a left-to-right basis with multiplication taking a higher precedence than addition and subtraction. Expressions containing relocatable symbols are discussed in the next section.

Examples

a) JMP $ + 14   b) MVI   A,01101110B   c) LXI   H,17H*3FH

ABSOLUTE AND RELOCATABLE EXPRESSIONS

A symbol is said to be relocatable if:

a) It is a label while the directive RSEG (see below) is in effect.

b) It has been set equal to a relocatable value with the EQU directive (see page 304).

c) It has been declared as EXTERNAL using the EXTRN directive (see page 305).

In all other cases a symbol is absolute; that is,

a) It is a label while the directive ASEG (see page 304) is in effect.

b) It has been set equal to an absolute value with the EQU directive (see page 304).

Relocatable symbols may appear in expressions under certain circumstances. The table below indicates the type of an expression in terms of the types of its components. In this table, R denotes a relocatable expression, A an absolute expression, and I an illegal combination.

	X:A Y:A	X:A Y:R	X:R Y:A	X:R Y:R
X+Y	A	R	R	I
X−Y	A	I	I	A
X∗Y	A	I	I	I

ASSEMBLER DIRECTIVE STATEMENTS

The I8085 assembler supports the NAME, END, ORG, EQU, EXTRN, PUBLIC, ASEG, RSEG, PAGE, SKIP, DB, DW, and DS directives. Labels may be used with the DS, DB, DW, END, ORG, EXTRN, and PUBLIC directives. The EQU directive uses a name field instead of a label field. A symbolic name, which is formed according to the usual rules, appears where the label field would normally be; the distinction is that the name field is *not* terminated with a colon.

In all cases, the directive itself must be placed in the operation field. The directives are divided into four groups (Assembly Control, Symbol Definition, Data Definition, Storage Control, and Listing Control) and considered individually below.

1. Assembly Control

i) NAME

Format: NAME   name

Description: The NAME directive gives the program module a name that can be referenced by the linker. < Name > is a string of characters formed using the same rules as for a symbol. The NAME directive is required and must be the first line in a source deck. Labels are not allowed.

ii) ORG

Format: optlabel: ORG   expression

Description: This directive changes the location counter of the
I8085 assembler by setting it to the value of the expression. The
value must lie in the range 0000–FFFF hex. The next memory location used by the assembler will be the location whose address is the
value of the expression. More than one ORG statement is permitted in an assembler program. If an initial ORG is not present,
the location counter is set to 0 by default. If a label is used, its
value will be the value of the location counter before it is updated
by the ORG. ORG's are ignored when the RSEG directive is in
effect.

iii) END

Format: optlabel: END   optexpression

Description: This directive must be the last statement in an I8085
program. Its purpose is to mark the end of the source program.
The label and expression are optional. If an expression is present,
the value of this expression is taken to be the start address of the
program. A start address of zero is assumed if no expression is
present.

iv) ASEG

Format: ASEG

Description: The ASEG directive indicates that all subsequent
source statements are to be assembled with absolute addresses. This
is the default setting and remains in effect until an RSEG is encountered

v) RSEG

Format: RSEG

Description: The RSEG directive indicates to the assembler that
source statements following are to be relocatable. This directive
remains in effect until an ASEG directive is encountered. All labels
defined while the RSEG is in effect will be relocatable symbols.

2. **Symbol Definition**

vi) EQU

Format: name   EQU   expression

Description: This directive evaluates the expression and puts the result in the symbol table as the value of the symbol in the name field. Note:

```
ABC    EQU    5
DEF    EQU    ABC
```

is legal, assigning the value 5 for DEF, while

```
ABC    EQU    DEF
DEF    EQU    7
```

is not legal because ABC will never get a value.

External symbols cannot be used in the expression.

vii) **EXTRN**

Format: EXTRN   symbol1, symbol2, . . .

Description: The EXTRN directive informs the assembler that symbols named in the operand field are not defined in this program segment, but defined elsewhere in another program segment.

Format: label   EXTRN   symbol

Description: The EXTRN directive in this format behaves similarly to the EQU directive. It is used to tell the assembler that "symbol" was a variable declared in a PL/M STAR program and "label" was the internal name used for that variable. This information is passed on to the linking loader. This statement is normally used only by the PL/M STAR compiler. Label is not declared in this program segment.

viii) **PUBLIC**

Format: PUBLIC   symbol1, symbol2, . . .

Description: The PUBLIC directive informs the assembler that the symbols appearing in the symbol list may be referenced by other program segments. The symbols must be defined in this program segment.

Format: label   PUBLIC   symbol

Description: This directive in this form is used to equate "label" and "symbol" to be the same symbol. This statement is normally generated by the PL/M STAR compiler and is not normally used by the assembly-language programmer. "Symbol" is the variable name, and "label" is the compiler internal name. Label is declared in this program segment, and may be accessed by other program segments.

3. Data Definition and Storage Control

ix) DS

Format: optlabel: DS   expression

Description: The DS (Define Storage) directive sets the location counter of the assembler to the current value of the location counter plus the value of the expression. The effect is that N successive memory bytes are reserved, where N is the value of the expression. The label is optional but, if used, its value is the address of the first reserved byte. Note that no values are stored in the reserved bytes.

x) DB

Format: optlabel: DB   expression list

Description: The function of the DB (Define Byte) directive is to store in successive memory locations the byte values of the operands found in the expression list. If a label is used with this directive, the value of the label will be the address of the location where the first byte value is stored.

The expression list is simply a list of expressions separated by commas. There is a limit of at most eight expressions per expression list. Each expression can be either an ASCII string constant, e.g., 'ABC, or a numeric expression, e.g., 15H, TEMP + 4, etc. For ASCII strings, the ASCII code for each character in the string is stored in successive locations. Numeric expressions store only one value, the value of the expression. If the value of a numeric expression is larger than 255 decimal, i.e., it cannot be held in one byte, the value is truncated on the left before the store.

Example

L1:   DB   5H,17,'AB,1759H stores

05	11	41	42	59

and the value of L1 is the address of the location where '05' is stored.

xi) DW

Format: optlabel: DW   expression list

Description: The DW (Define Word) directive stores in successive memory locations the 16-bit value of each expression in the expression list. Each 16-bit value is stored in least significant byte, most significant byte order. If a label is used with this directive, the value of the label will be the address of the location where the least significant byte of the first expression is stored.

The expression list is a list of expressions separated by commas. At most eight expressions can be used in a list. ASCII character strings of length one or two characters are permitted.

Example

L1:   DW   01F2H,0FH, 'AB stores

F2	01	0F	00	42	41

4. Listing Control

xii) PAGE

Format: PAGE

Description: This directive will cause printer to go to top of next page. There can be no label and no operands. The directive is not printed in the listing.

xiii) SKIP

Format: SKIP   n

Description: This will cause the printer to skip "n" lines in the listing. The directive is not printed. If the skip is past the bottom margin, the directive will go to a new page.

PL/M STAR SYNTAX SPECIFICATION

I. NOTATIONAL CONVENTIONS

In presenting the description of the PL/M syntax, the following notation will be used:

1. The symbol ":: =" should be read as "is defined to be."

2. The symbol "|" should be read as "or."

3. Strings in capital letters will denote PL/M symbols.

4. Strings in lower case letters surrounded by "<" and ">" will denote grammar definition symbols.

5. {x} will be used to denote 0 or more occurrences of the string x.

6. [x] will be used to indicate that the string x is optional.

7. (a|b|c|d| . . .) will be used to indicate that one of a or b or c or d, etc., should be selected.

8. {a|b|c|d| . . .} will be used to denote an occurrence of 0 or more strings where each string is a or b or c or d, etc.

9. {a|b|c} will be used to denote an occurrence of a string from the set {a, b, c, ab, ba, ac, ca, bc, cb, abc, acb, bac, bca, cab, cba}.

II. THE GRAMMAR

A) Character Set

ABCDEFGHIJKLMNOPQRSTUVWXYZ
abcdefghijklmnopqrstuvwxyz
0123456789
$' = / * + - ( ) . @ < > : ; , \$$
CR (carriage return)
LF (line feed)
TAB (tab)
SPACE (blank)

B) Identifiers and Constants

<identifier> :: = {$} < letter > { < letter > | < digit > |$}
<numeric constant> :: = <binary number>
                        | < octal number >
                        | < decimal number >
                        | < hexadecimal number >
<binary number> :: = {$} < bindigit > {$| < bindigit > }B
<octal number> :: = {$} < octdigit > {$| < octdigit > }(O|Q)
<decimal number> :: = {$} < decdigit > {$| < decdigit > }[D]
<hexadecimal number> :: = {$} < hexdigit > {$| < hexdigit > }H
<bindigit> :: = 0|1
<octdigit> :: = 0|1|2|3|4|5|6|7
<decdigit> :: = 0|1|2|3|4|5|6|7|8|9
<hexdigit> :: = 0|1|2|3|4|5|6|7|8|9|A|B|C|D|E|F
<string constant> :: = ' < charstring > '
<charstring> :: = any ASCII character; a single quote is represented by
                 two adjacent single quotes.

C) Program Components

<program> :: = <module> { < module > }[EOF]
<module> :: = <identifier> : <simple do block>
<simple do block> :: = DO;{ < declaration > }{ < unit > } < ending >
<ending> :: = { < label definition > }END[< identifier >];
<label definition> :: = < identifier > :

<unit> :: = <do block>
       | <basic statement>
       | <label definition> <unit>

<basic statement> :: = <assignment statement>
               | <call statement>
               | <goto statement>
               | <return statement>
               | <if statement>
               | <null statement>
               | <halt statement>
               | <enable statement>
               | <disable statement>

<do block> :: = <simple do block>
          | <do case block>
          | <do while block>
          | <iterative do block>
          | <repeat statement>

<assignment statement> :: = <left part> = <expression>;

<left part> :: = <variable reference>{, <variable reference>}

<call statement> :: = CALL <identifier> [<parameter list>];

:: = (<expression>{, <expression>})

<goto statement> :: = GO TO <identifier>;
                  GOTO <identifier>;

<return statement> :: = RETURN[<expression>];

<if statement> †:: = <if condition> <unit> [ELSE <unit>];

<if condition> :: = IF <expression> THEN

<null statement> :: = ;

<halt statement> :: = HALT;

<enable statement> :: = ENABLE;

<disable statement> :: = DISABLE;

<do case block> :: = DO CASE <expression>;{<unit>}<ending>

<do while block> :: = DO WHILE <expression>;{<unit>}<ending>

<iterative do block> :: = <iterative do statement>{<unit>}<ending>

<iterative do statement> :: = DO <identifier> = <expression> TO
                         <expression> [BY <expression>];

<repeat statement> :: = REPEAT;{<unit>}UNTIL<expression>;

---

†Ambiguity is resolved by matching ELSE with the most recent unmatched IF-THEN.

D) Expressions

```
<expression> :: = <logical expression>
                | <embedded assignment>
<embedded assignment> :: = <variable reference> : =
                                <logical expression>
<logical expression> :: = <logical factor>
                        | <logical expression> <or operator>
                          <logical factor>
<or operator> :: = OR
                 | XOR
<logical factor> :: = <logical secondary>
                    | <logical factor> AND <logical secondary>
<logical secondary> :: = [NOT] <logical primary>
<logical primary> :: = <arithmetic expression>
                     [<relational operator> <arithmetic expression>]
<relational operator> :: = < | > | < = | > = | < > | =
<arithmetic expression> :: = <term>
                           | <arithmetic expression>
                             <adding operator> <term>
<adding operator> :: = + | - | PLUS | MINUS
<term> :: = <secondary>
          | <term> <multiplying operator> <secondary>
<multiplying operator> :: = * | / | MOD
<secondary> :: = ( + | - ) <primary>
<primary> :: = <constant>
             | <variable reference>
             | <location reference>
             | <subexpression>
<constant> :: = <numeric constant>
              | <string constant>
<variable reference> :: = <data reference>
                        | <function reference>
<data reference> :: = <identifier> [<subscript>]
                      [<member specifier>]
<subscript> :: = (<expression>)
<member specifier> :: = . <identifier> [<subscript>]
<function reference> :: = <identifier> [<actual parameters>]
<actual parameters> :: = (<expression> {, <expression>})
```

<location reference> :: = (@|·)(<constant list> | <variable reference>)

<constant list> :: = (<constant>{, <constant>})

<subexpression> :: = (<expression>)

E) Declarations

<declaration> :: = <declare statement>
       | <procedure definition>

<declare statement> :: = DECLARE <declare element list> ;

<declare element list> :: = <declare element>
       {, <declare element>}

<declare element> :: = <factored element>
       | <unfactored element>

<factored element> :: = <factored variable element>
       | <factored label element>

<unfactored element> :: = <variable element>
       | <literal element>
       | <label element>

<variable element> :: = <variable name specifier>
       [<array specifier>] <variable type>
       [<variable attributes>][<initialization>]

<variable name specifier> :: = <identifier>
       | <identifier> BASED <simple variable>

<variable attributes> :: = PUBLIC[<locator>]
       |EXTERNAL
       | <locator>

<locator> :: = AT (<location>)

<location> :: = <numeric constant>
       |(@|·)<restricted expression>

<restricted expression> :: = <data reference> [(+ | −)
       <numeric constant>]

<array specifier> :: = <explicit dimension>
       | <implicit dimension>

<explicit dimension> :: = (<numeric constant>)

<implicit dimension> :: = (*)

<variable type> :: = <basic type>
       | <structure type>

<basic type> :: = ADDRESS
       |BYTE

<literal element> :: = <identifier> LITERALLY <string constant>

<label element> :: = <identifier> LABEL
     | <identifier> LABEL(PUBLIC|EXTERNAL)

<factored variable element> :: =(<variable name specifier>
        {, <variable name specifier> })
        [<explicit dimension>] <variable type>
        [<variable attributes>]
        [<initialization>]

<factored label element> :: =(<identifier> {, <identifier> })
       LABEL[(PUBLIC|EXTERNAL)]

<structure type> :: = STRUCTURE(<member elements>
     {, <member element> })

<member element> :: = <identifier> [<explicit dimension>]
     <basic type>

<initialization> :: =(INITIAL|DATA)(<initial value>
    {, <initial value> })

<initial value> :: = <expression>
    | <string constant>

<procedure definition> :: = <procedure statement>
     {<declaration> }{ <unit> } <ending>

<procedure statement> :: = <identifier> :PROCEDURE
     [<formal parameter list>][<basic type>]
     [<procedure attributes>];

<formal parameter list> :: =(<identifier> {, <identifier> })

<procedure attributes> :: = { INTERRUPT <interrupt constant>
     | <linkage>
     |REENTRANT}

<linkage> :: = PUBLIC|EXTERNAL

<interrupt constant> :: =0|1|2|3|4|5|5.5|6|6.5|7|7.5

III. RESERVED IDENTIFIERS

The identifiers in the following list are reserved and cannot be redefined by a programmer.

ADDRESS	END	OR
AND	EOF	PLUS
AT	EXTERNAL	PROCEDURE
BASED	GO	PUBLIC
BY	GOTO	REENTRANT

BYTE	HALT	REPEAT
CALL	IF	RETURN
CASE	INITIAL	STRUCTURE
DATA	INTERRUPT	THEN
DECLARE	LABEL	TO
DISABLE	LITERALLY	UNTIL
DO	MINUS	WHILE
ELSE	MOD	XOR
ENABLE	NOT	

IV. PREDEFINED IDENTIFIERS

The identifiers in the following list are predefined to denote PL/M STAR built-ins. They may be redefined by a programmer, but in doing so, the corresponding built-in routine is made inaccessible.

CARRY	OUTPUT	SHL
DOUBLE	OVERFLOW	SHR
HIGH	PARITY	SIGN
INPUT	RIM	SIM
LAST	ROL	STACKPTR
LENGTH	ROR	TIME
LOW	SCL	ZERO
MEMORY	SCR	

PL/M STAR BUILT-IN FUNCTIONS

LOW

> Form: LOW(expression)

The "expression" should yield a value of type ADDRESS. LOW returns the low byte of this value.

HIGH

> Form: HIGH(expression)

The "expression" should yield a value of type ADDRESS. HIGH returns the high byte of this value.

DOUBLE

> Form: DOUBLE(expression)

The "expression" should yield a value of type byte. DOUBLE returns the ADDRESS value that is formed by using 00H as the high byte and the value of the expression as the low byte.

LENGTH

> Form: LENGTH(variable)

where "variable" must be a nonsubscripted reference to an array.

LENGTH returns an ADDRESS value that is equal to the number of elements in the array denoted by "variable."

LAST

Form: LAST(variable)

where "variable" must be a nonsubscripted reference to an array.

LAST returns an ADDRESS value that is equal to the subscript value of the last element in the array denoted by "variable." Note that LAST(variable) $\equiv$ LENGTH(variable) -1.

ROL

Form: ROL(expression 1, expression 2)

Both expression 1 and expression 2 must evaluate to BYTE values. ROL rotates expression 1 to the left N times, where N is the value of expression 2. A BYTE value, the resulting value of expression 1, is returned. CY is also set according to the last value of b_7 that is rotated to b_0.

ROR

Form: ROR(expression 1, expression 2)

Both expression 1 and expression 2 must evaluate to BYTE values. ROR rotates expression 1 to the right N times, where N is the value of expression 2. A BYTE value, the resulting value of expression 1, is returned. CY is also set according to the last value of b_0 that is rotated to b_7.

SCL

Form: SCL(expression 1, expression 2)

Expression 1 may be either a BYTE or ADDRESS value, but expression 2 must evaluate to a BYTE value. Expression 1 is rotated left through the carry (CY) N times, where N is the value of expression 2. The final value of expression 1, BYTE or ADDRESS depending on the original type of expression 1, is returned.

SCR

Form: SCR(expression 1, expression 2)

Expression 1 may be either a BYTE or ADDRESS value, but expression 2 must evaluate to a BYTE value. Expression 1 is rotated right through the carry (CY) N times, where N is the value of expression 2. The final value of expression 1, BYTE or ADDRESS depending on the original type of expression 1, is returned.

SHL

Form: SHL(expression 1, expression 2)

Expression 1 may be either a BYTE or ADDRESS value, but expression 2 must evaluate to a BYTE value. Expression 1 is shifted to the left N times, where N is the value of expression 2. The bits shifted out of b_7 are shifted into CY; zeros are shifted in on the right. The final value of expression 1, BYTE or ADDRESS depending on the original type of expression 1, is returned.

SHR

Form: SHR(expression 1, expression 2)

Expression 1 may be either a BYTE or an ADDRESS value, but expression 2 must evaluate to a BYTE value. Expression 1 is shifted to the right N times, where N is the value of expression 2. The bits shifted out of b_0 are shifted into CY; zeros are shifted in on the left. The final value of expression 1, BYTE or ADDRESS depending on the original type of expression 1, is returned.

CARRY, SIGN, ZERO, PARITY, OVERFLOW

Forms: CARRY
SIGN
ZERO
PARITY
OVERFLOW

Each of these functions tests the respective condition code flags and returns 00H if the flag is reset (= 0) or 0FFH if the flag is set (= 1). PARITY should be used only with the I8085, and OVERFLOW only with the M6800.

TIME

Form: CALL TIME(expression);

Expression must evaluate to a BYTE value. TIME causes a time delay of $n * 100$ μseconds, where n is the value of the expression.

INPUT

Form: INPUT(number)

This function is used to support isolated input on the I8085. It returns the BYTE value that is input from the port designated by "number." "Number" must be a constant in the range 0 to 255 decimal.

OUTPUT

Form: OUTPUT(number) = expression;

This function is used to support isolated output on the I8085. Expression is evaluated and its value is output to the port designated by "number." "Number" must be a constant in the range 0 to 255 decimal. If expression yields an ADDRESS value, then the low byte of this value is output.

MEMORY

User access to the free area of memory is supported by including the implicit declaration

DECLARE MEMORY(0) BYTE;

MEMORY is treated as a BYTE array of unspecified length. If the user references MEMORY(0), the first free byte of memory is accessed; MEMORY(1) accesses the second free byte, etc.

STACKPTR

User access to the runtime value of the stack pointer (SP) is supported by this function.

variable = STACKPTR;

reads the SP value and assigns it to variable, while

STACKPTR = expression;

sets the value of the SP.

This built-in should be used with care to avoid conflicting with the compiler's use of the stack pointer.

SIM

Form: CALL SIM(expression);

Expression must evaluate to a BYTE value. The I8085 interrupt mask is set according to the value of expression.

RIM

Form: RIM

RIM returns a BYTE value that is equal to the current setting of the I8085 interrupt mask.

BIBLIOGRAPHY

1. Aho, A. V., and J. D. Ullman (1977), *Principles of Compiler Design.* Reading, Mass.: Addison-Wesley.
2. Anderberg, J. W., and C. L. Smith (1973), "High-level language translation in SYMBOL-2R." *SIGPLAN Notices,* 8:11.
3. Barron, D. W. (1969), *Assemblers and Loaders.* New York: American Elsevier.
4. Bartee, T. C. (1974), *Digital Computer Fundamentals.* New York: McGraw-Hill.
5. Bohm, C., and G. Jacopini (1966), "Flow diagrams, Turing machines, and languages with only two formation rules." *CACM,* 9:5.
6. Brooks, F. P. Jr., (1975), *The Mythical Man–Month.* Reading, Mass.: Addison-Wesley.
7. Corbató, F. J. (1969), "PL/I as a tool for systems programming." *Datamation,* 15:5.
8. Dahl, O. J., E. W. Dijkstra, and C. A. R. Hoare (1972), *Structured Programming.* New York: Academic Press.
9. Dardner, S. C., and S. B. Heller (1970), "Streamline your software development." *Computer Decisions,* 2:10.
10. Dijkstra, E. W. (1968), "GOTO statement considered harmful." *CACM,* 11:3.
11. Donovan, J. J. (1972), *Systems Programming.* New York: McGraw-Hill.
12. Garner, H. L. (1965), "Number Systems and Arithmetic." In *Advances in Computers,* Vol. 6. New York: Academic Press.
13. Gear, C. W. (1974), *Computer Organization and Programming.* New York: McGraw-Hill.
14. Graham, R. M. (1975), *Principles of Systems Programming.* New York: John Wiley & Sons.
15. Halpern, M. (1976), "Machine and Assembly-Language Programming," in *Encyclopedia of Computer Science* (Edited by A. Ralston and C. L. Meek). New York: Petrocelli/Charter.

16. Hilburn, J. L., and P. M. Julich (1976), *Microcomputers/Microprocessors.* Englewood Cliffs, N.J.: Prentice-Hall.

17. Hill, F. J., and G. R. Peterson (1974), *Introduction to Switching Theory and Logical Design.* New York: Wiley.

18. Intel (1975), "Interp/80 User's Manual." Intel Corporation, 3065 Bowers Ave., Santa Clara, California.

19. Intel (1977a), "MCS-85 User's Manual." Intel Corporation, 3065 Bowers Ave., Santa Clara, California.

20. Intel (1977b), "8080/8085 Assembly Language Programming Manual." Intel Corporation, 3065 Bowers Ave., Santa Clara, California.

21. Intel (1977c), "SDK-85 User's Manual." Intel Corporation, 3065 Bowers Ave., Santa Clara, California.

22. Intel (1978), "MCS-86 User's Manual." Intel Corporation, 3065 Bowers Ave., Santa Clara, California.

23. Intel (1978), "PL/M-86 Programming Manual." Intel Corporation, 3065 Bowers Ave., Santa Clara, California.

24. Intermetrics (1975), "PL/M6800 Language Specification." Cambridge, Massachusetts: Intermetrics Incorporated.

25. Kernighan, B. W., and P. J. Plauger (1978), *The Elements of Programming Style.* Second Edition. New York: McGraw-Hill.

26. Leventhal, L. A. (1978), *Introduction to Microprocessors: Software, Hardware, Programming.* Englewood Cliffs, N.J.: Prentice-Hall.

27. Leventhal, L. A. (1978), *6800 Assembly Language Programming.* Berkeley, Ca.: Adam Osborne and Associates, Inc.

28. Marks, J., C. L. Tondo, and C. L. Smith (1979), "PL/M STAR User's Manual: Release 2," Computer Science Department, Southern Illinois University at Carbondale, Carbondale, Illinois.

29. McCracken, D. D. (1978), *A Guide to PL/M Programming for Microcomputer Applications.* Reading, Mass.: Addison-Wesley.

30. Myers, G. (1976), *Software Reliability: Principles and Practices.* New York: Wiley-Interscience.

31. Motorola (1975), "M6800 Microprocessor Applications Manual." Motorola Semiconductor Products, Inc., Box 20912, Phoenix, Arizona.

32. Motorola (1976a), "M6800 Microcomputer: System Design Data." Motorola Semiconductor Products Inc. Box 20912, Phoenix, Arizona.

33. Motorola (1976b), "M6800 Programming Reference Manual." Motorola Semiconductor Products Inc., 20912, Phoenix, Arizona.

34. Motorola (1976c), "M6800 Cross Assembler Reference Manual." Motorola Semiconductor Products Inc., Box 20912, Phoenix, Arizona.

35. Motorola (1977), "MEK6800D2 Evaluation Kit Manual." Motorola Semiconductor Products Inc., 3501 Ed Bluestein Blvd., Austin, Texas.

36. Motorola (1977), "M6800 Simulator Reference Manual." Motorola Integrated Circuit Division, 3102 North 56th Street, Phoenix, Arizona.

37. Oliver, B. M. (1977), "The role of microelectronics in instrumentation and control." *Scientific American,* Vol. 237.

38. Osborne, A. (1976), *An Introduction to Microcomputers; Volume I: Basic Concepts.* Berkeley, Ca.: Adam Osborne and Associates, Inc.

39. Osborne, A. (1976a), *8080 Programming for Logic Design.* Berkeley, Ca.: Adam Osborne and Associates, Inc.

40. Osborne, A. (1976b), *6800 Programming for Logic Design.* Berkeley, Ca.: Adam Osborne and Associates, Inc.

41. Osborne, Jacobson, and Kane (1977), *An Introduction to Microcomputers; Volume II: Some Real Products.* Berkeley, Ca.: Adam Osborne and Associates, Inc.

42. Smith, C. L., and C. L. Tondo (1978), "PL/M*: A Retargetable Compiler." Second Annual Rocky Mountain Symposium on Microcomputers.

43. Stone, H. S. (1972), *Introduction to Computer Organization and Data Structures.* New York: McGraw-Hill.

44. Struble, G. W. (1975), *Assembler Language Programming: The IBM System/360 and 370.* Second Edition. Reading, Mass.: Addison Wesley.

45. Tanenbaum, A. S. (1976), *Structured Computer Organization.* Englewood Cliffs, N.J.: Prentice-Hall.

46. Toong, H-M. D. (1977), "Microprocessors." *Scientific American,* Vol. 237.

47. Weber, S. (1973), *Large- and Medium-Scale Integration.* New York: McGraw-Hill.

48. Wilkes, M. V. (1951), "The Best Way to Design an Automatic Calculating Machine." Manchester University Computer Inaugural Conference, July 1951.

49. Wulf, W. A., and M. Shaw (1973), "Global variables considered harmful." *SIGPLAN,* 8:2.

INDEX

INDEX

Absolute address, 146
Absolute load module, 145
Absolute loader, 137, 140
ACC (*See* Accumulator)
Accumulator, 6, 15, 27, 51
Address bus, 13
Addressing modes, 20
AL (*See* Assembly language)
ALU (*See* Arithmetic-logic unit)
Analog data, 267
Anderberg, 5
Arithmetic-logic unit, 6, 7
Array (parameter), 81
Array assignment, 76
ASCII code, 12, 138, 277
Assembler, 4, 93, 195, 225
  conditional assembly, 222
  error detection, 210
  macro prepass, 213, 215, 218
    definition phase, 218, 219
    expansion phase, 218, 219
  pass 1, 198, 213, 219
  pass 2, 198
Assembler function, 195
Assembly language, 4, 69, 93
Assembly-language programming, 190
Asynchronous, 112

Baud rate, 125, 134, 135
Binary coded decimal (BCD), 32, 59
Binding time, 141

Bipolar, 274
Bit, 7
Bit-addressable machine, 17
Bit-slice processors, 274
Bit transfer rate, 19
Block-structured language, 169, 186, 230
Böhm, 181
Bootstrap loader, 137, 139
Bootstrapping, 237
Branch-point table, 89
Brooks, 190
Buses, 6
Busy wait I/O, 115, 116, 117, 129, 176
Busy wait loop, 116, 129, 132, 134, 271
Byte, 13
Byte-addressable, 17
Byte size, 19

Call by value, 188
Carry flag, 10
Carry in, 10
Carry out, 10, 99
Cassette interface, 122, 123
Central Processing Unit, 6, 7, 25
Chip, 102
CML (*See* Conventional machine-language level)
Combinational circuits, 99
Compiler(s), 4, 227
Compiler Implementation Techniques, 237

Compile-time initializations, use of, 182
Computing power, 25
Computing system(s), 1, 122
    components, 2
Condition code register (flag register), 6
Control register, 112
Control unit, 6, 7
Conventional Machine Language Level, 4
Conversion, from base 10, 8
    to base 10, 8
Corbató, 190
CPU (*See* Central processing unit)
Cross assembler, 93, 225
CR (*See* Control register)
CU (*See* Control unit)

Dardner, 192
Data bus, width of, 13
Data transmission techniques, 109
Debugger, 241
    implementation, 245
Declarations, format of, 183
DIP (Dual Inline Package), 102
Direct addressing, 20
Distributed systems, 269, 270
Double precision addition, 73

EA (*See* Effective address)
EBCDIC Code, 12
Effective address, 20, 21
Emulation, 246
EPROM (Erasable PROM), 104
Expanding opcode, 19
Extending the subset assemblers, 210
External procedures, 186, 188

Feedback, 99, 100
Firmware, 2
Flip-flop, 99
Flow of control, 183
Forward reference problem, 198
Framing bits, asynchronous
    transmission, 113

Gates, 97
Global variables, 186, 231
    binding to a declaration, 171

Half-adder, 99
Halt instruction, 14
Handshaking, 270
Hardware, 2
    components, 5
    serialization, 112
Heller, 192
High-level languages, 4, 69, 153
High-level language programming, 190

I8085 microprocessor, 105
    accumulator, 51
    addressing modes, 52
    arithmetic instructions, 58, 59
    branch central instructions, 63, 64
    byte order, 51, 56, 74
    clock cycles, 107
    condition code register (CCR), 52
    data transfer instructions, 54, 55
    halt instruction, 57
    input and output operations, 65
    instruction formats, 52
    instruction register, 107
    integer compares, 63
    interrupt masks, 65
    logical instructions, 60, 61
    machine cycles, 107
    microcomputer systems, 111
    opcodes, 285
    program counter (PC), 51
    program status word (PSW), 51
    READ operation, 107
    register encoding, 53
    register pairs, 54
    RIM, 112
    Serial I/O Port, 112
    SIM, 112
    stack, 51
    stack, I/O, and machine central
        instructions, 65, 66
    stack pointer (SP), 51
    subroutine linkage, 63
    WRITE operation, 107
I8085 assembler, comments, 71
    conditional assembly format, 223
    conventions, 299
    DB directive, 71

DS directive, 71
DW directive, 74
ELSE directive, 223, 224
END directive, 71
ENDIF directive, 223, 224
ENDM directive, 212
EQU directive, 91
EXTRN directive, 144, 146
IF directive, 223, 224
IRP directive, 221
IRPC directive, 221
labels, 71
LOCAL directive, 215
MACRO directive, 212
macro facility, 212
ORG directive, 71
PUBLIC directive, 144, 146
REPT directive, 221
I8085S assembler, 195
  comments, 199
  DB directive, 198
  directives, 199
  DS directive, 198
  DW directive, 198
  GET$LINE routine, 200, 202
  HEX$CONVERT routine, 201
  INSTRUCTION routine, 203, 204
  memory layout, 205
  opcode table, 203
  ORG directive, 198
  PASS 1 routine, 199, 200, 205
  PASS 2 routine, 202, 203, 205
  predefined opcode table, 196
  predefined symbol values, 197
  symbol table, 201, 203
  UPDATE$TABLE routine, 201
Immediate addessing, 23
Implied addressing, 23
Index register, 21
Indexed addressing, 21
Indirect addressing, 21
Input/output, 108
  instructions, 111
  port numbers, 111
Instruction, addresses in, 14
  encoding, 17
  one-address, 15

three-address, 15
two-address, 15
zero-address, 16
Instruction counter (*See* Program
    counter), 22
Instruction formats, 14
Instruction size, 17, 19
Integer arithmetic, 10
INTEL 8085 microprocessor (*See* I8085
    microprocessor)
INTEL 80/85 Assembler (*See also* I8085
    Assembler), 94
INTEL 8086, 274, 275, 276
INTEL 8155 RAM, 111, 260, 270
  Command/Status Register, 260, 261
  strobed mode, 261, 262
INTEL 8251 Programmable
    Communications Interface, 129
  command instruction format, 130
  control register, 129
  mode instruction format, 129
  transmit data register, 132
  word framing, 130
INTEL 8355 ROM, 111
Internal procedures, 186
Interpretation, 3
Interpreter, 3, 4
Interprocessor communication, 270
Interrupts, 116, 253
  asynchronous nature of, 253
  I8085, 259
  M6800, 254
  priority, 117, 119
  service routine, 259
  uses of, 253
Interrupt I/O, 116, 117, 135
  example of, 263
Interrupt mask, 118
Interrupt sequence, 117, 118, 259
  differences between M6800 and I8085,
    119
Interrupt system, disabled, 117
  enabled, 117
Inverter, 98
I/O (*See* Input/output)
IS1A (*See* INTEL 8251)
Isolated I/O, 110, 112

Jacopini, 181

Label, declaration of, 171
Label table, 89
Levels, in a computing system, 3, 4, 69
Level transversal, 3, 195, 247, 250
Linker, 146
Linking loader, 140, 143, 144, 145, 148, 212
Load module, 148
Load routine, 123, 133
Loader, 137
  object module, 145
  records, 137
Local variables, 146, 169, 231
Location counter, 198
  maintenance, 198
Logical circuits, 97, 98, 100
Logical operations, 11
  notation for, 11

M6800 Microprocessor, 27, 102
  accumulator and memory reference
      instructions, 31
  accumulators, 27
  addressing modes, 29
  Arithmetic Logic Unit, 105
  arithmetic instructions, 31, 32
  bus control lines, 102
  byte order, 31, 74
  clock cycle, 102
  Condition Code Register (CCR), 28
  condition code register instructions, 49
  conditional branch instructions, 45
  cross assembler, 94
  control unit, 105
  data handling instructions, 36, 38
  data test instructions, 33, 35
  direct addressing, 29
  extended addressing, 29
  halt instruction, 40
  index register, 27, 41
  index register and stack pointer
      instructions, 41, 42
  indexed addressing, 30
  instruction format, 29
  instruction register, 105

integer compares, 45
interrupts, 45
interrupt mask, 135
interrupt mask bit, 117
interrupt system, 28
jump and branch instructions, 46, 47
logical instructions, 33, 34
microcomputer systems, 111
microinstructions, 102, 105
op codes, 281
overflow condition, 29, 43
program counter (PC), 27
registers, 27
relative addressing, 44
simulation, 241
stack, 27
stack pointer (SP), 27, 41
subroutine linkage, 45
two's complement (use of), 28
M6800 Assembler, assembler directives, 70
  comments, 71
  conventions, 289
  direct addressing, 94
  END directive, 69, 71
  EQU directive, 89
  extended addressing, 70
  FCB directive, 70
  FDB directive, 74
  immediate addressing, 75
  indexed addressing, 78
  labels, 71
  NAM directive, 70
  ORG directive, 70, 71
  RMB directive, 70
M6800S, assembler directives, 206
  comment convention, 206
  GET$LINE routine, 207
  INSTRUCTION routine, 209
  MODE routine, 208
  OINDEX routine, 208
  opcode table, 205, 206, 208
  operand field conventions, 206
  PASS 1 routine, 207, 208, 210
  PASS 2 routine, 208, 210
  predefined opcode table, 207
  REL routine, 209
  UPDATE$TABLE routine, 207

M6800S Assembler, 205
Machine language, 3
Macro, 212
  actual arguments, 216
  body, 212
  definition, 212, 213
  dummy parameters, 216
  end-of-definition marker, 212
  in-line expansion, 213, 214
  invocation, 212, 219
  naming statement, 212
  nested definition, 217
  parameter/argument mechanism, 215, 216
  table, 219
Macro assemblers, 212, 215
Maxi(s), 2, 24
MDS (*See* Microcomputer development system)
Memory, 13
  cost of, 192
  dynamic, 103
  static, 103
  volatile, 102
Memory-mapped I/O, 110, 112, 131
Memory resolution, 17, 18
Micro(s), 2, 24
Micro level, 4
Microcomputer architecture, 97
Microcomputer development system, 121, 138, 139
Microinstruction, 4
Microprocessor, 102
  applications, 267
  future directions, 274
Microprogramming, 4
Microprogramming Level (MP), 4
Microprograms, 4
Minicomputers, 2, 24
Module, communication, 185
  interface, 186
  "need to know" policy, 186, 188
Monitor, command keys, 123
  data keys, 123
Monitor program, 108, 123, 124
MOS Technology, 274

Motorola M6820 Peripheral Interface Adaptor, 254, 263, 270
  control lines, 256, 258
  control line settings, 270, 271
  control register, 254, 256
  data direction register, 254
Motorola M6850 Asynchronous Communications Interface Adaptor, 125
  control register, 125, 133
  receive data register, 134
  status register, 125, 128
  transmit data register, 128, 129, 135
  word frame, 127
MPIA (*See* Motorola M6820 Peripheral Interface Adaptor)
MSIA (*See* Motorola M6850 Asynchronous Communications Interface Adaptor)
Multiplexer, 105
Multiplexing, 105
Multiprocessor systems, 269, 270
Multiprogramming, 141
Multi-way branch, 87

Negative integers, 9
Nonnumeric data, 12
Number system, 7
  binary (base 2), 7
  decimal (base 10), 7
  hexadecimal (base 16), 8
  octal (base 8), 8
  suffix letter notation, 8

Object code, 137, 143
Object module, 148
  end of module section, 146
  external reference table, 146, 149
  identification section, 146
  machine instruction and constant section, 146, 148
  public entry table, 146, 149
  relocation directory, 146, 148
One-pass assemblers, 210
One's complement, 10
Opcode, 14
Opcode table, 195, 196, 198, 199

Operating System level (OS), 4, 69
Operating System Support, 247
OS (*See* Operating system level)
Overflow, 10

Parallel Interface Adaptor (PIA), 115
Parallel I/O, 109
  example of, 270
  ports, 111
Parameters, by reference, 81
  by value, 81
Parameter linkage, comparison of, 87
Parity check list, 12
Parity, even, 12
  odd, 12
PD (*See* Peripheral interface device)
Program Counter (PC), 6, 7, 105
  as pointer to arg list, 83, 86
Peripheral Interface Device (PD), 109
  connection, 110
Personnel salaries, effect on system cost,
    190
Position-independent code, 143
Program development techniques, 93
PL/M, arithmetic expressions,
    evaluation of, 160
  precedence relations, 160
  arithmetic operators, 159, 160
  array, 156
  arrays of structures, 156
  assignment statement, 162
  AT attribute, 157
  based variable, 157
    implementation of, 236
  blocks, 171
  built-in functions, 165, 166
  call by value, 167
  call statement, 167
  comment notation, 169
  compile-time initializations, 158
  compound statement, 162
  constant list, 161
  conversions, 162
  data types and constants, 154, 155
  declarations, 155
  DO CASE statement, 162, 163
  DO WHILE statement, 162, 163

  embedded assignment, 162
  expressions, 159
  external variables, 187
  function invocation, 167
  function type procedures, 167
  GO TO statement, 162, 165
    alternatives to, 182
    avoidance of, 183
    restrictions on, 171
  grammar, 154
  IF-THEN-ELSE statement, 162
  INITIAL, restrictions on, 171
  internal procedures, 169
  Interrupt Procedure, 263
  iterative DO statement, 162, 164
  label, 165
  label definition, 165
  language feature summary, 154
  location reference operator (dot
      operator), 161
  logical operations, 160
    precedence, 160
  macro facility, 159
  memory-mapped I/O facilities, 166
  multiple assignment statement, 162
  parameter linkage mechanism, 167,
      188
  procedures, 167
  procedure definition, 167
  procedure usage definition, 188
  program format, 168
  PUBLIC variables, 187
  relational operators, 160
    precedence, 160
  REPEAT-UNTIL statement, 162, 164
  simulation of call by reference, 168
  statements, 162
  structure, 156
  subroutine type procedures, 167
  variable name, 155
PL/M 6800, 153
PL/M 80, 153
PL/M Programming Language (*See*
    PL/M), 153
PL/M STAR, 153, 227
  built-in functions, 317
  grammar, 310

syntax specifications, 309
variable name/symbolic name
    association, 228, 231
Polling, 253
    software, 259
Predefined symbol table, 198, 199
Program indentation format, 184
Program readability, 189
    use of comments for, 189
Programmer productivity, 190
Programming environment, cost of, 191
PROM (Programmable Read Only
    Memory), 104
Punch routine, 123, 125, 129

RAM (Random Access Memory), 102
"Real" machine, 3
Real-time, 267
Receive shift register, 112
Register(s), 6
Register addressing, 20
Relative addressing, 22
    M6800, 30
Relocating loader, 140, 143, 212
Relocation constant, 148
Resident assembler, 122, 225
ROM (Read Only Memory), 103
    masked-programmed, 104
Runtime efficiency, 191, 192

Selector/multiplexer, 98
Self-assembler, 225, 226
Self-translator, 237
Sequential circuit, 100, 108
Serial I/O, 109
Shift register, 100, 109
SI loader (System Interface loader), 138,
    139
SIA (serial interface adaptor), 112, 127
Sign/magnitude, 9
Simulator, 241
Smith, 5, 153
Software, 2
Software engineering, 180, 181
Software life cycle, maintenance phase,
    189, 190
Software serialization, 112

Software systems, design and
    implementation principles, 181
    memory-space requirements, 191
SR (status register), 113
Stack, 16
Stack pointer, 16
State (of a sequential circuit), 100
Static chain pointer, 232, 233, 234, 235
Stepwise refinement, 185
Structured programming, 180
    control constructs, iteration, 181
        selection, 181
        sequencing, 181
Subroutine, closed, 212, 214
    open, 212
SYMBOL-2R, 5
Symbol table, 197, 198
Synchronous, 100, 102, 112
Synchronous transmission, 112
Systems programs, 121, 122

Tanenbaum, 3
Target language, 227
Text editor, 149, 150, 151, 174, 175, 176
    EDIT mode, 150
    INPUT mode, 150
Three-state devices, 105
Time slicing, 116, 141
Tondo, 153
Topdown design, 185, 186
Translation, 3
Translator, 3, 4, 5, 195, 227
Transmit shift register, 112
Two-pass assembler, 198
Two's complement, 10, 11
Type conversions, 228, 229

Unconditional branch directives, 224

Variable name, scope of, 179
Vectoring, 117, 253
Virtual machine, 3

Wilkes, 4
Word, 8
Word-addressable, 17
Word size, 19